BLOOD

The Paramount Humour

BLOOD
The Paramount Humour

EARLE HACKETT

Jonathan Cape Thirty Bedford Square London

FIRST PUBLISHED 1973
© 1973 BY EARLE HACKETT

JONATHAN CAPE LTD, 30 BEDFORD SQUARE, LONDON WCI

ISBN 0 224 00631 2

PRINTED IN GREAT BRITAIN
BY EBENEZER BAYLIS AND SON LTD
THE TRINITY PRESS, WORCESTER, AND LONDON
ON PAPER MADE BY JOHN DICKINSON AND CO. LTD
BOUND BY G. AND J. KITCAT LTD, LONDON

CONTENTS

INTRODUCTION 11

1. EVERYTHING FLOWS 13
2. THICKER THAN WATER 40
3. PUMP AND PIPES 58
4. THE HUMOURS OF IT 80
5. ONE MAN'S BLOOD 101
6. GRANNY, MIRACLES, DREAMS 115
7. LIFE CODES 129
8. ANOTHER MAN'S POISON 147
9. MOTHER AGAINST CHILD 158
10. FORENSIC AND SUCH 167
11. TWO SHOCKS 176
12. SHARED BLOOD 187
13. BLOOD AND IRON 201
14. BAD HUMOUR 214
15. THE BLEEDERS 232
16. BLOOD OF OUR FATHERS 240
17. HEARTACHE 255

FURTHER READING 278

INDEX 279

PLATES

In this book, fourteen engravings have been included to refresh the eye. They are reproduced from *Physica Sacra* by Johann Jakob Scheuchzer, a large work published in the early eighteenth century. It contains hundreds of examples of baroque copperplate art, and its text assumes intellectual continuity between biblical tradition and what were then the latest observations of natural science. For example, the plate dealing with the heart (facing page 64) relates to a quotation from Psalm xxxiii; and it shows a romantic picture of a heart-felt human situation; two coils of flexible pipe; the vessels, valves, musculature and anatomical openings of the human heart; and a mechanical two-chambered pumping device symbolic of the heart's working.

To my blood relations

ERRATA

Page 26, caption to diagram. This should read:
Methods of fluid-exchange in three worm types: *above*, round-worm (cavity-swill); *centre*, proboscis-worm (tube-squirt); *below*, flatworm (soak-through)

Page 38, line 23: for over 66 pounds (30 kilograms) *read* over 600 pounds (270 kilograms).

Page 131, caption to diagram, line 2: for makes *read* males.

Opposite page 176, caption to plate: for transcience *read* transience.

ACKNOWLEDGMENTS

First and most important, because it has been the greatest contribution, I thank my wife, Eileen, herself a laboratory worker, for fondly putting up (for years) with my habit of writing on untidy papers during what I have been selfish enough to call my 'spare' time.

I also thank five people, three of them associated with my publisher, who directly helped me to construct this book out of a florid first version. Dr Richard Kimber, colleague and haematologist at the Institute of Medical and Veterinary Science, Adelaide, read the manuscript. He pointed out errors, and gave me opinions which were later seconded by Catherine Storr. She advised certain pruning and some rewriting. Further long and detailed help was given by Clare Draffin. Robyn Wallis agreed that the illustrations (as opposed to the technical diagrams) should be chosen for mood, and so we have the engravings from *Physica Sacra*, a redoubtable – and beautiful – treatise written in the eighteenth century. Dr R. W. Beal, Director of the Red Cross Blood Transfusion Service in Adelaide, expertly read the final proofs.

I am obliged to the Trustees of the Wellcome Institute of the History of Medicine, London, for permission to reproduce fourteen engravings from *Physica Sacra*, and for supplying copies of the endpaper illustrations. For permission to reproduce the latter I am grateful to Messrs Sandoz Ltd, Basel, publishers of the book *Die Zehn anatomischen Tafeln des Walter Hermann Ryff* from which they are taken, and to the Kupferstichkabinett der Öffenlichen Kunstsammlung, Basel, owners of the original collection of woodcuts (Walter Hermann Ryff, Strasburg, Balthasar Beck [Pistor] 1541).

I had already used some of this book's themes in the radio programme 'Insight' of the Australian Broadcasting Commission. I thank Dr Peter Pockley, the head of the A.B.C.'s science section in Sydney, for his help in shaping these broadcasts. Many of them are contained in three booklets issued by the A.B.C., *Insight on Blood, More Insight on Blood* and *Organ Voluntaries*. The essay on spiders' webs and blood-clotting in Chapter Six also had its origin in a radio talk. It has been printed in the *Medical Journal of Australia* and I am obliged to the editors for permission to use it with some changes.

As for my sources generally, they are teachers, texts, lectures, travel, journals, colleagues, gossip, novels, newspapers – where does anyone get ordinary information? Everywhere. Being no originator, I must be borrowing ideas and phrases which others first set free. I apologize to those whom I do not acknowledge, but to give citations throughout would be pretentious, for it is not that sort of book.

I.M.V.S.   E.H.
Adelaide

INTRODUCTION

There is no shortage of irrational or unscientific ideas about the supposed properties of human blood. Mostly these are folk theories which neither survive practical tests nor lend themselves to fruitful application in a modern context. But they still influence our language and customs. As a result, we speak of blood brotherhood and blood-feuds; of the blood of our fathers, blood relations, blood poisoning and sang-froid; of princes of the blood who may own blood-horses, bloodhounds and blood-stones; and of people or ideas which are cold-blooded, blood-curdling, blood-thirsty, bloody-minded, sanguine, clottish or plain bloody stupid. There are similar ranges of expression relating to the heart and veins. In some ways the symbolism in these notions is in accord with current technical knowledge, but in others it only reflects 'epidemic pseudo-doxies' (Sir Thomas Browne's famous Greekery for 'vulgar errors'), which are better identified if ideas are to be clear.

Actually, although we believe we live in an age of enlightenment, the total weight of written superstition has never been greater, and even good newspapers are full of pseudo-psychology, fads, fundamentalism, occult lore and astrology. This is because entire literate populations are able to amuse themselves by reading and writing. In part, it is a form of playing-about, and not to be taken too seriously, but much old wives' talk is more than half believed.

There are those who get spots on the face because 'their blood is too rich' and patent medicines are still taken to cool or clean it. Among Anglo-Saxon peoples, betrothal rings are worn on the third finger of the left hand—the 'leech finger'—because it 'has a vein which leads directly to the heart'. It is widely known that blood-letting was once a common treatment for disease, so why has it been abandoned? Or hasn't it? And is it true that some of the seven layers of skin are missing from a haemophiliac so that he will bleed to death from a scratch? Or is it that his skin is too tight? And if not, then what *is* haemophilia anyway? and leukaemia? and blood pressure? and phlebitis? and pernicious anaemia?

Just how do you give transfusions? Are there vampires? Do cobwebs staunch bleeding? Is blood alive? Does a woman's blood run through the baby inside her? Is there a difference between the bloods of black and white peoples? How much blood is in you? What did a leech do? What about the miraculous annual liquefaction of the preserved blood of St Januarius, the patron saint of Naples? Do pelicans feed their own blood to their young ones? What was in the old apothecary's drawer labelled 'Dragon's Blood'? What blood tests are used when paternity is disputed? Can you really die of a broken heart? And dreams of blood, are they significant?

An examination of these and similar questions can reasonably be made into an unpretentious book, which will then become an easy bridge between *haematology* (the scientific study of blood) and what one may call *haematosophy* (or traditional bloody wisdom).

As a matter of fact, this is a bridge by which all beginners in medicine and human biology should travel; also all non-science undergraduates and secondary-school pupils, and others who like to read around a bit, or are told to do so. There are, too, those such as journalists, lawyers and policemen who find that they must acquire, at short notice, some general knowledge of blood if they are to understand what laboratory or medical experts are saying to them. And there are volunteer blood donors who would like to know more about the blood they give and where it goes. Too often they are left wondering. But perhaps the largest group of all are those who — quite simply — are curious, because they are disturbed by blood lore, half feared, half enjoyed.

Now look down, under the bridge, at the red river. There are great precedents for reputable streams turning that colour. Listen to Milton's *Paradise Lost*:

> Thammuz came next behind,
> Whose annual wound in Lebanon allured
> The Syrian damsels to lament his fate
> In amorous ditties all a summer's day,
> While smooth Adonis from his native rock
> Ran purple to the sea, supposed with blood
> Of Thammuz yearly wounded ...

CHAPTER ONE

Everything Flows

Everything flows, everything moves — many things move relatively, but everything moves intrinsically, unless it be reduced to the no-heat temperature of absolute zero. The page you are reading here, and you yourself, are made of mêlées of dancing particles, bumping together, ricocheting, so many and so small that the number which move *this* way is just about equal to the number which go *that* way. The warmer the paper, or you, or anything else, the faster the dance within. To the eye, the resulting gross movement is nil.

Three worlds

In fact, the terms 'printed page' and 'you' have triple meanings, for each refers to at least three worlds: three intervals in a cosmic tonic sol-fa. In the first place they are ordinary descriptive terms relating to things seen every day and established as entities in traditional human culture. In the second they are statistical probability statements about the average behaviour of these large collections of elementary bounding balls: molecules and atoms whose existence and rates of movement are inferred by physicists, chemists and mathematicians in an ultramicroscopic world observed for the most part indirectly. Thirdly, they are the even more elementary subatomic particles of which the molecules and atoms themselves are composed and whose existence can only be presumed, in a still more indirect and mathematical way, from reactions occurring under special conditions created by nuclear physicists and observed in their instruments; this world scarcely concerns us in this book at all.

There is an important difference between the molecular dance in the intimate structure of the printed page, and that in your body. In the first the scene is one of inexorably increasing disorder among the dancers, during which the paper will slowly age and crumble. But in the human body the dance proceeds at least for a time — a lifetime — through a state of increasing and then conserved order. Frenzy becomes jig becomes ballet, as matter becomes *organized* into complex human protoplasm for the growth, maintenance and repair of your body, your *organism*. The energy which promotes this change into organism is derived, in the last analysis a biologist can usefully make, from the sun, though often in a roundabout way. An organism is a system of matter which maintains and restores very complex interior relationships in the face of stimulation and disturbance.

The total organization in the body of one living individual is the sum of many concurrent cycles of building-up, interchange and breaking-down, like the barter on the floor of a bourse: a balanced confusion of supplies and demands, with atoms and molecules for the stock-in-trade. They are subject to the same inherent thermal jigging and bumping that goes on in non-living matter, but the living substance has such a configuration of energy concentrations and structure that needed par-ticles, moving like lightning but at random near the right places, will fit precisely into empty niches and be held there, and thus ordered patterns of increasing size are built up.

Diffusion in cells

Molecules are aggregations of atoms knitted together by electric influences. The more atoms in a molecule the heavier and more cumber-some it will be, and thus the less effective the knocks of its neighbours in moving it about and 'diffusing' it. Protoplasm, the basic broth of life in the cells of all living material, is a half-fluid half-jelly composed of large molecules which have been built from smaller ones. Many of these large molecules are aggregated and linked so that they form sheets or spheres or tubes or chains, all of which are submicroscopic and almost invisible, though to some extent they can be 'seen' with an electron microscope.

In liquids, dissolved substances diffuse steadily at different rates according to their molecular weights, the heavier the slower; and proto-plasm depends much on this diffusion of large molecules and is hampered if their rate of unaided movement is correspondingly slow. Further, the net movement of randomly diffusing molecules is always from areas of high to areas of low concentration: shake a pile of marbles on a flat tray and they will diffuse out sideways rather than rise up in a yet higher pile.

The simplest independent living organisms consist of single cells. A cell is a small collection of living protoplasm consisting of nucleus and cytoplasm, enclosed in a fine membrane or cell wall, the whole being commonly surrounded by water. The term 'cell', suggesting imprison-ment or monastic isolation, is not a good one, having been used first by an early microscopist to describe the fine structure of dead plant material. He saw only the desiccated skeletonic walls of areas which once contained living cells, but today cell walls as we understand them do not a prison make. They are quite permeable and often elastic.

Cells vary in volume, and most would be between pin-head and fine pin-point size, say between one millimetre (one twenty-fifth of an inch) and one-hundredth of a millimetre across. Over such distances there is relatively rapid diffusion of small molecules such as those of water,

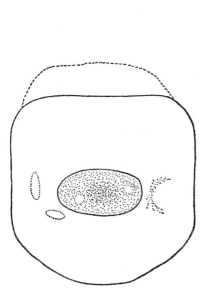

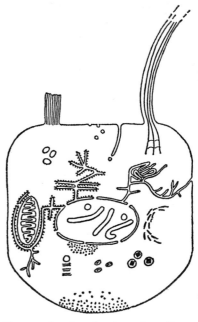

A cell, seen under the light microscope, with fine cytoplasmic structures faintly visible

The complex fine structure of a cell, seen under the electron microscope (Some of the different structures, shown diagrammatically here, may be repeated many times.)

H_2O, or common salt, NaCl; but a sugar such as glucose, $C_6H_{12}O_6$, or an amino-acid such as tryptophan, $C_{11}H_{12}O_2N_2$, will be more cumbersome and will diffuse only slowly within a cell. Haemoglobin—something like $C_{2954}H_{4414}O_{806}N_{780}S_{12}Fe_4$—will hardly diffuse at all. Nevertheless, ordinary simple diffusion probably provides sufficient exchanges to maintain life at minimal rates in the protoplasm of beings up to one millimetre thick.

Exchange of molecules between adjacent areas goes on both within the mass of the protoplasm, and between it and whatever medium is outside, usually water. Therefore some diffusion and transport of molecules has to take place through the cell wall, which acts as a complete barrier only to the passage of the very largest, such as haemoglobin. It transmits, sometimes selectively, most of those of the size we have just been considering, such as simple sugars or amino-acids, and these are typical of the 'food' of the cell.

For a simple cell to stay alive, food and dissolved oxygen must enter and waste products must be eliminated. If the cell had to rely upon unaided diffusion for this exchange, its size, shape and rate of living would have to be limited, for all its protoplasm must be near to the margins for transport of these substances by diffusion to be sufficiently fast.

Protoplasmic streaming

The remedy is for the cell protoplasm to mix continually by proto-plasmic streaming. Most living cells show this: a continual slow stirring of the protoplasm. In some it is directly visible under the microscope; in others it is best observed when the cell is photographed by slow cinematography and the picture is accelerated on the screen. This reveals the remarkable physical reconciliation achieved by living matter

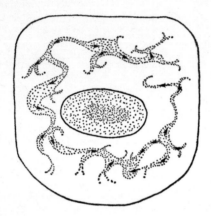

A living cell, showing the movement of the cytoplasm

—the regularity of a crystal accommodated to the chemical fluidity of a flame.

The streaming is brought about by local changes in the protoplasm from a dissolved to a jelly state (a sol-gel change) and vice versa. A jelly is semi-solid and elastic, while a solution is liquid and flowing. Slight changes in the local availability of some simple elements in the proto-plasm, particularly calcium, potassium and magnesium, may bring about a change from one state to another. When part of the cell is in the gel state, the elasticity makes it contract slightly, and squirts any proto-plasm in the sol state in a stream away from the gelled area. These changes from a fluid to a jelly state under the influence of calcium are echoed in the elaborate blood-clotting mechanisms of higher animals, where it is as though this basic jellifying property of protoplasm has been extended outside the cells into the liquid extracellular constituents of the blood, the cells still retaining a triggering action in the process.

In some species such as *amoeba* (from a Greek word meaning 'change') with a very soft extendible cell wall, the streaming is used as a means of locomoting the cell itself, which waddles and flows along on protrusible, false legs of protoplasm. This also becomes a method of eating, when the cell flows around a morsel of food. Such ebbing and flowing cannot be called 'circulation', but it illustrates the fundamental biological value of streaming movement within living material.

There are certain larger organisms (the slime-fungi or Mycetozoa) in which very marked use is made of this flowing power of protoplasm. In its ordinary form a slime-fungus looks like a spread-out mass of spittle, up to five centimetres (two inches) across, and is sometimes to be seen on decaying vegetable-matter. Closer inspection shows it to be all protoplasm, remarkable in that it is thousands of times bigger than an amoeba and not divided up by cell walls. It moves very simply by protoplasmic streaming, so that the whole patch creeps slowly and eerily along, a main current in the middle dividing and subdividing towards an advancing margin like a riverine delta, the hind part contracting before

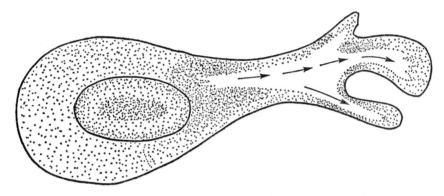

Protoplasmic streaming in a cell

flowing forward once again. When a moving slime-fungus encounters food which it can absorb, the direction of streaming is regularly reversed so that digested substances can be carried back and distributed in the body of the organism.

To return to minute free-living cells: if, as well as protoplasmic streaming, there is relative movement of water over the outside of the cell, then the diffusionary advantage is much increased, for supplies from outside will thus be constantly renewed and waste materials diffusing outwards will continually be borne away. Moreover, diffusion through the cell wall itself will be the more effective the steeper the gradient between concentrations inside and out.

Therefore a cell may anchor itself in a position where there is a natural flow of ocean or river current over it. Movement through water of the cell itself will, of course, achieve the same result, or perhaps — as with a great number of small organisms — an external current may be created in still water by the rhythmic lashing of the minute protoplasmic hairs on the cell's surface.

Against the gradient

At this point you may ask, Must not diffusion sometimes take place in the opposite direction, from an area of low to one of high concentration? For if not, how on earth can plants or animals accumulate concentrated stocks of rare or trace substances, as many of them are known to do? Or how can they build up stores of even, say, sugar, or hold their own protoplasm together? The answer is that the accumulation and regulation of such materials by living matter is certainly against the diffusion gradient, and is possible only as the result of expending energy and 'doing work'. Protoplasm has to do much active absorption of this kind. It must trap wanted molecules and carry them uphill, so to speak; for by random thermal jigging alone, they will run only down the slope.

Protoplasm does not do anything supernatural when it carries out such selective absorption. It captures needed particles with energy which is either obtained from sunlight or derived locally by allowing other molecules that are more easily obtained or more easily strung together to rip. (When molecules rip apart, they release available energy.) This is how living material drives the molecular chemical 'pumps' on its membranes which increase its organization at the expense of progressive disorganization somewhere else (such as in the sun). There must be some source of greater energy available before a less organized system can proceed to increasingly higher levels of organization, as happens when living matter assembles from non-living material. Protoplasm has no divine *perpetuum mobile*. It obeys the same 'laws' as non-living matter, particularly the famous Second Law of Thermodynamics, a probability principle of classical physics which we assume is applicable to all situations in the entire observable universe. This law has various implications: for example, that closed, organized systems of matter or energy tend to proceed to disorder; that the 'available' energy of the universe is running down; that where a hot body is in contact only with a cold one, the first will get colder and the second hotter, never the other way round; that entropy tends to increase.

Take a tray of red and green marbles and 'wind up the system' by putting all the red ones at one end and all the green ones at the other. Shake the tray at random. The red and green steadily mingle until mixing is complete. Shake as you may, the chances are so greatly against your being able, by random movement, to shake them back to their original ordered distribution of one colour at either end that you can say it will 'never' happen. The movements of the marbles are a model of the molecular working of the Second Law; they have diffused until there are no longer any gradients of concentration within the closed boundaries of the tray. You can see that the 'law' is a probability statement about segregations, or 'order within the system', and also that if you were dealing with only one molecule the 'law' would have no meaning.

If you want to re-create order you must add 'energy' by putting in your hand (in fact 'opening the system' to wind it again) and segregating marbles of one colour. That, roughly, is how protoplasm works: by open-system thermodynamics, using outside energy to chivy molecules against the diffusion gradient. Plants use radiant solar energy directly; animals use it indirectly by eating plants, for all flesh is grass.

The sun is very hot. The earth is relatively cool. Solar energy flows, at just a nice rate, in our direction. Some is trapped in such 'fossil fuels' as coal and oil. (There is a little non-solar energy being artificially released on the earth's surface from atomic and nuclear sources — now that we have learned how to tap them — and there are a few bacteria which can obtain energy by digesting mineral substances; but from the biological viewpoint such sources will never compare in magnitude with those in the sun.) If you ask where solar or nuclear energy ultimately comes from, no one can tell you. What does ultimate mean? Who wound up the universe? You may say that God did. If you want a more circular way of expressing ignorance you may talk of the 'properties' of subatomic particles and electrons, which is to say that the wound-upness of the universe is in the nature of things. Or you can say that the questions are not sensible. What does that mean? It means they waste time. What does that mean? And so it goes on.

Water, water everywhere

Next in the scale of biological complexity, above the one-celled organisms, are those which consist of a small number of cells making up single individuals (or 'undividables'). They, too, live mostly in water. Their structures vary: their cells may be in a simple mass, but hollow spheres, tubes and branching stalks are commonplace; all, or most, of their cells are in contact with the surrounding water and there is often a co-ordinated beating of protoplasmic hairs on the surface of suitably placed cells. The current created by this may be such that floating food-particles are directed towards a special opening into the interior of the 'animal'. You can think of the opening as the 'mouth', and the cavity inside as the 'stomach'. Thus different parts have different functions. This 'differencing' related to structure is simply called 'differentiation' and is an important biological idea.

Animals like this are usually composed of two distinct layers of cells, one covering the outside and the other lining the inside. For the most part each layer is only one cell thick, and so the animals are small and fragile. The largest of all the two-layered animals are the jelly-fishes, which secrete great quantities of non-living viscous jelly between their inner and outer layers. This gives them bulk so that they may drift in the oceans with some stability, which allows them to entangle quite large prey.

The sponges are another simple group which has undergone special development. A sponge is a loose collection of single cells which are cohabiting rather than forming part of a multicellular organism. The cells have a certain amount of individual independence, but they exchange molecular 'information' with one another sufficiently well to secrete a common openwork, non-living, flask-shaped skeleton of lime or flexible horny material which gives them support. They station themselves on this skeleton, which has numerous small openings and one

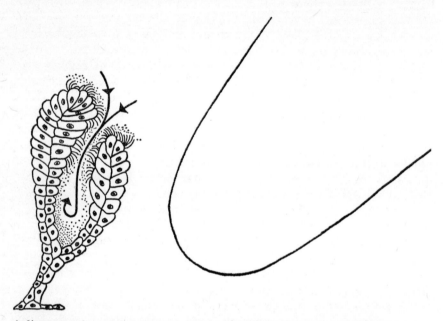

A diagrammatic section through a small two-layered aquatic animal, showing the beating of protoplasmic hairs. Its size is compared with the point of a fine sewing needle.

large one, so that by co-ordinated beating their protoplasmic hairs can create a water current which passes in through the small holes and out through the big one. This current brings in food and oxygen and takes away waste and carbon dioxide — not a circulation, but a well-contrived current in the external environment, like the ventilation system in some elaborate building.

Simple cellular life of this sort depends upon water, but no more than complex life. More elaborate animals have an internal wet environment enclosed within their skins so that they can individually control the composition of the watery surroundings required by their cells. It was

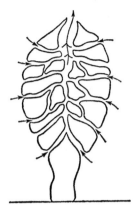

The movement of water through a live sponge — into the small holes and out through the large one

water-living animals which developed and perfected this system, and they carried it with them when they left the lakes and the oceans to evolve into dry-land species. We shall see how they created mechanical pumping systems to circulate the fluid, and how they made it ever more elaborate until the slow swirl of an ocean current was, in the end, replaced by the throbbing red river that flows secretly under the dry skin of a man.

Evolution

You will notice that here and there we are using 'purposive' language. It is difficult to avoid inferences of function, behaviour or intention in describing biological life-processes that are unconscious or blind. One may say, for example, that protoplasm 'depends' on diffusion; that it contains or exchanges 'information'; or that the cell 'needs' oxygen and 'must' get rid of carbon dioxide; or that they 'developed' pumping systems and 'left' the oceans to 'become' dry-land species. Such phrases do not imply that protoplasm is endowed with purposive consciousness or intelligence; they are simply useful ways of conveying ideas in a language where the everyday words have been moulded for thousands of years by a self-conscious human outlook so that they carry overtones of large-scale purpose, endeavour or need. Nor do they imply a belief in the existence of a life-force or of a Designer, being at least equally consistent with the hypothesis of evolution: the differential survival of variants under the influence of a blind natural selection of those organisms which are the more appropriately adapted to survive in their surroundings.

Living things, if they are to survive, 'need' to 'function' and 'behave' effectively in competitive or changing external circumstances. Of course, our view of this is retrospective. We look back at what happened and we say, 'In order to survive it "needed" to do such-and-such.' But this really means, 'Sufficient different random changes came about in certain living things for at least one of these to have resulted in more appropriate behaviour for survival in the circumstances, and the offspring which inherited that change survived, too, and produced larger numbers of descendants, as we have seen.' The smaller a target the greater the number of random shots 'needed' to hit it. Such a 'need' is not a felt want; it is a requirement for a certain performance; it is a 'need' for an arithmetical relationship to be satisfied. There is circularity here too, but while apparently purposive biological language is at worst tautological, it is at best a short-cut statistical expression of survival values.

It would be possible, but not easy, to avoid purposive phrases. I shall not even try. If the teleological implications do upset you – and it seems they upset some readers more than others – put in a *sotto voce* 'as if' every now and again: it is 'as if' the cell 'needs' oxygen.

There are many areas of science where the regularity-producing factors, but not all the regularities produced, lie outside the range of observation, often because they are in the past. Evolution relates to one of these areas of science. You can't 'prove' evolution; it is an intuitive account of 'what happened'. It offers what seems the most economical explanation – the one with the least content of unproven or unprovable assumptions – of how self-varying, self-reproducing complex matter, which we call 'living', progressed in time by natural selection to a variety of systems which contained ever greater degrees of organization.

Evolution does not require a propelling force other than the original winding-up of the universe, since it is a strange by-product of the universe's running-down, whereby events improbable at first sight are seen, after study, to be generated by the operation of the very principles of probability which they had seemed to deny.

As for the making of the inherited changes which lead to improvements in the capacity to survive, living matter makes use of a structural molecular chemistry which reproduces its kind with slight but just enough constant 'mistakes' for a number of unique try-outs always to be turning up. This in-built variability is a prerequisite of the evolutionary process, and any species will be eliminated if it loses its capacity to vary genetically in a varying environment. Individuals who have unluckily varied in a 'wrong' direction may show their inappropriateness in the form of 'disease'. The living scene is a long-term casino where play is compulsory, where few win, most lose slightly, and a few lose disastrously and with pain – which is the price of the survival of the rest.

Biological evolution has not taken place along a single narrow track, but by successions of radiating divergences. It seems that under the influence of natural selection a species of plant or animal slowly developed some entirely new feature, such as roots, or pollen, or a flower, or muscle, or lungs, or a circulatory system, or wings, or warm-bloodedness, or a shell-covered egg, or a placenta. Then the increased powers of survival, which such a novelty allowed, made it possible for that species to become the forerunner of a whole group of organisms which exploited the new advantage in a wide variety of environments, so that one proto-bird species, for instance, could then give rise to all the multiplicity of variations of the bird-type we see around us.

The very line which unwittingly pioneered the advance would itself quite probably be overwhelmed by those lines which subsequently perfected the new characteristic and thereby enjoyed the 'success' of being present on the earth in very large numbers. So there are missing links. For instance, we may find gaps if we look in a variety of currently living animals for a smooth sequence of changes by which our human blood circulatory system evolved. We will do better if we ask how various organisms (from the simplest to the most complex, but without close reference to evolution) effect adequate exchange of materials by means of fluid movement within themselves. The answers will show increasing elaboration as we look higher in the evolutionary tree — the branches of which, springing from the trunk and sub-trunks at irregular intervals, vary greatly.

Private ponds

Two-layered animals, in which the cells were covering and lining layers only, gave rise to three-layered ones. Middle-layer cells introduced a new versatility. They carried out storage and excretion, and formed the special male and female reproductive cells. They gave firmness and bulk to the body, eventually forming bone, cartilage, fibrous connective tissue, and muscle. They gave rise to the freely mobile blood cells, and to their close associates the scavenger cells which moved in the interstices of other tissues. They formed the walls and linings of the blood vessels and other fluid-holding cavities, and of those lubricated spaces within which heart, lungs, gut and joints could have freedom of movement.

Both on their own account and by giving structural support to particular areas of the covering or lining layers, they allowed the development of differentiated tissues, organs and body systems. A *tissue* is a cohesive collection of characteristic cells. The word, which comes from the French for woven cloth, embodies the idea, now a hundred and fifty years old, that there are a number of characteristic cellular webs and laceworks in the body, so that we can distinguish, for example, muscle tissue, connective tissue and glandular tissue. An *organ* is a tissue structure devoted to the specialized performance of a particular function, while a body *system* is a group of organs carrying out some general life-activity. For example, the human stomach is one of the *organs* of the digestive *system*, while the heart and blood are organs belonging to the circulatory system.

The simplest three-layered animals alive today are the flatworms.

Their middle layer, between the inner lining of the gut and the outer covering or skin, contains muscle, reproductive organs, and excretory cells which discharge waste through pores in the outer covering. In and around these special structures are large numbers of simple cells. Some of them form a supportive network and others wander around, like amoebae, on errands of scavenging or repair, in the spaces between other cells. These spaces may not be large, and the wanderer may have to squeeze to get through, but there is a potentially continuous space around all the cells within the body and it contains *tissue fluid*.

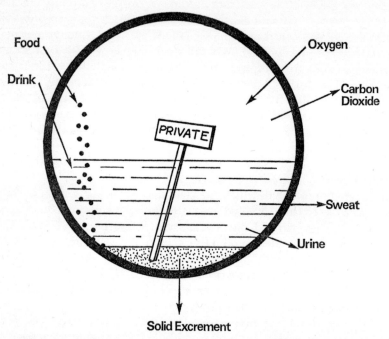

The *milieu interne*, with arrows indicating movements of gases, water and solids in and out through a relatively impermeable outer covering

Tissue fluid is mainly water, which bathes (or at least moistens) all the cells, including the undersides of those which form the outer skin and gut lining. Thus the flatworm, although it swims in a pond as an aquatic animal, carries within itself its own private pond: the enclosed watery environment, first mentioned a few pages back, which is kept clean by its own scavenging and excreting cells. This important biological concept was first understood by the great French physiologist Claude Bernard, who named it the *milieu interne*. These private ponds, underground rivers and sunless seas which surround the inner cells of three-layered animals, and which are kept constant by the excretion of unwanted waste, replenished by diffusion from the gut and protected by a relatively waterproof outer covering (the skin), allow an organism to withstand gross outside changes which would be enough to kill naked cells in a hard world. Most important, this arrangement makes the cells independent of constant external water.

The establishment of the *milieu interne* creates in an evolving aquatic organism the potential to become a large land-species absorbing oxygen from the air and needing only a regular drink to replenish the pond inside.

The flatworm is very small, and its gut is a branched tube which ramifies throughout its small body. The digested products of the food it takes in can be absorbed through the gut cells and dissolved in the tissue fluid which surrounds the middle-layer cells: it has not developed any special system of conducting-tubes to carry fluid to and fro within itself. It exchanges carbon dioxide and oxygen with the outside water through its skin, which presents the maximum surface for this purpose because of the worm's flattened shape. A parasitic tapeworm is flattened for much the same reason: so that it can present the maximum absorbing surface — relative to its volume — in the fluid, semi-digested, poorly oxygenated gut-contents in which it lives.

First blood vessels

The proboscis-worms are near relatives of the flatworm. They are so called because of the protrusible member with which they grasp their prey. They live in shallow seashore waters and are perhaps the most primitive animals to have a 'vascular' or tubed fluid-exchange system. Three simple longitudinal pipes with weak muscular walls — the blood vessels — lie embedded in their middle layer; one runs above the gut, the other two on either side of it and all join together at either end of the animal and are transversely interconnected by little side-branches. Within these tubes runs a watery 'blood' or 'plasma' in which a few cells float. In some proboscis-worms these cells contain haemoglobin, a variety of the same red pigment which colours human blood. It has a most powerful capacity for temporarily holding oxygen molecules.

There is no obvious pumping activity in the blood vessels of these worms, but their body movements — if there are indeed no co-ordinated contractions in the walls of the vessels — would keep the blood squirting to and fro. The presence of haemoglobin in some of them allows a rich supply of oxygen to be carried to muscles and other body systems. This gives a worm many survival advantages: it allows it, for instance, to be more active and aggressive than a flatworm in pursuit of food; and its tubed circulation has the greater effectiveness of a piped water-supply compared with the ooze that seeps through a riverine swamp.

Another large group of primitive animals are the round-worms, of which there are very many kinds, some of them parasitic. They have no

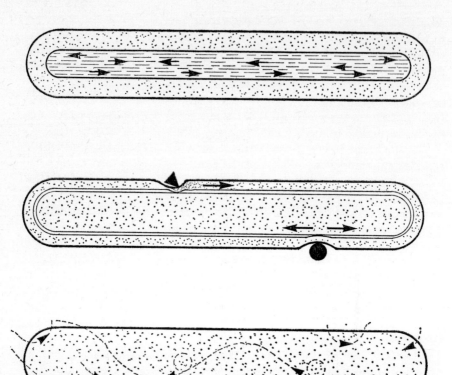

Methods of fluid-exchange in three worm types: *above*, flatworm (soak-through); *centre*, proboscis-worm (tube-squirt); *below*, round-worm (cavity-swill)

tubed circulatory system. Instead their middle-layer tissues open out to form a simple space around the gut, and this space is filled with tissue fluid which, freely flowing and flushed this way and that by the muscular movements of the body, aids in distributing food products and oxygen. If we now compare the fluid-interchange methods within deep tissues of these three worm-types, we may say that the flatworm uses a soak-through method, the proboscis-worm uses a tube-squirt method and the round-worm uses a cavity-swill method.

Now look at snails, slugs, whelks, oysters, clams, octopuses and squids. These are all molluscs. The basic design which they hit upon proved very adaptable, allowing the development of many different shapes and activities. Molluscs have vascular systems through which a thin blood circulates, and in which it is moved by specialized pumping organs, or hearts, which develop as exceptionally muscular dilatations of the vessels. These hearts massage the blood along usually by the rhythmic pulsing of two chambers acting one immediately after the other.

Molluscs have gills as well as hearts. These are organs with a large moist surface through which the blood runs in thin-walled vessels near the outside water or air, so that exchange of dissolved or gaseous oxygen or carbon dioxide with the external surroundings is made easy. A few of the molluscs have haemoglobin in their bloods, or one of the other pigments of the same type, such as haemocyanin which turns from colourless to blue when it takes up oxygen; but many molluscs have no respiratory pigment at all. In general, those molluscs which lead the most active lives have the most elaborate tubed circulatory systems. The squid, for instance, which swims at speed, has a main heart plus two auxiliary pumping stations which help to send the blood rapidly through its gills; it is also the mollusc with the most intricate fine branching of its blood vessels. In the more sedentary species, such as the clams, blood flows only partly in vessels, and partly in wide spaces and sinuses.

The worm shape is nature's favourite for living things which crawl into holes, and we find it again when we consider the common earthworm of our gardens. The most notable characteristic of this animal is the series of rings which divides up its long body into segments. Segmentation is an important feature of body organization. It offers the same sort of strategic advantages as does the division of one individual into many cells, for it allows specialization to develop locally in certain units without embarrassing the routine functions of the rest; such units of special activity may then more readily evolve into organs. All the complex higher animals show vestigial signs of transverse segmentation, though the divisions may be obscured in the mature individual: for example, the lines across the underside of a cockroach, or the backbone structure of a vertebrate are such indications.

There are two main blood vessels in the earthworm, one running longitudinally along the back (dorsally: *dorsum*, the back) and the other matching it on the underside (ventrally: *venter*, the belly). Many segmented branches connect the two main vessels transversely, and there is a rich system of fine hair-size vessels supplying the skin. The dorsal vessel is muscular, and rhythmic waves of contraction run along it from tail to head, driving the blood forwards along the worm. Flap-valves prevent any reversal of flow. At the front end, in adjacent segments, there are several pairs (five in the common species) of large muscular transverse vessels connecting the dorsal with the ventral vessel. These are 'hearts', and they contract rhythmically, forcing the blood into the ventral vessel — the distributing pipe — which has no muscle and therefore cannot contract. Under pressure from the hearts and from movements of the worm, blood flows in this vessel from head to tail and into all its lateral branches and capillaries. It is only in the hearts that the blood flows from the dorsal to the ventral vessel; it flows from the ventral to the dorsal one in all the other segmental connecting loops.

The arrangement in the earthworm differs from that which is found in the human and in all mammals, birds, reptiles and amphibians, where the *distributing* vessels (arteries) are muscular and contractile, and the *collecting* tubes (veins) are thin-walled and slack. Moreover, the blood of the vertebrates is distributed from head to tail along the body in dorsal, longitudinal vessels and returned forward on the ventral side from tail to head: the opposite of the earthworm's circuit. Further, the earthworm has a main nerve cord running along its ventral side, and in all the vertebrates this runs down the back.

The skin of the earthworm is thin and has a rich supply of capillary blood vessels because the creature has no lungs and must exchange respiratory gases through its skin. 'Capillary' means 'hair-like', but the capillaries, the smallest blood vessels of all, are finer than hairs. Their walls are composed of just a single layer of thin, flattened cells, and they run barely under the thin skin of the worm so that oxygen and carbon dioxide can diffuse across it readily—though with less facility than in lungs or gills. It is because it depends upon airborne oxygen reaching its skin that an earthworm will 'drown' in a pool of rain-water. Earthworms have cells and haemoglobin in their blood, but the pigment is in free solution in the fluid, non-cellular part; it is not within cells as in the proboscis-worms.

In nearly every segment of the earthworm there is a pair of excretory organs which are tube structures opening into pores in the skin. These organs selectively absorb and remove such fluid and waste material as is necessary to keep the worm's *milieu interne* in a steady state, so they can be regarded as primitive kidney units. To work efficiently they must be intimately in touch with the circulating blood, and so each one is supplied with a rich sheaf of capillaries. This is a structural necessity in animals having organs which filter off waste substances from the blood. In the vertebrates the general supply of blood to the kidney is always large, as you can see in a rabbit or sheep if you compare the size of the blood vessels connected to the kidneys with those supplying other organs of similar size.

Skeletons outside

The simple animals we have considereds of ar are soft-bodied. The limey or horny shell made by some of them is mainly an adventitious machine for retiring into, though indeed in the squids and cuttle-fish it gives some useful internal rigidity. But there is also that very big and success-ful group of animals which have a complete external skeleton. These are the arthropods ('the joint-footed ones'), which are well known because of the myriad forms in which they cover the earth: king-crabs, lobsters, centipedes, spiders, insects and bugs. They are segmented, and their outer protective armour makes them very secure inside, although it also creates problems of growing-up and of weight.

The circulatory systems of the arthropods are straightforward. They have a plain dorsal pulsating heart-tube with valves. Their blood has dissolved haemocyanin (a pigment containing copper, as haemoglobin contains iron) and is pumped sluggishly by the heart into vessels leading to the main parts of the body. These vessels do not branch into capillaries; instead the blood passes into sinuses and cavities in the tissues, where it circulates by the cavity-swill method. Then it flows back into a ventral space, from where, in the aquatic forms, the general movements of the body send it through the gill vessels. Here it gives up carbon dioxide and takes up oxygen and then returns to the heart.

One might think that these leggy beings, showing such a high level of complexity and rapidity of movement, would need capillary vessels to distribute their blood efficiently. However, their open circulatory plan is effective because their external skeleton provides such rigidity that fluid pathways in the intimate tissues remain permanently open. Such pathways do not need to be maintained by cell-lined tubes which, whatever their advantages, are an extra cell-barrier to contact between the blood and the tissues. (As we shall see, there is an equivalent situation in the vertebrates, in the marrow space in the hollow of a rigid bone, where there are no capillaries and the blood circulates through open areas in the jelly-like marrow, thus coming into direct contact with the tissue from which its own cells actually originate.)

Some terrestrial arthropods (such as spiders) have a sort of air-gill, known picturesquely as a lung-book; others (such as certain large insects) are equipped with a segmental series of thin-walled tubes in the main parts of the body which pass inwards from portholes in the outside skeleton, and this allows oxygen to diffuse directly to the tissues which require it and reduces the need for the carriage of respiratory gases in the blood.

But although we think of bloodstreams primarily as carriers of oxygen, they can, as we shall see, carry many things. Some bugs, for example, make use of the bloodstream to transport sperms to the ovary. The male bedbug penetrates the female in an arbitrary abdominal place, puncturing her outer covering and injecting his semen into her — a crude and random method by 'our' standards — and then his sperms are carried round in her circulation to reach and fertilize her eggs.

The blood of most arthropods contains very small cells which are able to move about, amoeba-like, by flowing. Not all their functions are known, but one might guess that scavenging is an important general activity. One other very important protective property has been observed: if the lining of a blood space is breached by an injury, the blood in it will begin to ooze away as the arthropod bleeds. Some of the mobile cells will then collect around the gap and try to fill it with their bodies, like the mythical Dutch boy who plugged the hole in the dyke. Having taken up their places they become immobilized and then tend to coalesce, losing identity as they merge into a plug of jellied protoplasm. In some species they can also release some agent into the surrounding plasma which causes a precipitation of gluey material which adds to the bulk of the plug. This is primitive blood-clotting.

It would be neat if we could now trace this clotting mechanism by continuous stages up to the seemingly elaborate reaction which occurs in our own blood, but this cannot be done. The arthropods evolved along a different path, and the fact that their blood exhibits a crude clotting mechanism shows that independent evolution of similar features can take place in different areas in response to a similar 'need'.

The terms *plasma* and *serum* will be used more and more frequently in the pages that follow, and should now be made clear—if we may leave developing circulations for a moment. When a sample of human blood clots, a clotting protein dissolved in it (fibrinogen) precipitates, as we shall see, as a jelly in which the blood cells become trapped. The jelly then slowly contracts, holding the cells but exuding a straw-

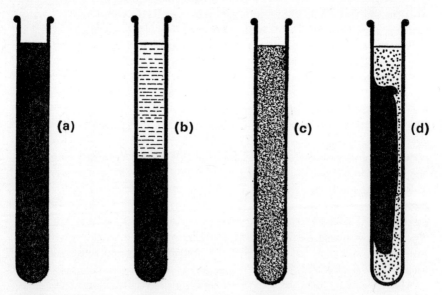

If a test tube of blood (*a*) is prevented from clotting by the addition of an anticoagulant (such as sodium citrate), the red cells will slowly sink down on standing, leaving a layer of straw-coloured *plasma* (*b*). If, however, no anticoagulant is added, the blood will clot (*c*), and then the clot will slowly contract, exuding a straw-coloured fluid, *serum* (*d*).

coloured juice: serum. The process is like whey separating from curdled milk, and 'serum' originally meant 'whey'. Serum lacks fibrinogen but it still contains all the other proteins and dissolved substances which have not been involved in the clotting reaction. Much medical testing of blood samples is carried out on serum because it can be obtained so simply, quite free of cells. It contains all the circulating antibodies, and the laboratory investigation of these is often called *serology*.

The word 'plasm', as used in proto*plasm*, originally meant 'formed' or 'moulded', but in 'plasma' the meaning has changed somewhat. Plasma is almost the same as serum except that it contains fibrinogen and other substances involved in the clotting reaction. If a sample of plasma is required, an *anticoagulant* which will prevent clotting must be added immediately after the blood is taken.

The physicists are at present stealing the word 'plasma' from the biologists, and giving it a wholly different and spectacular meaning. At very high temperatures — around a million degrees centigrade — gases pass into a state where their constituent atoms disintegrate. Negatively charged electrons become separated from their orbits around the central, positively charged nuclei of the atoms. The gas has become a 'plasma' and its freely moving electric charges make it a better conductor of electricity than a metal. This kind of plasma has been described as 'the fourth state' of matter.

If we now return to that point in the evolutionary sequence where the primitive three-layered animals first appeared, and instead of flatworms look at the echinoderms, or tough spine-skinned creatures which include sea-urchins and starfish, we find a group which, believe it or not, *is* supposed to be directly on the path leading to the vertebrates, including us. Echinoderms are slow-living, and except for the starfish can manage with a very simple circulatory system. Between their body walls and digestive tracts is a large space filled with fluid that is kept moving by the beating of microscopic hairs. This fluid bathes all the organs and conducts digested substances from the gut wall to the rest of the organism. In the starfish, some vessels connect with this space and run radially into each limb of the star, and small extensions project from these into the outside sea-water as delicate tubes covered with thin membrane. These act as 'skin-gills' for the exchange of oxygen and carbon dioxide with the outside environment. In a related species, the sea-cucumber, the plan is the reverse. A pair of branched tubes arises from the hindmost part of the gut and these extend inwards into the body-fluid cavity and end blindly. Through them the animal can send a rhythmic flow of sea-water to and fro, and this is its way of 'breathing'.

A special and peculiar character of all these spine-skinned animals is a low-pressure hydraulic system by which sea-water is conducted along tubes into soft 'tube-feet'. These move by becoming turgid or lax according to the pressure of water inside them, and have suckers at their tips for gripping solid surfaces. This specialized bit of plumbing is not connected to the general body-fluid cavity mentioned above, though doubtless the water in it performs simple respiratory-exchange functions in the 'feet' and the tubes which supply them. (There are some animals, mentioned later, which make use of the bloodstream itself for hydraulic enlargements or extendings of the body.)

The most rudimentary youthful or larval stage of these starfish, sea-urchins, sea-cucumbers and sea-lilies resembles that of the next group, which is still farther along the evolutionary path leading in the end to man.

Backbones beginning

Backbones begin with creatures that have curious names: the sea-squirts (*Ascidian tunicates*, 'Like wineskins in their underwear') and the lancelet (*Amphioxus*, 'At both ends sharp'). Amphioxus has gill-slits through which sea-water moves. It also has colourless blood which flows through vessels leading to the gills. The circulatory layout of the sea-squirts is not so elaborate.

Sea-squirts lead an inactive life and therefore do not need an intricate system of circulating blood. But they have one unique feature: a simple tubular heart which reverses the direction of the blood-flow at regular intervals – say thirty beats in one direction and then thirty in the other. This is done with two pacemakers which have reciprocating sensitivities.

Amphioxus is different, being a small muscular primitive fish and a more obvious ancestor of us vertebrates. Its blood is pumped forward to the gill-slits by a contractile ventral vessel and then passes back down the body in a pair of dorsal arteries to be distributed to the capillaries of the muscles and the intestine. ('Ventral' means on the belly side, that is, below if you're a worm or a fish or a four-legged vertebrate. 'Dorsal' means on the back side, that is, above. Man has assumed an upright position, and so for him ventral and dorsal are the equivalent of anterior and posterior.) Amphioxus has no heart, but it is the first character we meet who has a liver, and the blood-flow through this organ involves a new and important principle.

In a vertebrate animal, the products of the digested swallowed food are absorbed into the capillaries of the intestinal wall, and dissolved in the blood which runs into a special vein leading directly to the liver. There the vein divides again into fine capillaries, so that the blood will come into intimate contact with the liver cells. The vein is the *hepatic portal vein*, and its name refers to the 'gate of the liver', the *porta hepatis* by which the vein enters. Perhaps we may again jump ahead a little in order to consider the origin of this name.

In ancient times the appearance of the liver of a newly sacrificed

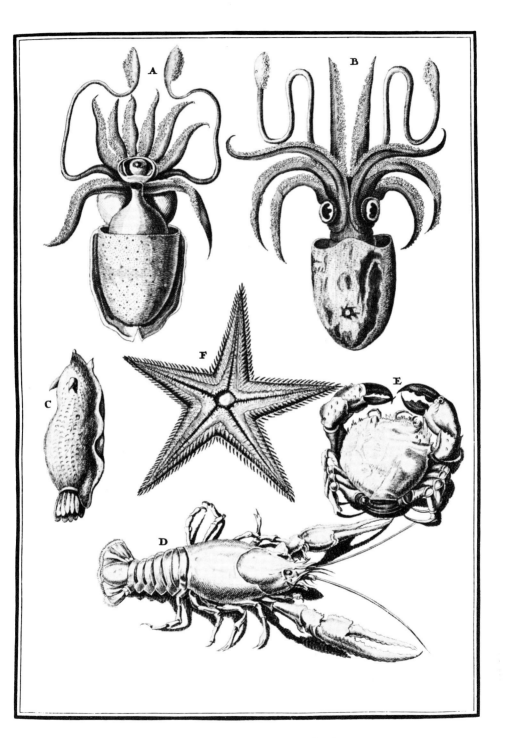

Molluscs, arthropods and an echinoderm

animal (bird, goat, sheep, ox) was commonly used to foretell the future, particularly the outcome of a proposed political or military action. It was believed that the liver was the organ in which emotional feeling, and life itself, was seated, and in which food was turned into blood and charged with 'natural spirit' which was then supposed to be distributed round the body. At the moment of death, when the Gods visited the body to snatch back this spirit, one might consequently expect to see some imprint of the 'divine intention' on the liver.

The shapes of individual human and animal livers vary slightly from body to body, and the ancients made an elaborate catalogue of areas, edges, fissures, knobs and so on, all of which had significance for the seer, who recognized in them not only a 'gate', but 'rivers', 'paths', 'mountains', 'the tooth', 'the ear', 'the finger', etc. Divination by the liver alone is *hepatoscopy*. *Haruspicy* or *extispicy* is soothsaying by observing *all* the inner parts of a sacrifice. Foretelling the future specifically by the entrails of men is *anthropomancy*.

The haruspices were important officials throughout the history of ancient Rome, from its foundation to the time of Constantine. They believed that the left side of the sacrificial victim was unlucky. To the Romans the left was the hostile side and the right was friendly, and the belief survives in such words as 'sinister' and 'dexterity'. The right part of the liver was consulted in matters concerning the questioner himself, the left for anything involving other parties. Now, after two thousand years, the modern physician still examines his recumbent patient from the right side, the surgeon operates from the right, and the pathologist (who perhaps is the inheritor, more than any of his medical colleagues, of the arts of the haruspex and the anthropomancer) performs his necroscopies from the right. Who says doctors aren't conservative?

The liver of a vertebrate carries on multiple functions of sorting, cleansing, storing and processing many of the substances deriving from the food. The blood leaves the liver again, collecting once more into a single vessel, which in the case of amphioxus joins the main ventral stream as it passes forward to the gills. In the proper fishes, this ventral blood tube becomes a muscular pulsating heart which drives the blood through the series of looped arterial arches running along its gills.

Fish heart

The heart of a fish is an S-shaped tube. One turn of the S is very muscular; this is the *ventricle* ('little belly'), the muscular pumping chamber. At the entrance and exit of the ventricle are small flap-valves so arranged that blood can move out of this chamber in one direction only: towards the gills. It does this as the ventricle contracts. As the ventricle relaxes after each beat, it refills from a reservoir at the entrance turn of the S.

Except for some in icy seas, fishes are red-blooded and have haemo-globin in their blood cells. The idea was thought up by the proboscis-worms, abandoned by the echinoderms (evolutionarily speaking) and hit on again by the fishes. The haemoglobin of non-backboned animals, which is in free solution in their blood, consists of very large molecules — perhaps to prevent its escaping into the tissues through the exchange-holes in their blood-vessel walls, which are of ordinary-molecule size. (When human haemoglobin escapes from a red cell, it quickly becomes bound to a particular plasma protein — haptoglobin — which effectively

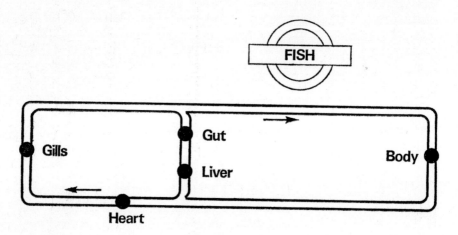

increases its molecular weight about four times.) If, in the vertebrates, small-molecule haemoglobin at the customary blood-strength were in free solution in the plasma and not enclosed within blood cells, their blood would be very thick and viscous, and the flow along the walls of their capillary vessels would suffer from stasis and drag. This dis-advantage would offset any increased ease of oxygen-exchange which might seem to be possible if there were no hampering blood-cell wall.

The blood which passes through the heart of a fish is lacking in oxygen because the hungry tissues have taken it from the circulation; at the same time, it is rich in carbon dioxide which they have produced. When the blood reaches the gills it picks up fresh oxygen, and its carbon dioxide washes out as it passes through the capillaries in contact with the water. The pressure of a fish's heart-beat drives the blood as far as the gill arches but here the gill capillaries, which are fine and numerous, slow down the flow of blood, so that it resumes its journey round the body at low pressure.

Myxine (the Hag), a very primitive sea fish — only a stage or two beyond Amphioxus in evolutionary terms, and a long way before the proper fishes — has a many-hearted circulation. It (or she?) has a 'conventional' vertebrate heart pumping blood through the gills, and no less than *three* subsidiary hearts which, severally, send blood through the liver, and return it from the head, and from the tail.

The amphibians evolved from the early fishes. The reptiles evolved from amphibians. The birds, and the mammals, evolved from the reptiles. An important factor in this metamorphosis was the development of lungs for breathing air. Lungs are spongy structures connected to the mouth and nose by a branching air passage. They are formed of intimately divided air spaces which have a moist lining generously served with blood capillaries. Because of the numerous wall divisions, exchanges of oxygen and carbon dioxide between the blood in the capillaries and the air breathed in and out of the lungs take place over a very large surface. Of great help to the amphibians was a rearrangement of the circulatory system whereby the blood from the lungs immediately returns to the heart for an added pressure-boost for its journey around the general circulation of the organs and tissues of the body.

From a heart-and-a-half to two hearts

In the frogs and toads the 'refreshed' blood from the lungs (*pulmonary* blood) mixed in the heart to some extent with the 'exhausted' blood returning from the general circulation, because there was an incomplete division within the heart for keeping the streams separate. Nevertheless,

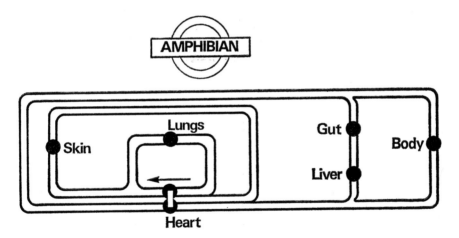

these amphibians found it quite good enough for their part-dry-land, slow-tempo existence. The air they could now breathe contained far more oxygen than the water. And their thin, moist skin had a good blood supply too, and acted as an additional membrane for oxygen-exchange in either water or air.

The growth of the dividing wall which created—from the original fish heart—a 'heart-and-a-half' in the frogs and toads, continued further in the reptiles, and further still in the birds and mammals, until the 'heart' became a matching *pair* of pumps. These pumps were quite separate, but since they had developed from one musculature, there were all the advantages of unified control and action: so today the human heart, which is two hearts, beats as one. Clearly each side must put out the same volume of blood with each stroke, if there is not to be a dangerous 'piling-up' on one side or the other in a high-pressure circulation. Effective muscular co-ordination might have been harder to achieve if two entirely separated hearts had developed in vertebrates, one for the pulmonary and one for the general circulation.

Perhaps future mammals will require an accessory abdominal heart in the portal vein, or a cranial one in the circle of arteries at the base of

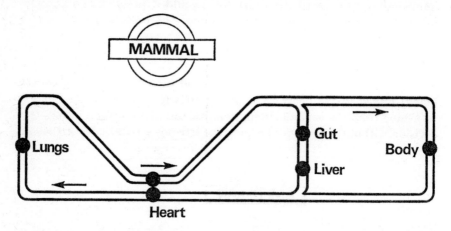

the brain, to improve the efficiency of the blood-flow through the liver or to the cerebral hemispheres. A renal heart and circulation which would send all the blood of the body through the kidneys each time round (like the pulmonary circulation) is another possibility. A 'Design for Better Bodies' competition among biology-minded chemists, engineers, architects or communications experts could provide many stimulating ideas. It is often said, for instance, that anyone knowing some optics could design a much better lens system than that of the human eye. This is quite true, but the difficulty is to arrange to grow one and see with it.

The basic circulatory system, even in warm-blooded mammals, is evidently still open to evolutionary 'improvement'. For example, the pigeon has large blood spaces in its breast muscles. These muscles move the wings, which are small for a heavy bird and therefore have to beat with great force for short periods immediately after take-off and while gaining altitude. The blood spaces are fed by arteries and fill up with oxygenated blood while the bird is at rest. They then act as reservoirs for the stress periods when the wing-beating muscles need to be super-charged with oxygen. Again, some of the bats (which are, of course, mammals) have muscular areas surrounding the veins of their thin, membranous wings. These accessory 'hearts' help to return blood to the central parts of the circulation.

If it were necessary for survival, could the reshuffling of a few hundred human genes recapture, maybe at some opportune moment of embryonic growth, the ancient arrangement of Myxine and produce a new human with interesting throbs in neck, belly and pelvis? After all, the circu-latory and nerve-cord arrangement of Amphioxus is, roughly speaking, the earthworm plan upside down, though the same does not apply consistently to other parts, such as the relative position of the mouth. So perhaps we backboned species are worms that turned over at a critical point in our evolutionary development? And if we have that sort of evolutionary potentiality, and allowing for the fact that an embryo during growth recapitulates the evolutionary development of its species, retaining some features and discarding others, why then can we not now evolve the hagfish type of circulatory adaptations if we need them?

Such simplistic possibilities may not be worth discussing in view of the fact that the evolution of the circulatory systems of the earthworm, the lancelet, the hagfish and man each took many millions of years, and major modifications to any of them would presumably take as long again. But, all the same, evolution is a mechanism for generating apparent unlikelihoods. And evolution has now produced the human brain. And the brain is thinking about manufacturing genetic material in the laboratory—which could be very dangerous, but also a great short-cut in evolutionary time.

Circulation in large plants

Having considered the whole animal kingdom, it would be improper to neglect the plants, for the green ones on whom we red animals depend have circulatory problems too.

Briefly, the smallest primitive microscopic plants, like their animal counterparts, live their active lives in water, and so their exchange problems are solved by simple diffusion and protoplasmic movement. Again as with the animals, it is the larger forms which need elaborate circulatory systems, particularly those which live on dry land. Big land-plants are sessile, they do not move. As they grow larger they send their roots deeper and deeper into the soil, and extend their leaves higher and higher towards the open sunlight. The biggest trees can grow to 400 feet (120 metres) above the ground. The leaves at their tops constantly require much water which must be conducted upwards, against gravity, from the roots. In the sunlight the green leaves make sugars which are carried as a weak syrup down to various parts of the plant for conversion into other material or for storage. The superficial woody parts of a tree and the 'ribs' and 'veins' of stems and leaves contain systems of small tubes which carry the water up and out; they also contain end-to-end chains of elongated communicating cells through which the sugar syrup passes, usually in the opposite direction to the flow of water.

In order to make the sugar, the green leaves require sunlight for energy, carbon dioxide gas which they take from the air where it is present in low concentration, and water. There are small orifices in the otherwise impermeable surfaces of leaves, and these allow air to enter and come into contact with cells lining the microscopic spaces inside. The surfaces of these cells are wet with a film of water in which the carbon dioxide can dissolve. (Compare the moist cells which line the lungs of a vertebrate and which absorb oxygen.) For this reason, and because water is one of the ingredients of sugar, the plant needs a lot of it, but the plant also *loses* water through the orifices in the leaves. The amount of water which evaporates in this way is very great: for example, for every one-pound (0.45 kilogram) weight of tubers produced by a potato plant (by the storage of the sugar it makes in the form of starch), it loses, uncontrollably, over 66 pounds (30 kilograms) of water by evaporation—more than 60 gallons (270 litres). This water levy a dry-land plant must pay is part of the price of leaving its ancestral sea, and it is the reason why it must stand with its water-seeking roots in the ground.

There is no contractile pumping tissue in a green plant—no heart, no throbbing arteries. But water can move from the roots up the stems and trunks at the rate of half an inch a second when the sun is warm on a tree with many leaves. Roots extend through soil which, though it may seem dry, consists of multi-millions of very small particles each surrounded by a microscopic film of water. This water diffuses directly into hair-like cells which grow out of all roots and curl closely around the soil grains. Diffusion pressure in the roots is sufficient to force water some way up a tall tree. At the same time, the cells in the leaves far above are losing water, which is flowing from their vessels and thus pulling up more water from below. The microscopic pores in the cell walls from which the water evaporates are so small that fluid cannot 'fall back' down the tubes of the trunk when air is drawn in through the leaf orifices, as could happen if both they and the tubes were of a large bore. At this tiny order of size the behaviour of liquids in tubes is not the same as it is in everyday large-scale experience. In effect, the combined evaporation 'pull' from the top of the plant and diffusion pressure 'shoving' up from the roots below is enough to make the sap flow right up through even the tallest tree-trunks.

The pressures and tensions involved are considerable, and the conducting tissue of large plants is reinforced to cope with them. It might be thought that a column of water would break into bubbles of water vapour or of dissolved air if it were mainly drawn up, like a steel wire, by the evaporation pull from the leaves above. (After all, a lift pump will draw water no higher than about twenty feet — six metres — up from a well.) However, experiments have shown that sap can withstand considerable tension and will remain in a continuous column, perhaps being prevented from breaking by the presence of dissolved protein. Nevertheless, just as it is easy to 'explain' the pumping 'mechanism' of the heart if you ignore the chemical levels of the problem of just how and why each minute muscle fibre contracts over and over again at the right time and to the right extent; so also it may be that the flow of sap depends for its final reliability on some molecular mechanism that requires energy to be expended by the living protoplasm of those cells which accompany the conducting tubes of the stems and trunks of green plants.

CHAPTER TWO

Thicker than Water

Somewhere, as we have seen, in one of the worm stages of animal evolution, blood became significantly thicker than water. By the time wriggling worm had evolved into backboned fish, blood had many of the functions it has in our own bodies today. In fact it is doubtful whether many genuinely new molecular features have appeared in earth's living matter since that time; it has been more a matter of the exploitation of capabilities which were already present in primitive form in the first vertebrates. The animals of the sea adapted themselves to its temperature, to its currents, its tides, and to the substances dissolved in it. In their own private internal circulations the range of salts remains somewhat the same as in the primitive sea-water in which their basic cellular natures evolved.

Prick your finger and suck the flowing blood. It's faintly of the sea, with a richer underlying taste. The sea doesn't contain salt simply because fundamentally seas are salty and rivers fresh. Rivers are slightly salty too, for rain falling on the land dissolves traces of the mineral salts of the earth and carries them to the rivers. The rivers flow to the sea. Originally the sea was as fresh as the rivers, but the heat of the sun evaporates water from its surface, leaving behind the salts which, as the ages go by, become ever more concentrated in this vast still. Today's seas are saltier than those in which life first evolved.

And now, night and day, the cells of all the air-breathing backboned animals — whether frogs or finches, lizards or lemmings, humans or whales — are nostalgically juggling with atoms and molecules in order to be able to swim for ever in a latter-day version of the fossil seas of their far, far distant fathers — ancient mariners who never knew dry land or smelled flowers, four hundred million years ago.

Warm blood

In one most important respect, however, our blood is different from cold sea-water: it's warm. Everyone knows that birds and mammals are 'warm-blooded' and all other vertebrates are 'cold-blooded'. The distinction is long established, but although it seems simple it needs some elaboration and explanation. For instance, the warmth of warm-blooded animals is not essentially in their blood: the slow furnaces of all vertebrates are the chemical reactions in their muscles, livers and other active cell systems. The blood distributes this heat around the body; it does not itself generate heat. The warm-blooded animals keep warm because they have developed surfaces which can prevent heat loss. A bird is insulated by air trapped in its feathers; most mammals achieve the same result with hair, which covers a layer of insulating fat.

For fine control of temperature there are centres in our brains which act as thermostats, sending out nerve impulses which open up or shut down the small blood vessels of the skin. Here there are sensory nerve-endings by which we feel hot or cold objects, but also these nerve-endings 'tell' us whether our skin is relatively hot or relatively cold. If we get too hot we flush and sweat to dissipate heat through the skin, which consequently 'feels hot'; too cold, and the blood-flow to our surface decreases as the blood vessels of the skin shut down, so that outwardly we turn pale and the skin 'feels cold'. But this is only because heat loss from the body is being minimized; the temperature deep inside us does not fall. At the same time involuntary muscle contractions (shivering) may generate extra warmth in the deeper layers.

The importance of the 'I feel hot' and 'I feel cold' sensations is greatly overstressed in urban societies where we have developed the habit of complaining about them — crouching in front of a heater or turning on the electric blanket when we 'feel cold', or reiterating that the summer days are 'too hot'. Both are conventional responses: we are only talking about natural regulating mechanisms of skin, blood and sweat, which under most ordinary conditions keep our internal temperatures constant no matter what we do or say.

Much of the effectiveness of the heat-regulating mechanisms of birds and mammals depends on the physical properties of water, which is the main constituent of blood and sweat. Water has a higher specific heat than any other common liquid or solid: this means that it can absorb a lot of heat without getting much hotter itself. It has a high conductivity too, so it is very effective in transferring heat from the deeper to the superficial layers of the body. It has a very high latent heat of evaporation — more heat is needed to evaporate it — which makes it very effective as sweat. Incidentally, you can't sweat blood, in spite of the well-known phrase.

A 'cold-blooded' lizard on a rock cannot control its temperature. It has to take up the heat of its surroundings. On a cold day it is cold-blooded, and on a warm sunny day, warm-blooded. Whereas the timing throughout each day seems uniform to us — with our bodies and brains working at constant speed because of our constant temperatures — the lizard would find (if it had the faculty) that hot days, when it would move faster and get more done, seemed to last longer than cold ones. Watch ants on a hot day and see how much they do. They double their activities for every 10°C rise in temperature and halve them for every 10°C fall. Indeed, someone with a good ear for music can learn to tell the daily temperature from the note given out by local humming insects whose rate of wing beat, or stridulating 'song', will vary accordingly.

Blood bankers chill blood to reduce its living rate so that it will stay alive longer before transfusion. Surgeons may chill a whole living human body, overcoming its heat-regulating mechanisms and reducing its rate of living, so that it can temporarily manage without a blood supply (i.e. without circulating oxygen or nourishment) during an operation on the heart or blood vessels.

All of this points to one advantage of keeping a constant warm body temperature: the processes of the body, and particularly those of the brain, then run at a steady fast rate which makes it possible to get plenty done and to have consistent 'experience' from day to day no matter what the temperature of one's surroundings. The biological 'clock in the head' keeps regular time. When your body temperature rises, as it does in fever, the days may appear long, though not everyone seems to experience this. Perhaps more important, your body's chemical mechanisms accelerate, and unless you can take in extra food to satisfy their increased energy requirements, your own tissues will be consumed. That is why muscle-wasting and weight loss is usual in persistent fever. The hoary adage 'Feed a cold and starve a fever' is absolutely bad treatment. It is based on the old humoral pathology and on an analogy with the behaviour of fire—and realizing this, a discerning Irish physician of the nineteenth century, Robert J. Graves, who gave his name to Graves' Disease, said he would like his epitaph to be 'He Fed Fevers'.

One might ask, Why 37°C (98.4°F)?—for all earth's creatures with a constant warm body temperature maintain it within a degree or two of this point on the thermometer. The reason is not known. It is possible that this temperature is the highest which can be sustained by some of the vital protein structures of the body without soon becoming coagulated or denatured. Or perhaps we are the children of some very early forms of life which lived in warm shallow water where a higher temperature was never experienced, and those germs and amoebae developed fundamental molecular patterns of life to which we are still bound. However, both of these explanations would seem to be invalidated by the fact that many quite complicated aquatic species, including arthropods and fish, have evolved varieties which today can live in hot springs at higher temperatures than this. Anyway, 37°C is as high as *we* can go for long periods with safety. If we *could* live at a steady temperature of, say, 80°C, we would need to eat continuously to produce enough heat, and grow a thick fleece like a merino sheep in order to conserve it. We would have to take care not to go up a mountain, where we would boil in the reduced atmospheric pressure. On the other hand, our inner machinery would run at sixteen times its present pace, so that assuming the human life span remained the same, we would each then be able to fit in about twelve hundred years of our present rate of thought and 'experience' before dying.

The elephant and dragon

Clear ideas about the difference between warm- and cold-blooded animals have slowly developed over the last three hundred years — out of the invention of the thermometer and an understanding of the physical nature of heat. Before this even the best people were confused. There is, for instance, the tale of the ancient enmity between the elephant and the dragon. Pliny the Elder, who perished in the eruption of Vesuvius in August of A.D. 79, gives an account of it in his exhaustive *Natural History*, a great storehouse of ancient errors.

The animal known as the dragon in Pliny's time was a large tropical serpent of the boa-constrictor type; it was not found in Italy, so his knowledge of it would have been from hearsay. Later, in the Middle Ages, dragons became more mythical and elaborate, with wings, legs and a tendency to breathe fire, until in the end they resembled the sort of monster that St George took on.

According to Pliny, India was the place where the largest elephants and the largest dragons were to be found. The dragons there were perpetually at war with the elephants. This was because the dragons got overheated in the torrid summer and sought out the elephants, whose blood was quite remarkably cold. The dragons, Pliny said, would lie in wait in trees, watching the path the elephants would take on their way to the river to drink. Then a dragon would coil itself around an elephant's legs and trunk, fixing its teeth behind the ear where the poor beast could not protect itself, and would greedily suck out all that lovely cool elephant blood. The elephant would faint and fall, and crash to the ground, carrying with it the dragon — now so stupefied by its huge, jumbo-sized drink as to be unable to wriggle away. The enormous weight of the dying elephant would crush and burst the dragon, and out would pour a rare mixture of hot and cold bloods which, congealing to solid matter on the ground, could afterwards be gathered up by people of the locality.

Now this dragon's blood (also known as Indian cinnabar) was, according to Pliny, the only pigment with which a painter could give a proper representation of blood in a picture. Moreover, he condemned physicians who confused it with mineral cinnabar or minium in making medicines — and rightly so, for cinnabar, or vermilion, from the mines is poisonous red sulphide of mercury, and minium is poisonous red oxide of lead, while the *Sanguis Draconis* of the apothecaries is harmless.

There are no facts to support the story of the elephant and the dragon. The elephant's blood was and is as warm as yours, while that of a dragon —if the dragon was a snake—was cold by night and warm by day if it lay in the sun. All the same, you could, up to a few years ago, buy an ounce of *Sang. Drac.* out of the drawer at any old-established chemist's shop. It is a red resin exuded upon the fruits of a tree in the East Indies, but for the European city merchants who received and traded the substance it was indeed, up to three hundred years ago, real dragon's blood. The Jews used it homoeopathetically to heal circumcision wounds and it remained in the pharmacopoeia but, like other resins and balsams, as time went on it fell out of therapeutic use. It was still used to redden varnishes, to stain marble and sometimes to colour dentifrices; also, more recently, to protect those parts not to be etched in zinc line-engravings. But today, with synthetic materials of all kinds to replace it, you will have difficulty in getting dragon's gore.

Inspire, expire

If the dispersion of heat by the blood can be likened to some kind of commercial heating and cooling system that depends upon the movement of fluids in pipes, there are similar analogies which indicate the other main functions of human blood. They read like the brass plates of a successfully diversified business: Gas and Special Transport, Cross-Channel Communications, Scavengers Inc., Stock Exchange, Irrigation Services, The Disinfecting Co. Ltd, Self-Sealing Inner Tubes, Prospectors' Samples, Security Patrols, Acid Safety.

Human life is intimately associated with breathing. In ancient times one took in a part of the 'world spirit' with each breath, and lost it when one breathed one's last. The 'wine spirit' (which could be made visible by distillation) could, if swallowed, have marked effects on behaviour. The similarity of meaning between 'spiritual' and 'spirituous' in our language today is a mark of the very real confusion of ideas which these concepts once involved. Nowadays, to 'expire' has become synonymous with dying, whereas to 'inspire' which originally meant to 'breathe or blow into' now means 'to stimulate creatively'; inspiration can 'set the soul on fire'.

The physical fire or metabolism of the body is like a burning coal, with the pace slowed down. Oxygen unites with carbon, producing energy and carbon dioxide. The energy drives the machinery of the body, and some is wasted as excess heat, as in a fuel-burning engine. We have already seen that oxygen in air comes from green plants which use the energy of sunlight to build sugars from carbon dioxide. The plant needs some of the oxygen produced in the process to drive its own cell engines, but it has a surplus left which wafts into the air. We animals are completely dependent on green plants for the release of oxygen from carbon dioxide. Fish get their oxygen from the air too: oxygen dissolves in water. So fish are often to be found in the tumbling parts of streams or near the surface or where the waves are breaking, for there the water is well oxygenated through mixing with air. And so all flesh is grass, but in the same sense all grass is sun, so the herbs needn't get too upstage about their primary position.

The French chemist Lavoisier, who in 1777 showed that combustion requires oxygen, became aware that physiological 'respiration' is a similar process: that the body takes in 'oxygen' (which he named) and slowly 'burns' it. This elucidated the muddled *pneuma* of the ancients, the essential inspired constituent of the air which charges blood with 'vital spirit'. Lavoisier's fellow countrymen cut off his head in 1794, saying that their new Republic needed no savants. The next day a French mathematician remarked, 'Il ne leur a fallu qu'un moment pour faire tomber cette tête, et cent années peut-être ne suffiront pas pour en reproduire une semblable.'* (He was wrong – though he did say 'perhaps' – for Pasteur was to be born in 1822.)

More oxygen dissolves in cold than in hot water. When you raise the temperature of water in a glass vessel, you can see bubbles rising to the surface long before it boils. These are bubbles of air (including oxygen) which can no longer remain in solution as the temperature rises. On a warm day your goldfish gasps – from the lack of oxygen in his warm water. His personal temperature rises too (because he can't control it), which forces all his body cells to work faster, so that they need extra oxygen, of which there is now less than usual – cruel dilemma. Put in some ice, stir the water to oxygenate it and he'll revive. In Antarctic seas where sea-water slaps against ice faces, the amount of oxygen dissolved is so great, and (because of the cold) the need for it so greatly reduced, that certain fish can carry sufficient oxygen in their blood without any respiratory pigment. So they have no haemoglobin and their gills and blood are colourless – not 'bloodless fish', as they are called, but haemoglobinless.

Very young eels are transparently flat and leaf-shaped – quite unlike the adult fish – and although they live in warm seas, this shape enables them also to do without haemoglobin; instead they obtain their oxygen by diffusion, like flatworms. When they grow up they produce red blood as they adopt the rounded eel-shape.

Haemoglobin, the red iron-containing pigment of blood, has a great affinity for oxygen when that gas is plentiful, as it is in the air breathed into the lungs. But haemoglobin will readily release oxygen if it is in a situation where free oxygen is scarce, as it is among the live cells of working tissues. Haemoglobin gives blood an oxygen-carrying capacity

---

* 'Only a moment was required to sever that head, and perhaps a century will not be sufficient to produce another like it.'

eighty times greater than this would be if the oxygen was merely dissolved in a watery plasma, as it is in those Antarctic fish.

A man at work needs about a gallon (4½ litres) of oxygen gas a minute. If there were no haemoglobin in human blood, it would require about 300 gallons (1,360 litres) of plasma to carry one gallon of oxygen, and his heart would therefore have to pump 300 gallons per minute. Such a heart would be big: it would have to weigh between 50 and 60 pounds (22 to 27 kilograms) — one-third the weight of a man — instead of one pound (half a kilogram), and it would cause the chest to project two feet (60 centimetres).

When haemoglobin gives up its oxygen, it becomes capable of taking up some carbon dioxide, which it carries to the lungs. The rest of the carbon dioxide is carried in the plasma, dissolved as bicarbonate.

The human red cell is disc-shaped, as are such cells in all the vertebrates. In birds, reptiles, amphibia and fishes the red cells are nucleated

Human red cells (*left*) are discs with a depression on each flat surface. In the bone marrow the developing red cells are nucleated (*centre*), the nucleus becoming smaller and denser until finally extruded. The red cell of an amphibian or of a fish (*right, to same scale*) is also flattened, but it is much larger and remains nucleated in the circulation.

and tend to be much larger than in mammals, where they lose their nuclei before being released into the bloodstream. Losing the nucleus has certain consequences for the red cell — if you can still call it a cell after it has lost such a vital part. It becomes an oxygen-carrying pawn, a zombie, a specialist working superbly but unable to be diverted to anything else. Nearly all the space in the cell is now occupied by haemoglobin, and since a non-nucleated corpuscle needs very little personal oxygen for its restricted private life, it carries a maximum amount of oxygen to the point of delivery.

The centre of the human red cell is thinner than the edges. This gives it a large surface relative to its volume and allows oxygen to diffuse rapidly to all parts. It also allows it to swell and shrink, and to be squashed through narrow capillaries without its surface being subjected to serious mechanical shearing or bursting strains (as would happen if it were, for instance, a sphere). Being flat, its sides can move in and out like those of an oil can. (A human red cell cannot repair itself. After three or four months in the circulation it is old and battered, and is eliminated and replaced.)

Added together, the surfaces of all the red cells of a grown man become an area something like ten tennis courts. This seems enormous —and of course it is if you think of it as an oxygen-exchanging sheet being towed round and round inside the body by the heart engine — but the analogy is only pointing up the fact that when material is divided up small, its surface area greatly increases. (As material division gets towards molecular size, you begin to realize that the reaction between, say, a dissolved acid and a base in a test tube must involve so much 'surface' that the two will meet in a resounding clash, and so no wonder there is fizzing and heat.)

Common carrier

Many substances which are formed in one part of the body are carried in the bloodstream so that they can influence other parts, as a dye thrown into a rivulet can act as a signal when it reaches a place downstream. For example, the pituitary gland at the base of the brain releases substances into the bloodstream which on reaching specific targets will variously stimulate growth, thyroid-gland activity, adrenal-gland activity, sex-gland activity or the secretion of milk in the breasts, and so on. Here the blood is providing a common communication channel, as the post office provides a means by which we can post letters to one another.

A blood function of a similar kind is the transport of dangerous substances in safe form. For example, the body has important physiological uses for certain metals, such as copper and iron, which in a raw state are violently active, chemically speaking; and in the plasma there are proteins which specifically bind or hold iron and copper molecules while they are being moved around the body. This inactivates them during transport and also prevents their being filtered out into the urine, because the protein molecules to which they are bound are large. In the same way, if some haemoglobin, or any of the yellow pigment which derives from it, has been released into the plasma from a broken red cell, there are appropriate proteins in the plasma to bind each of them. Other substances, such as enzymes and certain drugs, also travel in the bloodstream in a bound state.

Some theorists go so far as to suggest that because there is such a variety of special soluble protein molecules for so many particular functions, one should think of the circulating plasma as the complete mobile dissolved counterpart of the fixed tissues of the body. Perhaps the vertebrate evolutionary process modified certain protoplasmic and cell-wall structures in such a way that they became part of the fluid plasma of the blood. Many of the particular plasma proteins turn up in slightly different forms in different individuals, the variations being inherited, so that the blood reflects individual constitution. This indicates how much information a doctor may hope to get from a sample of human blood, for this blood is a much thicker and more complex soup than the thin fluid circulating in a primitive fish. Like a prospector who seeks traces of minerals in a piece of rock, a physician can send a specimen of his patient's blood to a laboratory, and have measured any of the hundreds of items which, being normal or deranged in the body, generally reveal themselves in the circulation. One could even say that an advanced 'function' of the blood is to provide an examination point for the diagnosis of disease or the establishing of identity.

The total number of nucleated cells in the adult human body is somewhere around 100,000,000,000,000. In some tissues, such as brain

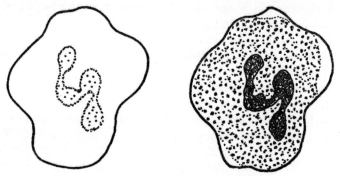

'White' blood cells are colourless when examined under a microscope (*left*), but the microscopist usually stains them with red and blue dyes (*right*) so that nucleus and cytoplasm are clearly distinguished.

or muscle, cells do not continue to divide once the part has fully grown, although they take in food substances and release waste material. On the other hand there are parts of the body where cells normally have quite a short life of days or weeks. They die off and are replaced by others dividing. When such cells are not on a surface (such as the skin or the lining of the gut) which constantly sheds itself to the outside world, there is considerable accumulation of cell debris. So the body has to clean out its own tissues.

It does this through the activity of a family of special cells with streaming tendrils of cytoplasm. Like amoebae, these are able to corner and engulf the dead bits, digesting them so that the soluble components can be re-used or excreted. Some of these engulfing cells are anchored in the linings of certain blood spaces; others wander through all the fluid-filled gaps in the tissues of almost any part of the body, and take distributive joy rides in the bloodstream. Such cells have no haemo-

The microscopic structure of woody plant tissues, which contain
small tubes carrying water

globin, and so when seen in blood (under the microscope), they are called the 'white' blood cells or leucocytes (Greek *leukos*, white), also phago-cytes (Greek *phagein*, to eat). In stained microscopic preparations they take up the red and blue dyes and so have a purplish look. There are far more of them outside the bloodstream than in it, and in this sense they are not exclusively blood cells as the red cells are. On a flat surface they spread out in the shape of fried eggs and move like amoebae, but in the flowing blood they are rounded. There are three main types: fast-crawling, slow-crawling, and those which are fixed to the walls of blood spaces in the spleen, liver and lymph nodes. The fast movers are 'polymorphonuclear leucocytes'; the slow ones, slightly larger, are 'mononuclear leucocytes'. These names signify the type of nucleus: that

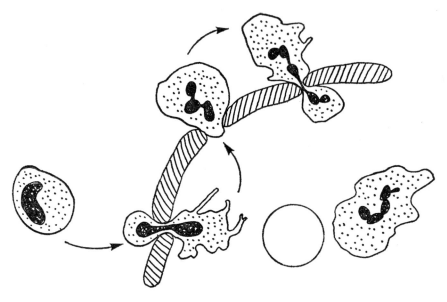

Polymorphonuclear leucocytes — a fast-moving phagocyte which, by squirming between the body's tissue cells, draws its nucleus into a series of lobes. The disc represents a red cell on the same scale.

of the first kind is usually like a short string of rough beads, while that of the second is a single rounded lump. Both start off with a round nucleus, but the fast-moving type squirms and pushes its way through the narrow spaces in the capillary walls, and between the tissue cells, and in so doing its nucleus gets dragged out into lobes which do not re-form into a single round mass. It is possible to tell whether a poly-morphonuclear cell is young or old by counting the number of lobes in its nucleus: the more lobes, the longer the period of its active existence.

When waste particles are taken into scavenging cells and 'digested', the process is similar to that which takes place in the gut. Here, conventional food is broken down by enzymes into its soluble molecular components and these are then distributed in the bloodstream. They are offered to organs such as the liver for building or rebuilding into complex structures, or to other parts for 'burning' to release energy, or for storage. What cannot be used is excreted by the liver in bile and by the kidneys in urine. So the blood is an irrigation channel bearing liquid nourishment to nearly all the body's 100,000,000,000,000 cells, and also a general-exchange pool for raw materials. Think how useful it would be if a constantly moving belt passed one's own house and all other houses in the land, and if on to it one could put anything which was surplus or waste and take from it anything one wanted – a nice substitute for the exchange and retail trades. Items not taken by anybody within a given time would be concentrated and dumped.

The life processes in all the cells of the body have a general tendency to produce acid substances, but most of the processes themselves operate best in a slightly alkaline environment. This creates a dilemma when an organ like a muscle is hard at work. The amount of acid produced is excessive, and there has to be some way of neutralizing it or the muscle cells would quickly go out of business. (An organism which has not solved this kind of dilemma is the germ that sours milk. It produces so much lactic acid that it kills itself – which is one of the reasons why cheese 'keeps'.) The plasma proteins and red cells of the blood are able to take up excess acid and hold it until sufficient has been eliminated or chemically neutralized. This buffering function is of great physiological importance.

The sieves and filters

The spleen is an organ containing large numbers of the anchored type of scavenging cells. Its structure is spongy and the blood passing through it flows sluggishly around the walls of spaces lined with the scavengers. The current is slow enough to allow the scavengers time to stretch out their tendrils of cytoplasm to catch worn-out cells and drifting pieces of irregular material. The scavengers take up red cells which are at the end of their life span, battered by a three- to four-month journey round and round the body, travelling maybe a mile a day in capillaries. The spleen cells digest them and return the proceeds to the general commonwealth. All the blood which leaves the spleen enters the portal vein, thus ensuring that the products of this important scavenging organ go directly to the liver to be resynthesized as far as possible into useful material.

The spleen evolved by the congregation of groups of scavenging cells and blood spaces originally disposed along the wall of the intestine. This makes it easier to understand how it comes to have vascular connections which drain with those of the intestine into the portal system of the liver, which also developed from the wall of the gut, somewhat higher up than the spleen.

The spleen, though important, is not the only assembly of cells which sieve and clean the blood. The liver, bone marrow and lymph nodes also have some activity of this kind, in addition to their other functions, and the whole scavenging-cell system throughout the body is capable of multiplying generally or locally to meet emergencies. Consequently it is possible for a surgeon to remove the spleen without seriously endangering life, and other parts of the body will take over some of its work. By contrast, the liver has unique biochemical functions of vital importance, and so one cannot live without it — even though, like the spleen, it is a discrete organ and potentially removable by surgical technique.

We have noted already that soluble wastes which are not re-used or stored are excreted, usually by the kidneys. The fundamental unit of

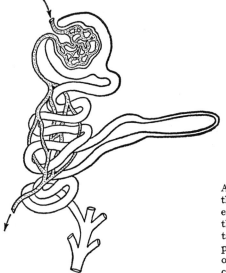

A microscopic kidney unit, one of many thousands in a human kidney. Blood enters at the arrow and passes through the capillary bunch in which filtration takes place. The liquid filtering out passes along the coiled tube, where much of it is absorbed back into the blood. The concentrate which reaches the lower branched collecting tube is urine.

Urine

the kidney is a special bunch of small capillaries pushing into the top end of a coiled kidney tube. There are many thousands of these bunches in a mammalian kidney and they arise very directly from the kidney arteries so that the blood pressure in them is relatively high. The walls of the capillaries in the bunch are sufficiently porous for water and soluble blood substances of small molecular size to be pressed through this filter into the kidney tubules — in fact everything liquid in the blood passes into the kidney tubules through this strainer except cells, platelets, plasma proteins, and bodies such as fat globules. The walls of the kidney tubules are supplied on the outside with blood that has already passed through the capillary filter. The very active cells of the wall then reabsorb (or 'pump', in the molecular sense) into the blood such filtered substances as must not be wasted, including much of the water, salts and vitamin C, and all the sugar. Thus every day about 45 gallons of fluid (200 litres) filters through the kidney capillaries, and 44½ gallons are 'biologically' reabsorbed by the walls of these tubules. The remaining half gallon (about two litres) is the concentrate called urine. It runs into a series of collecting tubules which eventually link to form one large tube (the ureter) from each kidney. The ureters connect to the urinary bladder, which is emptied at the owner's convenience. Blood from the kidneys returns directly to the inferior vena cava (see next chapter), and so does not flow through the portal system of the liver; there would, indeed, be no functional advantage in its doing so.

The renal blood-flow is strong and the pressure high: a quarter or more of our circulating blood goes through the kidneys each time around. If they were to act as filters with absolute efficiency, then all our circulating blood should go through the kidneys every time around, as it does through the lungs. This would perhaps require yet another pump (a renal one, as we already have a pulmonary one — the right side of the heart) and the kidneys would then have to be centralized, as the lungs are, in the circulatory plan. In which case urine might have to be passed through some orifice at the upper end of the body. This would then probably prevent the human male from economically using the same organ as waste-pipe and inseminating tube, but you never know what clever compromises the evolutionary process might be able to make in a hundred million years or so.

The kidney has considerable control over the pressure and quality of the blood that passes through it. If the pressure or the oxygen-content drops persistently, the kidney releases substances that bring about a rise in pressure or a speed-up in the production of red cells in the bone marrow.

Defence

The material scavenged by white cells includes any 'foreign' or not-self objects entering the internal parts of the body. These may be invading germs, or thorns or other particles which have pierced or otherwise entered the soft surfaces, or perhaps food material which has somehow been absorbed without being completely broken down by the digestive mechanisms in the gut.

When a scavenger cell deals with a living germ capable of causing disease (that is, capable of colonizing your body for a period and thereby taking over sufficient body materials to injure you noticeably), the cell is not so much 'clearing up' as 'defending'. No defence organization can exist without lines of communication; battle cannot be joined locally unless soldiers or missiles can be marshalled. In this regard the circulating blood is the prime organ distributing the defence of the body and making it effective at particular points. Without the circulation to carry it, a mobile leucocyte relying on its own powers of locomotion (amoeboid movement) would take an hour to cover a tenth of an inch (two and a half millimetres). But hundreds of millions of white cells are brought by the bloodstream into locally injured or infected areas. A very large localized collection of them makes the creamy white fluid known as pus.

As well as the two types of scavenger cell in the blood, there is another white cell commonly seen — this is the lymphocyte. It is smaller than the others and moves slowly. It has a large nucleus and little cytoplasm.

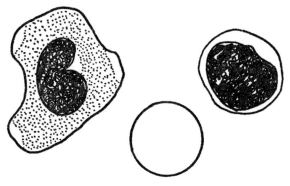

A slow-moving blood phagocyte (*left*) and lymphocyte (*right*) with red cell to scale.

Classically it is described just as a 'small round cell', and until recently it has been something of a mystery. Lymphocytes exist in large numbers in lymph nodes, in areas in the wall of the gut, around the throat ('tonsils') and back of the nose ('adenoids') and in the thymus gland in the neck. They turn up in hordes in areas where certain chronic infections are present, such as tuberculosis. They are not phagocytes — that is, they do not grossly engulf solid particles, as the polymorphs and large mononuclear cells do — but they play a part in antibody production. All this sounds vague, considering that pathologists have been looking at them through good microscopes for a hundred years. The fact is, however, that a microscope can deal only with a thin slice of tissue or a thin film of blood. The cells in such preparations are usually dead, and if they *are* examined alive they are too small, and the sample too special, for their general activities in the body to be studied. However, they can now be tagged with radioactive materials, so that their movements amongst all the other cells can be traced to a limited extent.

This widely travelling population of 'small round cells' may look uniform but in fact it conceals many differently acting types. Some of them can transform into large mononuclear cells which are phagocytic. Most are in a state of endless patrol, forming an early-warning system which moves out of the circulation into the tissue fluids and then back to the blood. If on this journey an individual lymphocyte encounters some foreign or other irregular 'antigenic' material which fits to a specific molecular pattern in its structure, or if it receives such material from another cell or phagocyte, then it may move to a lymph node or similar area. There it divides to produce a line of daughter cells all manufacturing an antibody specifically active against that foreign or irregular material which is then known as 'antigen' because it stimulated antibody production. Antibody is a protein which may dissolve freely in the blood plasma, or in the other body fluids. Or, according to type, it may be fixed to wandering members of the cell system which produced it. Or it may fix to other body cells, such as those of the skin, or the muscle cells in the tubes of the lung. Antibodies can be regarded as disinfectants, killing or conditioning or specifically marking foreign (or perhaps discarded 'self') material, so that this is more readily 'noticed', caught, digested or swept away by scavenger cells.

The lymphocytes that have antibody attached to them are dependent upon a special relationship with the thymus gland. This neck gland evolved from a front-end mouth structure in the simpler vertebrates; it is an intimate mixture of primitive outer-layer cells and primitive lymphocytes, and consists of the type of tissue from which the first lymphocytes appear to originate in an embryo. A lymphocyte, in fact, is a detached, internally wandering cell which has 'outer-covering' origins. Perhaps this is why it is adapted to 'recognition-and-specific-response' types of protective activity.

If the thymus gland is removed from newborn mice they grow up without the capacity to make a lymphocyte-fixed type of antibody, though they can still make other kinds such as those which are freely dissolved in serum. But the ability to make these is probably also dependent upon certain lymphocytes having an association with other special areas of the body, such as particular patches in the lining of the intestinal tract.

Antibody means simply what it says, 'a body which acts against'. Originally it was a medical jargon-word indicating function; that is to say, the term did not commit anyone to defining just what antibody was, for (like many other biological items which proved to be composed of very large molecules) it had some puzzling physical properties. And *antigen* means, as we have said, 'that which provokes the production of antibody'. In the heyday of late nineteenth-century immunology, antibody and antigen were always defined in this way, in terms of one another with happy circularity. This worried outsiders who believed that non-circular definitions would be more respectable. It is only recently that molecular biology has revealed the precise chemical nature of specific antibody activity and of molecular antigenicity, though the actual cell mechanisms of antibody production are not yet clear.

It is best to speak of 'an antibody molecule' when that is what is meant. Such molecules are present in the blood plasma in enormous numbers. 'An antibody' can mean a class of such molecules all having the same activity against one chemically distinct antigen. 'Antibody' (without the article) can mean 'antibodies in general'.

When a local part of the body is disturbed by physical or chemical injury or by the presence of material released by germs, it usually responds by becoming 'inflamed'. The cardinal signs of inflammation have been known since the days of Hippocrates and Galen, when they were listed as *rubor, tumor, calor, dolor* ('redness and swelling with heat and pain').

Inflammation is a defence reaction which brings more blood to the threatened part. There is a local release of substances from injured cells, which causes the small blood capillaries to dilate and microscopic pores to open in their sides. This in turn increases the local flow of blood and allows large molecular substances, such as antibodies, to escape locally from the blood plasma into the spaces between the tissue cells. Scavenging and other defence cells also move out through gaps which open in the capillary walls. Thus in an inflamed area, the tissue fluid becomes something like whole blood plasma containing numerous white cells, whereas normal tissue fluid, or 'lymph' (see next chapter), is mainly water and plasma salts with only a few white cells and small-size proteins.

Scattered in millions through the bloods of mammals are small sensitive cell fragments, the blood *platelets*. These little bodies are manufactured by large cells known as *giant cells*, whose evolutionary ancestors were probably hole-pluggers. They live in the bone marrow and their cytoplasms shred off edge-fragments into the blood as it flows past them. The platelets are part of a trigger mechanism which springs into immediate action whenever an accidental break occurs in a blood vessel. Swirling along in the blood, they are continually falling and drifting like blown snowflakes against the linings of the blood vessels. But if this lining should be broken or altered physically, the molecular balances are changed in the local plasma. This immediately causes platelets touching the damaged area to stick there and release their contents, like snowflakes melting. The factors inside them promote plasma reactions which lead to local coagulation of the blood, to the

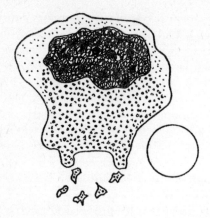

A giant cell making platelets by shedding its cytoplasm into the bloodstream. The disc represents a red cell on the same scale.

accumulation of more bursting platelets and to the development of a firm clot. This, together with the production of substances which make the broken vessel contract, will usually staunch the bleeding.

Platelets are also capable of ingesting bacteria and foreign particles, in a similar way to the white cells, but at a lower order of magnitude. An infection of bacteria in the bloodstream (septicaemia) can result in so many platelets being 'used up' that the clotting mechanisms are disturbed.

We noted that in the sluggishly flowing blood of crabs, insects and other arthropods, there are giant cells that cluster around any breach in the wall of a blood space to repair it. This is almost certainly the case in every primitive multicellular animal with an internal fluid compartment. The mammals and birds, however, have high-pressure circulations, much speedier than those of other animals, and a leak in any of their blood tubes is a potential danger-point. Through it much blood could be rapidly lost, until the circulation collapsed like a flat tyre. In such an emergency there would be little physical opportunity for amoeba-like cells, crawling at a tenth of an inch (two millimetres) an hour, to plug a leak. The speedier platelet mechanism has developed accordingly.

The value of blood

From everything said so far, it is very obvious that vertebrate blood is a liquid with complex structure and vital functions. It is valuable stuff. As it flows, bright scarlet, from a wounded body, it is visually more spectacular than splintered bone, burst liver or a mess of brains. But once it has left the owner, its usefulness ends, except in the very special case of transfusion; it is valuable in its place, not in itself. For example, as organic fertilizer for plants it has no magical advantage over dead fish or rotten vegetation. Like them it contains plenty of nitrogenous substances—the building-blocks of proteins—as well as a high concentration of the particular salts and metals used by many forms of life. But before a plant can get this nitrogen from a dose of blood, or from fish, liver, a dead body or anything else, it has to wait for the soil bacteria to rot the proteins down to their very minor components. Flesh becomes grass again with the help of microbes. When you put that 'Special Blood Manure' around your tomato plants or rose bushes, as many gardeners do, you are doing nothing 'special'—except pandering to an unconscious thought that scarlet love-apples and mystic roses must surely need red blood to make them swell and bloom to full perfection.

And yet ... and yet ... did not roses and anemones grow from the blood of Adonis? A fabulous purple flower sprang from the fallen blood of Hyacinthus. Where Attis bled, the scented violet bloomed. And the Empress Helena discovered basil, the royal plant, spreading long after from the blood of Christ at the place of the Cross.

CHAPTER THREE

Pump and Pipes

Go to a good engineering firm and ask them to make you a reliable, compact, automatic pump about $\frac{1}{250}$ of a horsepower, as big as a man's fist and weighing rather less than a pound (about 450 grams). It must have an output which can be varied from one gallon to 8 gallons (5 to 35 litres) of thickish fluid per minute. For the most part it must idle smoothly along at the lower rate, beating about 40 million strokes a year. It will work usually against a head equivalent to 6 feet (2 metres) of water, but at times this may be doubled, and then it must automatically increase its force. Similarly it must be sensitive to any increase or decrease in the pool of fluid from which it is pumping, responding immediately by acceleration or deceleration, or by increased or decreased stroke as the case may be. It must also accept signals which may reach it electrically from other pieces of machinery or from control centres elsewhere. It must react, too, to signals in the form of dissolved substances reaching it in the fluid being pumped. Its valve closures must not damage millions of suspended cells which will form almost half the volume of this fluid. It must never stop in an average run of 60 to 80 years, during which time each of its chambers will pump 65 million gallons (about 300 million litres) of blood.

The remarkable machine

Such analogies show how remarkable a machine the human heart is. We are all familiar with pumping-engines and the distribution of fluids by means of pipes. It is easy to find mechanical parallels for any physiological process involving muscular action. This seems platitudinous. In the seventeenth century it was revolutionary. William Harvey's 'discovery' was to think of the heart and blood vessels as machinery. But he did not think any less of a traditionally important organ because it displayed mechanical qualities. 'So the heart', he wrote, 'is the beginning of life and the sun of the microcosm, as similarly the sun deserves to be called the heart of the world.'*

The human heart is nearly all muscle, a hollow lump of red meat expanding and contracting with each beat about as much as a half-

---

* *Ita cor principium vitae et sol microcosmi, ut proportionabiliter sol cor mundi, appelari meretur.*

58

opened and re-clenched fist. Those who have never been taught any biology sometimes do not realize that most 'meat' is muscle. Lean beef, chicken, fillet of sole, lobster, the white part of a clam or a scallop: all are the contractile tissue known as muscle.

When you run up a hill and lie exhausted at the top, not only can you feel your heart pounding in your chest; you also seem to be able to hear it. The noise is mainly that of the blood pulsating in the arteries in your head, but also it is the knocking of the heart against the underside of your ribs or breastbone — especially if you are lying curled on your left side so that your chest wall is pressing on the most muscular side of the heart. But put your ear directly over someone else's chest where the beat is most obvious and listen carefully. Many thousands of medical students have been taught to distinguish the rhythmic sounds described to them by teachers in various ways, but most often as something like *lubb* and *dup* — lubb-dup ... lubb-dup ... lubb-dup ... *Lubb* is low pitched with a roaring quality — perhaps more like *lurb* — and it represents the main contracting phase, the pushing stroke which closes the valves between the chambers and forces the blood out into the large, elastic arteries; while *dup* — perhaps more like *drup* — is the abrupt click as the other valves close to prevent the blood flowing back from the arteries while the chambers refill from the veins and the heart muscle relaxes. The second sound is therefore like the bang in a water-pipe when a tap is turned off suddenly.

Your heart, lying under the lower end of the breastbone, is, as anyone will tell you, 'on the left' (i.e. on your left). The place where it knocks most forcibly on the chest is indeed well over to that side, but the whole organ is not as left-sided as this seems to indicate; really it is fairly central, particularly when you are standing up. It slides further over to the left when you lie down, and in X-ray photographs taken with the patient in this position the heart's shadow is distinctly left-sided. Its position in the chest is determined partly by its left chambers, which are more muscular and thicker-walled than those on the right, and partly by the great blood vessels, which enter and leave the heart asymmetrically. (Much blood passes through the liver on its return journey to the heart, and the liver is on the right side; hence the bulky right-sided development of the large returning hepatic veins.)

Very few internal organs in the chest or abdominal cavity are perfectly bilaterally symmetrical. The two compartments of the body have essentially central-line tube systems, but by evolutionary contortions and additions these have twisted away from a primitive simple vertebrate layout so that now the bland external symmetry of chest and belly is a misleading guide to the disposition of what lies within.

But given an evolutionary need for internal non-symmetry, we might still ask why this should always adopt a same-sidedness in all members of a species. Why not a random distribution of either-sidedly arranged people? There is no good answer to this one, because very occasionally (about once in two years in every large city hospital) a human turns up with total body structure transposed, left to right, as in a mirror. Such people appear to function normally. Their condition is called 'situs inversus', or 'dextrocardia', and is a dreadful trap for medical students doing the clinical parts of their final examinations.

Moving machinery needs smooth, lubricated surfaces. The heart, attached by blood vessels at its upper end, lies in a wet slippery bag: the *pericardium* (literally 'the thing around the heart'). The bag allows the necessary freedom of movement so that nearby organs are not pulled and tugged as the heart beats. If the heart suffers a stab wound,

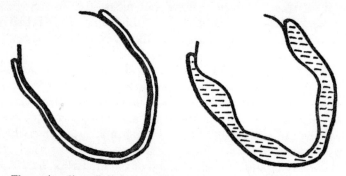

The pericardium (*left*), a wet, slippery bag. If fluid enters it in quantity (*right*), the bag fills up and compresses the heart, preventing it from working properly because its chambers cannot refill after a beat.

blood squirts into this bag and fills what was previously only a potential space, and as the bag tightens, the blood then begins to press on the outside of the thinner-walled top heart-chambers, preventing them from filling. This seriously hampers the function of the heart and is why such wounds can be almost immediately fatal.

Each side of the heart has two chambers, the auricle (or atrium) above, and the ventricle below. (*Auricle*, little ear: part of each is triangular and looked to the ancients like the ear of a dog; *atrium*, a court or an entrance hall; *ventricle*, little belly.) Blood flows from the auricles to the ventricles. There is no effective direct opening between the two sides of the heart in the normal adult. The heart is cone-shaped, the base attached above, and its apex under the left border of the lower end of the breastbone. Whoever designated a heart in the shape which is cut on trees, or drawn on cards for St Valentine's Day, must have been thinking of a heart slit in two or opened out. He was a butcher lover.

The beating heart

On each side between auricle and ventricle there are flap-valves (*valva*, the leaf of a folding door) so that blood can flow only from the auricle to the ventricle; it cannot return because of the valves slamming like doors in a wind. The valves are made from thin, tough folds of the lining membrane of the heart, and are prevented from blowing inside-out by fine, tendinous strings which attach the edges to the walls of the ventricles. (It was once thought that when the spirit of the heart was broken it was these 'heart-strings' which snapped.) The valve on the right side has three flaps, and that on the left has two. When the left-sided two-flap valve was closed, it reminded the Renaissance anatomists (*ana*, through, *tome*, a cutting) of a bishop's mitre, and since then it has been known as the mitral valve. It is said that T. H. Huxley made the gibe to a bishop that the valve on the left side was named mitral because bishops were never in the right. The tone of this remark reflects the sharp debate in the nineteenth century between the Christian fundamentalists and the apologists for evolutionary biology.

The auricles contract first, loading the more muscular ventricles with blood. Then the ventricles clench, and squirt blood into the arteries with great force. When the right ventricle contracts it forces blood up the pulmonary artery on a short journey to the lungs. The left ventricle is more muscular than the right; when it contracts it sends blood into the aorta, the main distributing pipe, at high pressure, on its way to all parts of the body. (The term *aorta* is ancient and obscure; it may signify 'air-carrier' as 'artery' does. Blood runs out of these thick-walled rigid vessels when cut or butchered, leaving them like empty pipes, and so it was thought by some of the ancients that they carried only air.) Reflux from the pulmonary artery or the aorta back to the ventricles is prevented by three small, cup-shaped, pocket-like flaps grouped in a circle at the beginning of each of these great vessels. These valves do not have restraining cords, for the round opening which each guards is firm and relatively narrow, and they have tough free rims which prevent them from blowing inside-out when they fill.

Heart muscle in a vertebrate differs from its other muscles, which are made up of bundles of individual fibres. Heart-muscle fibres are connected to one another by branching bridges so that their protoplasm communicates over wide areas. This allows the protoplasmic chemical changes that constitute a wave of contraction to start at one special point and then to spread all over the heart by conduction through the bridges. In the adult mammal a ring of non-muscular, fibrous tissue insulates the muscle fibres of the auricles from those of the ventricles; this prevents the wave spreading directly from the former to the latter. In the wall of the right auricle there is a small area of primitive muscle

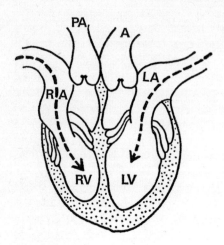 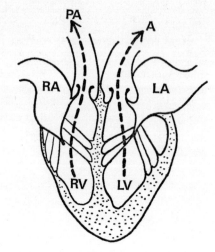

The auricles (RA, LA) contract first, sending the blood into the ventricles (RV, LV) through open flap-valves. Meanwhile the blood in the pulmonary artery (PA) and in the aorta (A) is prevented from running back into the heart by closed, cup-shaped, pocket-like valves.

Then the ventricles contract, and a rush of blood closes the flap-valves through which the blood entered from the auricles. The pressure of ventricular contraction opens the pulmonary and aortic valves, forcing a volume of blood into the pulmonary artery and into the aorta.

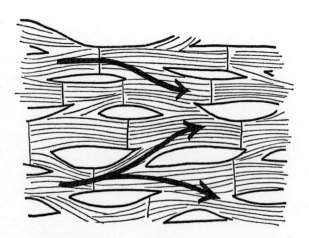

A wave of contraction, which spreads over a wide area of heart-muscle fibre.

cells such as are found in an embryo. This small part is called the pace-maker — and it generates the impulse which initiates each cycle of contraction.

At rest, the human heart beats about every eight-tenths of a second. A wave of contraction, started by the pacemaker, spreads over both auricles. They contract, blow open the intervening valves and fill the ventricles with blood. The wave of contraction then reaches another small special area in the dividing wall between the two auricles. This, the atrioventricular node, is continued as a bundle of tissue which runs down like a wire through the ring of insulating fibrous tissue into the wall between the ventricles, where it divides and branches widely,

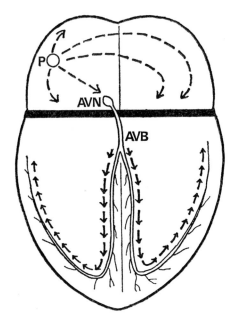

A heart-beat begins at the pacemaker (P) in the right auricle. It spreads to the left auricle through the heart-muscle fibres. When the contractile impulse reaches the atrioventricular node (AVN), it is conducted down through the atrioventricular bundle (AVB) and then spreads in the ventricular muscles. Disturbances of the bridges between muscle fibres, or of the conducting bundle, can lead to irregular or abnormal contractions.

mingling with the ventricular muscle. The contraction impulse of the auricles is conducted down through this atrioventricular bundle and then spreads in the ventricles from below upwards, forcing the blood from the right ventricle into the pulmonary artery, and from the left ventricle into the aorta. The whole wave of contraction passing over the heart lasts for about half a beat; during the other half, the muscle is passively resting, dilating, refilling.

In a beat of the heart the right and the left side contract at the same time, each putting out and refilling with the same quantity of blood. In effect two hearts are beating, because there is no mixing of the blood from left to right, but they beat synchronously because they have developed from the same interconnected muscle tissue.

The arteries

Every tissue, and particularly every muscle, needs oxygen. The heart is supplied by two small vessels which run from just above the flap-valves at the beginning of the aorta where it leaves the left ventricle. They encircle the heart like a crown or garland (*corona*) and are called the coronary arteries. Blockage of any part of these vessels ('coronary thrombosis') can damage the heart muscle because muscle fibres which are deprived of oxygen will die. The human coronary vessels are relatively small and easily blocked.

The first large branch of the aorta was described by Galen in his writings, but he gave it no particular name. Such was his authority, which lasted a thousand years, that later anatomists called it the 'innominate' artery rather than presume to correct him. It runs up, dividing in its turn, to supply the right arm and the right side of the neck and head. Next, the arteries for the left side of the neck and head, and that for the left arm, arise separately from the aorta. The large neck arteries are the carotids (from a word meaning 'to throttle'). The aorta and its large branches are very elastic, which smooths the thrusts of blood from the left ventricle, just as a chamber of trapped elastic air will convert the spurts of a force pump into a continuous flow from a tap.

Curving up, over and downwards, the aorta then plunges between the lungs and along the backbone at the back of the chest and abdomen, running through the diaphragm. Then it gives off some important branches which supply the stomach, spleen, intestines and kidneys. The kidney arteries are short and broad, giving the kidneys a large blood supply at high pressure. When it reaches the pelvis the aorta forks into two main trunks, each one supplying leg and buttock.

The winding course of the main blood vessels is remarkably constant from body to body. This has, of course, been observed over several centuries now during careful anatomical dissection. It is possible to make such dissection easier by injecting the blood vessels after death with coloured solidifying substances which stretch and fill them so that their tracks can be more readily picked out. The whole vascular pattern of an organ like the heart or kidney can even be displayed without dissection by rendering the muscle soft and translucent with further chemical treatment so that the branching vascular structure can be seen directly. The same patterns can be photographed in most living or dead organs by injecting a fluid which is opaque to X-rays into the main artery supplying the part, and by taking an X-ray radiograph when it has been distributed to all the fine arteriolar branches. This is X-ray angiography. It is useful for discovering blockages in blood vessels caused by clots or by the pressure of tumours. A newer approach is to inject a harmlessly minute amount of radioactive material into the

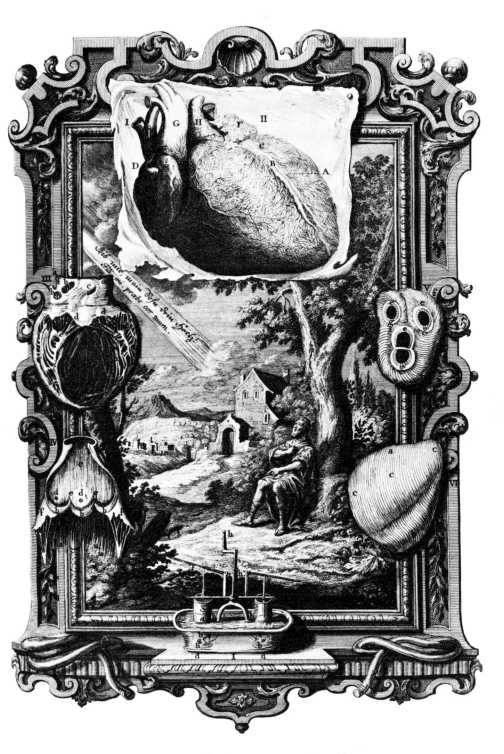

The heart: a reliable, compact, automatic pump

circulation and to map the area of its distribution in various parts of the body, using sensitive scanning instruments.

The arteries divide, branch and rebranch as they run to their destinations. Many of the minor branches reconnect or communicate with twigs from other main branches. For this reason there are often several alternative routes by which blood can flow to a part, and when this is so, it does not make all that much difference if one small artery gets blocked. There are some parts of the body, however, where small arteries do not intercommunicate. These are called end-arteries, the most important of which are the minor arteries of the brain, the central artery to the back of the eye, the vessels of the kidney, and most branches of the coronary arteries of the heart itself. If any of these becomes blocked, the part of the organ supplied will die for lack of oxygen. In the brain this produces *apoplexy* (Greek, 'a striking down') or stroke, and results in paralysis or death because some of the brain tissue has been suddenly destroyed. (The extent of the paralysis depends precisely on how much and what part of the brain dies.) The effect used to be likened to being struck by an external force. It seemed like the act of God.

Blockage of arteries is a major cause of disease in civilized humans, who are, at any rate at this stage of their evolutionary and social development, exceptionally prone to degenerative changes in the blood vessels.

The final branches of the arteries (called arterioles) end in their physiological *raisons d'être*, the hair-sized capillaries where most of the functions of the blood are performed and to which the arteries are conduits. Across the thin walls of these capillaries, the exchanges occur between blood and tissues. In each adult human there are enough capillaries to go more than once around the world. The pressure drops as the blood passes through this fine meshwork and finally trickles through to the veins. The veins have thinner walls and are more lax than the arteries, beside which they often run. There are more of them so their flow of blood is slower, and it is, of course, in the opposite direction.

The veins

The largest vein returning from the lower part of the body, the *inferior vena cava*, runs on the right side of the aorta along the front of the backbone, up to the heart. It brings blood from the lower limbs and the kidneys. It does not receive branches directly from the spleen, stomach or intestines, because the blood from these parts first travels to the liver in the large portal vein, so named because it runs into the groove which, as we have seen, the ancients called the *porta hepatis*, the gate of the liver. 'Portal' blood from the spleen, stomach and intestines is processed in the fine blood spaces between the columns of liver cells and then passes into the inferior vena cava through the liver vein. This portal shunt* in the circulation is remarkable, and is best understood by tracing its probable evolution.

A simple one-celled animal engulfs food particles, digests them and uses the products to build its own 'body' or to release energy. The chemical substances (enzymes or ferments) necessary for this are present inside the cell itself. A simple multicellular animal has specialized cells lining the gut which carry out digestion and absorption for themselves and for the rest of the body. Progressive evolution promotes an increasing concentration of these specialized digesting cells so that they become organs (stomach or pancreas, for example). Digestion no longer needs to take place inside cells if some organ or organs can pour out digestive juices directly, or along a duct, on to the food in the intestine, in order that the products can be absorbed farther down the gut.

The primitive vertebrate liver was originally a digestive gland, an outgrowth of the upper intestine. Its cells were particularly rich in enzymes which poured as a digestive juice along a liver-duct on to the food in the gut. As the vertebrates developed they made greater and greater demands upon their intestinal tracts for digestion and absorption. At this stage one could imagine a vertebrate intestinal designer saying, 'If only we could think up some kind of a loop line for putting the stuff twice through the important parts of the gut!' Such a recycling is common in chemical and mechanical engineering.

It was a transport problem eventually solved by the bloodstream: the food wasn't put twice through the gut, but was shunted by the blood through a second enzyme battery. The blood which drained from the intestinal capillaries in primitive vertebrates contained the products of digested food, and it ran near the liver in a network of veins on its way back to the heart. At some stage it began to pass through the liver, which, with rich enzyme resources, easily reverted to intracellular methods of further digestion or processing. The vertebrates that evolved the new arrangement prospered, and their descendants began to send all their gut-blood along the portal vein to flow through a second set of capillaries in the liver, the cells of which have now become their bodies' supreme molecule-manipulating factories, largely relieving the gut-wall of this function. The liver breaks down, builds up, stores, manufactures, neutralizes, purifies, disposes. It still uses its main duct to the intestine, but to channel away the bile, which is mainly a mixture of waste products but has some digestive function; conditioning the

---

* Today the anatomical term 'portal' no longer means 'pertaining to a gate' but simply 'any blood shunt of the liver type'. For instance, fishes and amphibians have 'renal portal systems' but no tradition of gates to their kidneys.

intestinal contents for the action of other secretions, and facilitating the absorption of fats. Clever old liver. Its 'functions' listed in any textbook of physiology sound like a roll call of the divisions of a great chemical industry.

The blood returning from the head runs into the jugular veins (*jugulum*, the throat) on each side of the neck. Each of these unites with an arm vein, and then all join to form one large vessel draining the whole of the upper part of the body. This great vein from above and the great vein from below (the superior vena cava and the inferior vena cava) separately enter the right auricle of the heart. The only other venous opening into this chamber is a small vein returning blood from the heart muscle itself.

Blue bloods

Arteries run deep in the body, but many veins lie only just under the skin, where they can be seen by virtue of their contents. Veins themselves are colourless but the blood in them is bluish; the colour of 'reduced' haemoglobin from which the oxygen has been removed in the capillaries.

The nobles of Castile lived a protected, well-washed indoor life. They claimed to have inherited blue blood (*sangre azul*), because their veins showed clearly through thin-skinned aristocratic hands and arms and necks, in contrast to those of the rough, thickened, dirty, sunburned skin of the hard-living, hard-working Spanish peasant, or the dark skin of Moor or Jew. Had the hidalgos (the name merely means 'sons of something'), who called themselves 'Dons', claimed to have been descended from king-crabs on the same evidence, there would have been nearly as much sense in it, for, as it happens, this arthropod has blood containing haemocyanin pigment. But only a very, very breathless aristocrat is blue-blooded.

Blood is pumped from the right auricle to the right ventricle and then up the pulmonary artery, which divides to distribute branches to both lungs. In the lungs these break up into fine capillary vessels which run very close to the air spaces in which breathed air circulates, drawn into the lungs by movements of the rib-cage and diaphragm. Carbon dioxide is released and fresh oxygen is taken up by the red cells. The freshened blood returns from the lungs in the pulmonary veins, two trunks of which enter the left auricle from each side through four separate openings. Then the blood passes into the left ventricle to begin another circular journey.

Pulses and blushes

Arteries are muscular, springy tubes. When the left ventricle contracts, it forcibly sends a volume of blood into the aorta. This acts as a shock impulse which travels as a wave through all the ramifications of the arterial system and can be felt as the 'pulse'. It keeps time with the rhythm of the heart, usually about seventy beats a minute. The speed with which the pulse wave is transmitted depends upon the elasticity of the arterial walls. In youth, when the arteries are supple, it travels more slowly than in old age, when the walls stiffen. If the arteries were wholly rigid it would be transmitted almost instantaneously, but as things are, the rate of propagation of the shock wave is about six yards (five and a half metres) a second. This is about twelve times as fast as the ordinary rate of blood-flow in the main arteries.

The walls of arteries have their own little blood vessels (the *vasa vasorum*, vessels of the vessels) which enter them from the outer coat. They arise from distant branches, they travel obliquely, and they do not penetrate entirely through the arterial wall for this would weaken it and encourage leakages. For the same reason the arterial wall cannot be supplied by vessels leading out directly from its own interior.

Muscle fibres in the walls of arteries are supplied by fine nerves which cause them to contract or relax. This either narrows or dilates the vessels and so the resistance to the flow of blood can be made greater or less under the influence of the central nervous system.

Similar nerves run to the heart and can either increase or decrease its rate of contraction. If they are cut, the heart will still beat at a steady rate, for although the pacemaker is influenced by nervous control, it is not completely dependent upon it. The heart nerves are connected to unconscious centres in the brain, which in turn are in touch through other nerves with sensitive endings in the wall of the right auricle and in the aorta and carotid arteries. These endings are responsive to stretching. If the pressure on the right side of the heart increases — that is, if the amount of blood being returned to the heart by the veins builds up — this stretches the wall of the right auricle and the circuit of nerve impulses promotes an increase in the rate of the heart. If the blood pressure on the other side of the heart should build up in the aorta or carotid arteries, the same sort of control brings about a slowing-down. These are not the only means by which the force of the heart and the resistance to flow in the vessels are controlled.

Everyone knows that emotion, fear or pain, can affect the pulse, or make you go red or white in the face. This is mediated not only through the brain centres and nerve pathways just mentioned, but also by the secretion into the bloodstream of solutions of active chemical substances which can accelerate or decelerate the heart, and constrict or relax the small arteries in different parts of the body. Adrenalin is an example. It increases the heart rate and constricts the blood vessels of the skin and the abdominal cavity. It is released into the bloodstream from the two small adrenal glands, each lying near a kidney, which are under the close control of parts of the nervous system. Other glandular areas of the body release other active substances, such as bradykinin, serotonin, pituitrin and so on. Thus there are multiple balancing nervous and chemical influences upon the circulation, with local variations so that blood can be selectively concentrated in or excluded from the small vessels of different organs. Such a multiplicity of fail-safe controls is what is commonly found in a complex animal body when the functioning of vital systems is investigated.

Blushing is the despair of some people. It gives them away, because it operates partly below the conscious level. Under ordinary circumstances adjustments in blood-flow through the skin are automatic and are concerned with the maintenance of a steady body temperature and blood pressure. The latter means a balance between the output of the heart and the resistance, determined by the state of contraction or 'tone', of the thousands of arterial branches into which the blood is being pumped. But the deep centres of the brain can appreciate danger and other expectations, such as the presence of a potential mate, and can ring nervous changes upon the vascular system, shunting blood around to produce effects that are familiar to us, like blushing, pallor, erection or fainting.

When you are pale with terror, the blood has left your skin and intestines, and is pouring through the muscles where you need it for a physical ordeal. When you are flushed with pleasure, the situation is more or less the opposite. But blushing with embarrassment is a puzzle. It seems to indicate a conflict in the mind of a young person and involves a feeling of inadequacy. As a non-verbal signal on the face and body it must go back to the dawn of our race. Tears and laughter, frowns, snarls, smiles, eye movements, and so on, are a basic non-word currency of social communication. The blushing girl or youth is instinctively giving the rest of us in the herd some valuable information about an inner attitude. Blushing means, 'You disturb me deeply.' Tactfully, one should understand it as, 'Please take me no further in this matter.'

When the ears 'burn', it may be (as the convention has it) that someone is talking about their owner; probably a secretly vain or apprehensive owner only *believes* it to be so. Clothing limits the location of the surfaces by which we humans can exchange skin-colour signals: some kinds of monkey are not so hampered.

The erection of the male penis and the swelling of the female clitoris are good examples of vascular hydraulics. The parts that stiffen are networks of veins, the outlets of which are guarded by rings of involuntary muscle. Nerve impulses close these rings, and at the same time cause dilatation of the local arteries and capillaries which then pour blood into the venous network. This fills up until the pressure is high and the organ swollen and hard.

There is a reptile, the 'horned toad' (strictly *horned lizard*) of the hot American deserts, which is reputed to be able to squirt blood from its eyes. And indeed it can. As in any other vertebrate, its blood ordinarily flows up into its head along the internal carotid arteries and comes back by the jugular veins. But in this animal a jugular constrictor muscle can squeeze these veins and prevent the return of blood, so that the lizard gets a swelled head. The blood spaces fill up behind and around its eyes, making them pop out and giving them a bloodshot look; and in a few species the pressure in the eyelids can rise to such a level that blood will break out and spray up to a distance of six feet (two metres). This blood carries with it some irritant substance deriving from the eye membranes and is a discouragement to predators that might fancy the horned toad for dinner. The reptile squirts blood only when disturbed or threatened, but it uses the same head-swelling mechanism more moderately to shed an old skin from its head at sloughing time and also to help remove sand particles from its eyes.

Among insects, a good example of vascular hydraulics is provided by the larvae of some large dragonflies that live under water. Like most insect larvae they are just specialized eating-machines. (Most adult insects are just specialized breeding-machines.) They have big eyes and jaws. When a suitable victim moves into range, the muscles of the body wall contract, so that blood — which, as in other arthropods, is in open spaces inside the body — is suddenly forced with great pressure into the head and neck, extending the formidable mouth-parts which shoot forward mechanically with high speed and accuracy to grab the prey.

Flow

The heart rates of animals vary inversely with their sizes. The rate in a small bird or mouse may be hundreds of beats a minute, that of an elephant or a horse some twenty to thirty. A man with a big heart is likely to have a slower pulse rate than the average man: during training, an athlete's heart may increase in muscle and size and the resting pulse rate may fall to forty or fifty beats a minute. This enlargement is no different from that of any other muscle which is vigorously and regularly exercised. A boy or girl whose pulse is naturally slow may have an inborn capacity for feats of athletic endurance, such as swimming or long-distance running, because such hearts usually have enormous reserves of output which come into action on acceleration of the beat.

The pressure in the arteries grows less and less as their branches become smaller, for the resistance to flow in small-calibre tubes is very great and the heart's pumping pressure cannot be maintained along them. By the time the blood has entered the capillaries, the pressure is about a quarter of what it was in the aorta.

The capillaries are very small, very delicate, slightly leaky tubes. It is their business to be leaky, so that the watery parts of the blood can ooze out through their walls into the spaces and interstices of the body and back again, and so that oxygen carried by the haemoglobin can freely diffuse to the tissue cells which need it. By the time blood has been through the capillaries and is once again moving in larger tubes, its pressure has dropped further, for the veins are slack and loose-

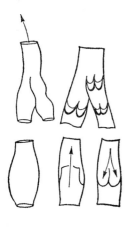

When veins are cut open, their valves can be seen: pairs of pockets with openings towards the heart.

walled and there are very many of them. With the pushing pressure so low, you will wonder how venous blood can get back to the heart from, say, the lower limbs of a standing man.

The veins of the limbs contain valves—pocket-valves in the walls—which are arranged with their openings towards the heart so that blood can flow only in that direction. Many veins are constantly compressed and massaged by the movements of the muscles and elastic tissues amongst which they run. Every side-pressure on a vein is converted by the valves into a movement of blood towards the heart. If you think your leg muscles are not in action as you stand or sit still, try and stay still consciously. Slight fidgeting is almost irresistible. Many tall four-legged animals have more difficulty than we in lifting blood back to the heart against the pull of gravity. Watch a tethered elephant in a circus or zoo: far from standing still, the animal sways about as though in a high wind, using its leg muscles to massage the blood back up from those great feet.

Blood moves rapidly in the aorta—think of a thick garden hose gushing hot blood at between one and 8 gallons (5 to 36 litres) a minute (a big watering-can holds about 3 gallons, or 14 litres). However, in the smaller branches of the arteries the velocity of blood is only 3 to 6 inches (7 to 15 cm.) per second, while in a capillary it is reduced to about one inch (2½ cm.) a minute. At times, in some of the inter-connections of a capillary network, the flow may be nil, and in a resting part of the body quite a proportion of the small blood vessels may be in this shut-down state. The blood-flow through a resting muscle, for instance, is many times less than when it is actively contracting. In a vein the flow is between one and 6 inches (2½ to 15 cm.) per second, according to size — the larger, the faster.

Over particular parts of the circuit, average times are: arm vein to heart, 7 seconds; arm vein to heart to lung to heart to arm artery to arm capillaries to arm vein, 24 seconds. Only some of the blood runs at these speeds; the measurements given are for blood flowing by the fastest route. Circulation times are markedly faster during muscular exercise or after injection of adrenalin. In the resting human the flow per unit volume of tissue is greatest through the brain, kidneys, thyroid gland and liver.

But there are some parts of the body where no red blood penetrates at all, such as the lens and cornea of the eye. These organs have to be crystal clear, and so they cannot have blood vessels. They are composed of cells which live at a slow rate, picking up enough nutrients and oxygen from the clear fluids secreted into cavities of the eyeball. Cartilage (gristle) is another tissue which has no blood vessels, but bone, apparently the most solid of all, has a very rich central blood supply.

Each bone has a nutrient artery which runs a tortuous course before entering it; this is to allow for some play among movable surrounding muscles. Bones need a large blood supply because they are more than mere structural girders: they act as storehouses for calcium, and blood is the carrier of this element in the body, and they also protect the delicate marrow, where the blood cells themselves are grown before being shed into the circulation.

The brain is the best organ of all, humans must say, because, elaborate and self-conscious, it is *their* great gambit in the inter-species survival stakes. Blood is pumped up to the brain through four separate arterial channels, two on each side of the neck. These are the right and left vertebral arteries, which run up along the backbone, and the right and left internal carotid arteries, which pass up in the neck muscles and enter the base of the skull near to the innermost parts of the ears. All these four vessels join to make a ring around the pituitary gland. This ring is the Circle of Willis (an English seventeenth-century physician), which equalizes the flow from the four sources before the supply enters the cerebral arteries of the brain.

There are other equalizing and adjusting circuits, both on the arterial and venous sides of the circulation. For example, the azygos veins (*azygos*, 'without a spouse': the veins are not paired symmetri-

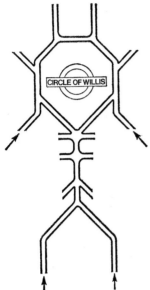

The Circle of Willis: an elaborate set of shunts which receives blood from four neck arteries (*arrowed*) and distributes it to the brain.

cally) run along the back of the thorax and abdomen to form a connecting channel between the inferior and superior venae cavae, equalizing any excessive return of blood either from the upper or from the lower part of the body, or relieving a blocked or congested inferior vena cava.

Lymph

The movement of fluid across the capillary wall depends upon *osmosis*. Diffusion across membranes has been mentioned before, but osmosis has not, though it was relevant to the short account of the movement of water into the roots of a green plant. Osmosis occurs when a membrane is permeable to small molecules but not to larger ones, and where the larger are still small enough to 'hold' the water in which they are dissolved. (When something dissolves in water, the water also dissolves in it, because the forces between the molecules operate mutually. But 'dissolving' refers only to smallish molecules: really big ones produce suspensions, not solutions, when added to water.) For example, when the holes of a membrane in water are big enough to transmit, say, water but not sugar molecules, and if there is sugar on one side of the membrane only, the sugar will seem to 'draw' water across. It is the thermal jigging of molecules which provides the movement, the water molecules moving wherever they *can* go without obstruction. The force with which they penetrate the sugar (measured by the hydrostatic pressure required to stop them) is the osmotic pressure. Now the blood pressure coming from the pumping force of the heart is greater at the arterial end than at the venous end of a capillary. The capillary wall is permeable to water, dissolved gases, salts and sugars, but not to plasma proteins (except in 'inflamed' tissues). Some of the plasma-protein molecules (the albumins, mainly) are just small enough to exert a slight osmotic pressure. The hydrostatic pressure at the arterial end of the capillary is enough to push water, with dissolved oxygen, salts and sugars, out into the tissue spaces, but at the venous end the hydrostatic pressure has fallen below the osmotic pressure of the plasma proteins. This causes a flow of fluid back from the tissue spaces into the blood. The total

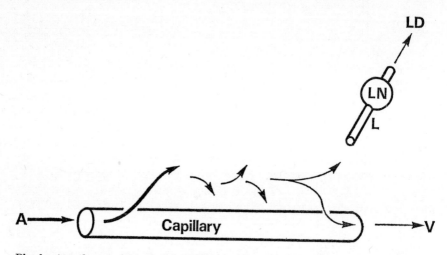

Blood enters the arterial end of a capillary at relatively high pressure (A), which squeezes water and small-molecule dissolved substances out through the wall into the tissue spaces. At the venous end of the capillary the pressure is lower (V), and some fluid is drawn osmotically back into the bloodstream. The excess (lymph) eventually finds its way back to the bloodstream through small lymph vessels (L), which run through lymph nodes (LN) and finally enter main lymph ducts (LD), which empty into the great veins.

result, however, is that more fluid passes into the tissues than returns immediately to the blood. The excess is the *lymph*.

The lymph seeps around the cells outside the bloodstream. The cells of the body have walls which can be regarded as semi-permeable, and the amount of water they take from the lymph and 'hold' depends not only upon their sugary or salty contents, but also on the amount of pumping 'work' done by their lining membranes. However, they generally have some osmotic relationship with their surroundings.

A separate system of lymph capillaries and lymph vessels (often called 'the lymphatics') collects the lymph and eventually channels it back to the blood by two main lymphatic ducts, which drain on each side into the great veins near the heart. The walls of lymph capillaries are more permeable than those which carry blood, and cells, proteins, fat globules and all manner of materials can enter. The lymphatic system has numerous small valves which ensure that the flow in the tubes is in one direction only, and as with the veins, every small movement of the body passages the lymph on its journey back towards the heart.

All lymphatics pass through lymph nodes (sometimes called 'lymph glands') which are set like stations along railway lines (the lymphatic system can be outlined by angiography in much the same way as the blood vascular system). Lymph nodes are important structures for the defence of the body against injurious agents travelling in the lymphatic pathways. Germs infecting, say, a finger, or some other part, may tend to spread undesirably, particularly along the lymphatics, but then they can be trapped in the lymph nodes, which swarm with mobile cells, lymphocytes, scavengers and antibody-formers. These attack and destroy the invading organisms, and the number of active cells in the node rapidly increases. This explains why an inflamed, lumpish enlargement of the draining lymph nodes occurs, for example, in the elbow and armpit when a finger or hand is infected, in the groin and behind the knee when a foot or leg is involved, in the neck when germs attack the throat or the scalp, and so on. One can also appreciate that if infected soft tissue is immobilized in a firm dressing, the germs are less likely to spread dangerously along the local lymph channels than if it is massaged, scratched or forcibly squeezed—hence our use of immobilizing bandages, slings and plaster to treat infected parts.

The skin is exceptionally rich in lymphatic capillaries. Certain medical injections are given carefully into the skin when the intention is to put material directly into the lymphatic system; a deeper injection into a muscle is more likely to result in its absorption into the bloodstream.

The intestines are rich in lymphatics. This is probably important for the defence of the body because of all the strange items, germs included, which are taken as food. Although most digested food material absorbed by the walls of the gut passes directly into the bloodstream, some of it, particularly the fat, goes straight into lymphatic channels in the frond-like intestinal lining. Such fat, of course, does not then go through the portal system to the liver—at least not on its first time round the body.

The placenta

The amphibians invented the lung. The reptiles came up with the waterproof egg-shell. Birds hit on feathers. But outside of self-conscious thinking, for sheer evolutionary cleverness give me the placenta, a great mammalian invention, greater even than hair. (One might object to any exaltation of vertebrate genius by saying that molluscs or insects have waterproof egg-shells, lungs, hairs, and feathers of a kind, whereas many plants have a placenta of sorts. But these are toys compared to the complexity of the mammalian gadgets.)

The placenta is a local extension of the egg, in which an embryo is packed up with a food supply sufficient to see it through its early development. Eggs of fishes and reptiles carry a food supply in the form of a yolk in a sac, which becomes incorporated into the gut of the growing embryo. A large leash of blood vessels spreads over the sac to absorb the yolk food and carry it first to the liver, then to the heart and body generally.

The eggs of some fishes are fertilized by the male sperm while still inside the female, by physical mating of the two sexes. There is nothing revolutionary about this: many molluscs and arthropods have been doing it for millions of years. Copulation is essential for any species whose eggs are later to be laid fertile and with an impervious shell; but it also allows the embryo to develop without a shell, so long as it remains within the egg-tube of the female. In some fishes, amphibia and reptiles, the embryo grows with the blood vessels of its yolk sac pressed close to the blood supply of the wall of the female egg-tube. In this way some exchange of oxygen and carbon dioxide can take place, but it is not very effective: too many layers of cells intervene.

A new human egg is freed every month during non-pregnant periods of a woman's fertile life, unless she takes hormonal contraceptive pills which prevent this ovulation. The egg will be fertilized high up in the female reproductive tubes by a sperm which swims up to it, if unobstructed mating takes place within a few days after its release. The fertilized egg then drifts slowly down to the uterus, and when it is about ten days old it sinks into the uterine wall. Then it behaves just like an invading parasite. Its outer layers digest and erode the maternal tissues and eventually grow as frond-like processes into the maternal blood spaces of the uterus. These fronds contain foetal blood. Their outer layers become extremely thin, so that ultimately there is minimal impediment to exchanges between the bloods of mother and foetus, but they do not mix. These fronds become the placenta, or 'afterbirth', a temporary uterine 'lung' for the foetus, which is attached to it by the umbilical cord of blood vessels. The disadvantage of being forced to take oxygen at second hand across the placental barrier is overcome by the foetus having a modified circulation and a kind of haemoglobin (haemoglobin F, for 'foetus') different from that of a normal adult (haemoglobin A, for 'adult'). Haemoglobin F has some resemblance to the haemoglobin of aquatic animals. It has a greater affinity for oxygen than haemoglobin A, which helps the transfer but still leaves the embryo living at a reduced oxygen tension, like a man on a high mountain. On the other hand haemoglobin F seems to have disadvantages for adult life, and by the time the infant is born its cells are already beginning to make haemoglobin A, and F is fading out.

Another function of the placenta is to exchange heat between the two circulations, maternal and foetal. The foetus generates heat like any other living mammal, but being locked in the uterus it has no exterior exposed parts from which heat can be dissipated—no sweat, no radiation, no surface conduction to take it away. The mother, through her circulation, has to distribute the heat of two. Small wonder pregnant women may be seen in light clothing on a cold day, having never felt better in their lives, warm and pink-faced with their bounding circulations. They look radiant because they are radiators.

The placenta can successfully parasitize the maternal uterus without

The human placenta and umbilical cord

provoking an immunological reaction of the graft-rejection type. How it does so is a mystery, because half of the genetic constitution of the placenta—and foetus—derives from another individual, the father, and is theoretically 'foreign' to the mother.

The human placenta is not precisely the equivalent of the primitive yolk sac, but the stalk by which it grows from the foetus is attached at almost the same place. This stalk lengthens to become the umbilical cord, giving the foetus freedom to move and to be born. The cord contains two arteries and one vein, which conduct foetal blood to and from the placenta. The spiral twists of the three vessels of the cord, and the way they spread out and divide over the placenta, are reminiscent of the root and main stem of a vine. This, together with the symbolic resemblances between wine and blood, accounts for the old belief that an afterbirth buried under a newly planted vine will ensure its productivity.

As the foetus grows, it recapitulates to some extent its own evolutionary history. You are probably familiar with the concept that the developing animal 'climbs its own family tree'. This is broadly true: there is a stage when fishy and reptilian patterns are present in the layout of the circulatory system. You will remember that the fish heart pumps blood into a series of looped arterial arches running along the gills, and that the amphibian and reptilian hearts are not fully separated into right and left sides. A remnant of one gill artery persists in the human foetus as a wide-open short circuit (the *ductus arteriosus*) between the pulmonary artery and the aorta. Similarly, there is an oblique opening (the *foramen ovale*) between the right and left auricles, which allows some blood to move straight across from the right to the left side as long as pressure is higher on the right. The diagram may help to make this plainer.

Oxygenated foetal blood returning from the placenta passes through the foetal liver and into the inferior vena cava, by which it flows to the right side of the foetal heart. But just as it enters, a ridge deflects much of it through the foramen ovale across to the left chambers, from which it is pumped into the aorta and then to the body and placenta again, by-passing the lungs.

The placenta is a huge open capillary bed and offers little resistance to blood-flow. However, the lungs of a foetus are solid, because they have no air in them, and their resistance to blood-flow is great. Consequently, most of the blood leaving the right side of the heart moves readily from the pulmonary artery to the aorta through the ductus arteriosus.

The effect of these short circuits is that in the foetus both sides of the heart work together in parallel to pump blood into the aorta at high pressure and speed, and the consequent rapidity and high flow-rate of the circulation through foetus and placenta overcomes any disadvantage that may be inherent in a second-order circulation inside a pregnant uterus.

At birth a number of things happen quickly. The blood vessels in the umbilical cord undergo a contraction, and shut down, no matter whether the cord is tied, broken, chewed or left alone. This stops the flow of foetal blood through the placenta. The sudden resistance in such a main channel causes the pressure in the heart to rise and it beats more forcibly. Then, without a placental circulation, the baby begins to go short of oxygen. This stimulates the breathing centre in its brain, and nerve impulses are sent out which make the chest muscles heave. The baby gives a gasp. The previously solid lungs begin to fill out with air, like compressed petals unfolding. The lung capillaries become straightened out and dilated, and the resistance to a flow of blood through the lung from the right side of the heart falls away dramatically.

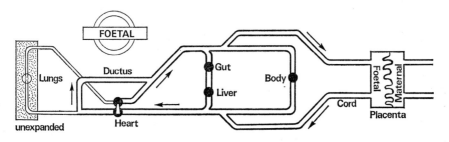

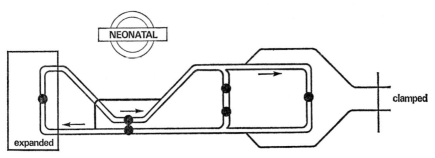

Changes in the foetal circulation at birth, when the offspring has to adapt rapidly to a neonatal (newborn) state

As the pressure becomes lower in the right side than in the left — the reverse of what it was before — the foramen ovale closes like an oblique clack-valve, and the two sides of the heart begin to act in series, no longer in parallel. Some time later the ductus arteriosus closes too, apparently by contraction of the muscle in its walls. In the normal child both these openings then become permanently obliterated by the growth of fibrous tissue. When, rarely, they do not, congenital heart disease may result.

CHAPTER FOUR

The Humours of It

So far, in this book, we have described medical and biological ideas about circulating blood that are consistent with current science. But in the past blood has been 'explained' in quite different ways. Our present notions have developed out of those earlier ones — not smoothly, but by fits and starts — over the past two or three thousands years. The process began in Egypt and Mesopotamia, and round about 500 B.C. it moved to the countries around the Mediterranean which had become intellectually active.

The Pythagoreans

There was then, in the extreme south of Italy, a group of Greek colonists interested in philosophical interpretations of nature and in following a way of life consistent with them. Their leader was the famous Pythagoras, a man of great intellect and ascetic habits. He was a vegetarian, but he forbade the eating of beans. He owed some of his notions to the civilization of Egypt, which he had visited. He believed that a man's body contained a spirit or soul which was sufficiently independent of the flesh to migrate to another body after death. He was adept at manipulating numbers and ratios, which he became convinced were the basis of all existence and experience.

He, or his later followers (who attributed all their views and discoveries to their leader), concluded that inspection of the natural scene revealed a series of pairs of contraries. Much-quoted ones were light and darkness, single and multiple, straight and curved, odd and even, limit and unlimit, rest and motion, good and bad, right and left, square and oblong, male and female. Such pairs they believed were the basis of all experience and natural order. Further, they supposed that graduated scales must stretch from each extreme to its contrary and that the gradations along each scale could be told off in numbers.

As a practical demonstration, a stretched lyre-string was used to illustrate the direct numerical harmony between the length of the string which was plucked and the musical pitch of the note that resulted. This was a display of concordance between the material world of the lyre-string and the inner world of the person who heard its tune.

The Pythagoreans assigned numbers to spatial relationships. One was

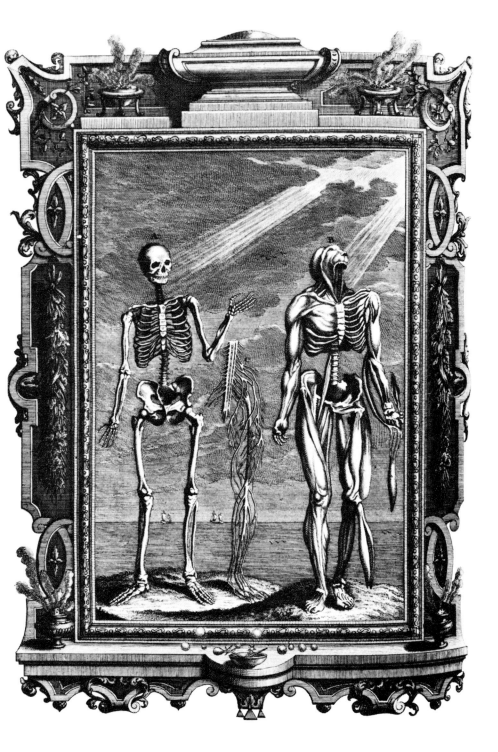

A human skeleton, and dissections displaying certain muscles and
the nerves of a leg

a point, two was a straight line, three was a surface, four was a solid. All material things were composed of points which were arranged in lines which enclosed surfaces which covered solids. Four was a square number, the product of equals, therefore just and perfect. It became a suitable pattern for the ideal man or the ideal world. Man and the world about him 'felt' like two separate modes of existence; but maybe each had echoes of the other. Maybe the body of man was a little universe or microcosm, and the world outside his body was a great universe or macrocosm, and maybe each was 'like' the other.

It does not greatly matter now whether this idea originated in Europe in Pythagorean thinking, or whether it came from Egypt or the East or through some other Greek school. But it was to be a persistent and developing notion, and one which might be used to explain the physiology of the body in wholly material terms, providing the 'outside' world was the one taken as the standard for reference. However, for the time being (which was to be the next two thousand years), the notion was persistently confused by the supposed presence of 'spirits' in the body.

Spirits defy definition. Not being solidly material they suffer from 'non-conservation of category', like an infant's thought-forms; they swell and diminish, mutate and merge. Consequently, when confronted with a sample of material reality, they can still escape final denial. And indeed, there are aspects of the external world (for example, distillation and magnetism) which seemed to many of the ancients to confirm the existence of spirits.

Greek thinkers noted that there were differences between arteries and veins, and that the blood moved. According to whether the heart, the liver or the brain was thought to be the prime organ controlling the rest of the body, various functions were tentatively ascribed to blood: perhaps its movements had to do with sleep; perhaps it distributed heat and animation. Some schools carried out animal dissections; others made dogmatic statements based only on speculation or the 'authority' of venerated teachers.

About one hundred years after the Pythagoreans, the Greek school of medicine became personified in Hippocrates. His system denied the interference of spirits. The body and its diseases were part of a natural process, obeying natural laws, and since there was a general tendency in nature to restore harmony after disturbance, in disease the healing power of nature should be assisted, not interfered with. Such a philosophy required one to have a view of 'nature' and its harmonies. The followers of Hippocrates were accurate observers of disease but they did not experiment or dissect; their 'model' of nature was essentially a piece of mystical Pythagorean numerology.

They accepted that both in the microcosm (the little universe of a

6

man's body) and in the macrocosm (the great universe outside) there must be harmonies between various contrary qualities or states of matter. Taking the number four as a guide, they accepted that both in Man and in the world there were two major pairs of qualities and states which, like stretched lyre-strings, would make the four points and the four sides of a square.

Four elements, four humours

The four fundamental qualities of non-living matter were reckoned to be the two pairs of contraries: hot and cold, wet and dry. The four elemental substances were air, earth, fire and water. Air was steamy vapour, warm and moist. Particles of earth were cool and dry. Fire was a kind of energetic influence, dry and warm. Water, a liquid, was cool and wet. As each element shared two qualities, the harmonies of the world outside a man could be represented thus:

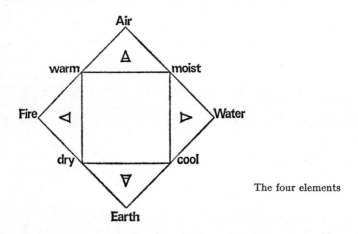

The four elements

The Greek school outlined a similar scheme for Man, believing that microscosm and macrocosm must somehow reflect one another. The 'elements' of a living body were hard to discern, especially if you didn't dissect much. Perhaps it was concluded that overall harmony inside the wet fleshiness of a living body must consist in items which ran and mingled together. Such were body juices and fluids, or 'humours'. It was reckoned that the four important humours were blood, lymph (also called pituita, or phlegm), yellow bile (choler) and black bile (melancholy). These were not as clearly defined or described as the scientifically analysed body fluids we are familiar with today. Information about them was derived from crude butchering knowledge, from ritual sacrifice of animals, from observation of battle wounds and from inspection (as is explained later in this chapter) of blood clotting in a dish.

The four humours were accorded the same overlapping pairs of properties as the four elements. 'Hot', 'cold' and 'wet' were easy enough to match, but the quality of 'dryness' may have seemed difficult to reconcile with the essential flowing nature of a 'humour'. However, the bitterness of gall, which 'dries up' the mouth, has remained one of the alternative senses of the word 'dry', and we still apply it particularly to the description of wines (and even to a variety of 'humour', as we *now* understand that term).

In the 'complexion' or 'constitution' or 'temperament' of a healthy person the four humours were 'well-tempered', they kept a nice equal balance or harmony. If they got out of trim, there was discord (or dis-harmony, dis-ease, dis-temper).

Blood was usually accorded the same position in the microcosmic

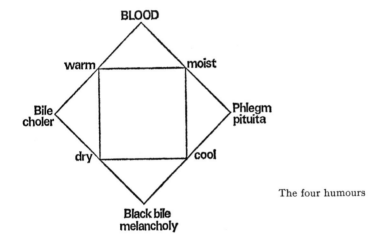

The four humours

system as air in the macrocosmic system. Phlegm corresponded to water, melancholy to earth, and choler to fire. Sometimes choler and blood were interchanged, but air, after all, was breath, and breath was life, and life was a living influence or 'pneuma' carried in the arteries and somehow related to the blood and the lungs. The living body soon died if it was deprived of air by smothering. Correspondingly, breath was a living influence which, blown into a body, could 'inspire' it. Similarly, blood was life, for loss of blood could kill a man or an animal in a few minutes, more quickly than any other disordering of the humours. Besides, one could see moist, steamy air rising from the freshly shed, warm blood of a sacrifice. So Blood was the Paramount Humour.

The careful clinical observations of the Hippocratic school showed that certain diseases (those we now know to be caused by germs, and particularly malaria) tended to run a regular course. This fitted well with the Pythagorean tradition of numerical explanation, and ideas were established about critical days on which these diseases would be expected to take natural turns for the better or worse. The treatments of the Hippocratic doctors were supportive, dietary, herbal, harmless. They were interested in the pulse and they knew that it beat with the heart, but they were concerned with its strength and quality, not its rate. The doctrine of the four humours was good enough for them because it 'explained' all they saw, mainly on the surface. Humours moved and flowed. Blood was in the veins. The aorta and arteries contained air, as every butcher told them, for being thick-walled and opaque, the cut ends of these vessels gaped emptily in a slaughtered beast.

Aristotle and Galen

Aristotle, who lived a little later, was a great classifier and expounder of knowledge and his influence lasted a long time. He accepted a humoral hypothesis that the heart was a source of fiery bodily heat, so that one had to breathe air and bring cold humours from the brain to cool and moderate it. For him the heart was also a seat of intelligence, distributing its influence through the arteries, which contained hot, bounding, mystic, airy pneuma. And at the same time, tendinous strings attached to the valves of the heart were in some way connected up, again rather mysteriously, to all the other tendons in the rest of the body, as in a marionette. (We still speak of things tugging at our heart-strings.) For Aristotle had noted that parts at which free movement occurred, such as the wrists, were well supplied with tendons, which he regarded as the prime movers. (He mistakenly took it that the muscles were concerned only with sensation.) In his books he divided animals into two groups — those With Blood, and those Without.

This humoral explanation of the nature of blood and disease had an attractive mathematical neatness. It was as evident then as it is now, that the medical and physiological scene is full of complex interactions and individual variations. This makes one eager for simple explanations, but unfortunately it also means that such explanations are unlikely to be right. In medicine today, the doctors are drawn, from time to time, to some simple, symmetrical, easily grasped theory of the nature of a puzzling disease, only to find, again and again, that the idea does not stand up to experimental test. But in ancient times the experimental test was seldom made or understood.

One of Aristotle's best-known pupils was Alexander the Great, whose conquests spread Greek influence widely. A notable medical school developed in Alexandria, and the ideas of Hippocrates and Aristotle were taught. However, a variation developed there in regard to blood, and for a time the humoral explanation of disease was displaced by a theory of 'plethora'. This was based on the supposition that food was absorbed into the portal vein and became blood in the liver. This blood ascended to the right side of the heart in the inferior vena cava and was then pumped to the lungs; it also was distributed to the body and limbs through the veins. (So far, this represents a standard Hippocratic or Aristotelian view.) But the arteries, on the other side of the vascular system, contained that rather indeterminate airy spirit, 'pneuma', and there were some small communicating vessels between the ends of the veins and the ends of the arteries. Now if too much blood were present on the venous side (because of overeating, for example), this would cause a 'plethora', in which blood would move across the connections to the arterial side, causing such disease as inflammation, fever, and disorders of the pulse. On the other hand, if an artery was cut, allowing some pneuma to escape, then blood would rush across from the venous to the arterial side to fill the vacuum, again causing plethora. This meant that a wound should be firmly bandaged to prevent the escape of pneuma, a vital spirit. The habit of treating severe bleeding with a ligature around the wrist, ankle or thumb, in order 'to tie the soul in', must go back to this time. And when a little of the vital spirit was thought to discharge itself through the nose in a sneeze, it was the ancient custom to cry to Jupiter or to say 'Good health!', as today we say 'Gesundheit' or 'Bless you!', to guard against all of this spirit 'expiring' or passing out like a soul, and life along with it.

Four centuries passed. Christ was born, and died. The Roman Empire straddled the known world. The medical school of Alexandria was still there, and Galen (the Serene) became one of its famous products. His views followed on from those of Hippocrates and Aristotle. He denied the doctrine of plethora and reasserted the system of the four humours. He stated that the arteries contained blood and not airiness, though this blood was charged with vital spirit. He promulgated considerable new knowledge both of anatomy and of the results of experiments. He was at the same time a reactionary and an innovator; and, unknown to him, his work was to stultify progressive thought on the structure and function of the human body for more than a thousand years.

He believed that the liver, heart and brain were the three prime organs of the body. Digested food was absorbed from the gut and carried by the portal vein to the liver, entering by the porta hepatis. In the liver, food was turned into blood charged with 'natural spirit', a kind of nourishing essence and a necessity of life. The 'natural spirit', according to Galen, was then distributed to the body along the veins by an ebb-and-flow movement of the blood. Impurities from the body were absorbed at the same time into the venous blood and were returned to the liver and then to the right side of the heart, whence they ascended in the pulmonary artery to the lungs to be exhaled. (Galen pointed out that animals kept in a closed space died because of the accumulation of these impurities.) Some of the blood then passed from the right to the left side of the heart through invisible pores in the wall between the ventricles, and mingled with air brought from the cool lungs in the pulmonary vein. In the hot heart this gave rise to a more vigorous 'vital spirit', or pneuma, which was responsible for the warmth of the whole body when it was distributed along the arteries. A third essence, the 'animal spirit', was formed in the brain when the 'vital spirit' reached it. This spirit was separated and distributed along the nerves which Galen thought of as being hollow during life, and it was responsible for movement and sensation.

The trinity of spirits added up to a composite soul. One can see it was largely made up of subjective experiences of eating, breathing, skin warmth, heart pulsation, muscular movement and sensation. Today if we showed Galen the biochemistry of sugar ('natural spirit') in blood; the oxygenation ('vital spirit' or pneuma) of blood; and the electrochemistry ('animal spirit') of nerve and muscle tissue, he would probably agree that his tripartite 'soul' was accounted for—that this sort of thing was what he 'meant' anyway by these 'spirits'.

Animal dissection was widely practised by Galen's time. The fact that the blood circulated could have been 'discovered', if the inquiring attitude of the Greeks had been maintained a little longer and had been joined to practical experiments. However, there was one main psychological block to be overcome. Mediterranean thinkers from warm, dry countries regarded the bloodstream as analogous to the irrigation streams of their field crops. It was therefore easily 'thinkable' that the blood's runnels should branch and rebranch in arteries or in veins until finally it should all soak away into thirsty earth. After all, the liver purified the blood and turned it to a perfect nourishing fluid. Why then should there be anything left over after this blood reached the body's hungry members? They would absorb it totally. The analogy thus tended to prevent a 'discovery' of circulation, even though for the educated an image of the full meteorological circulation of water in nature was available in the works of Aristotle.

There are odd periods in history when particular human ideas then current can achieve remarkably wide dissemination, authority and persistence because of circumstances. For example, the English tongue was once the language of a small, local, island people, but it was borne around the world at the critical time when they gained sudden ascendance in seafaring, commercial and industrial techniques, so it became established as an international language. In the same way, a minor eccentricity of behaviour in the first organizer of a human institution, such as an original court of law, or even a cricket club, can establish traditions which may be carried on unquestioned by successors for centuries, and which can influence countless others which derive from them. The Galenical doctrines benefited in such a way.

Galen was a confident man, with ideas not only about movements and functions of the blood, but about everything. He outlined the cause and cure of all known diseases dogmatically, without hesitation. He wrote down his beliefs in four hundred books, of which about ninety survive, and proclaimed himself a monotheist who could see the designing hand of one God in all nature. This made him acceptable to Arab, Hebrew and Christian. Many of the facts in his system were accurately observed and he certainly represented a peak in the knowledge and practice of medicine. Admittedly, some of his ideas were quite wrong: for example, the doctrine, derived from humoral pathology, that 'laudable pus' is necessary for a wound to heal (whereas in fact, the gathering of pus — suppuration — indicates that the body is defending itself against the complication of infection, something a wound can well do without). Nevertheless, had Galen's work been taken as a basis for further research after his death, things would have developed rapidly. As it was, the historical process resulted in his ideas being crystallized in the institutions of Christianity (which was then 'taking' in the Roman Empire as opportunely as the English language 'took' around the world in the eighteenth and nineteenth centuries). The Christians had an understandable hankering for single indisputable written authorities, and a medical system which incorporated a doctrine of a 'soul' was particularly in accord with their religious beliefs. Consequently, for well over a thousand years it came to be taught and believed that there were four humours and that blood flowed through invisible pores from the right ventricle of the heart to the left. And why, Father, does it do so? Because otherwise, my son, the 'vital spirit' could not be formed. But of course, Father, how silly of me to question it.

The tradition of the humours

In *Pantagruel*, François Rabelais, physician and writer, gives an account of the humoral theory as it was still being taught, fourteen hundred years after Galen:*

> Life consisteth in blood; blood is the seat of the soul; therefore the chiefest work of the microcosm is, to be making blood continually. At this forge are exercised all the members of the body; none is exempted from labour, each operates apart, and doth its proper office. And such is their hierarchy, that perpetually the one borrows

---

* *Gargantua and Pantagruel*, Bk III, ch. 4 (Everyman edition, Dent, London, 1929), translated by Sir Thomas Urquhart of Cromarty, who died at the accession of Charles II 'of joy and laughter at His Majesty's coming to his own again'.

from the other, the one lends the other and the one is the other's debtor.

The stuff and matter convenient, which nature giveth to be turned into blood, is bread and wine. All kind of nourishing victuals is understood to be comprehended in those two, and from hence in the Gothish tongue is called companage. To find out this meat and drink, to prepare and boil it, the hands are put to work, the feet do walk and bear up the whole bulk of the corporal mass; the eyes guide and conduct all; the appetite in the orifice of the stomach, by means of a little sourish black humour, called melancholy, which is transmitted thereto from the milt [spleen], giveth warning to shut in the food. The tongue doth make the first essay, and tastes it; the teeth to chaw it, and the stomach doth receive, digest, and chilify it. The mesaraic veins suck out of it what is good and fit, leaving behind the excrements, which are, through special conduits, for that purpose, voided by an expulsive faculty. Thereafter it is carried to the liver, where it being changed again, it by the virtue of that new transmutation becomes blood. What joy, conjecture you, will then be found amongst those officers, when they see this rivulet of gold, which is their sole restorative? No greater is the joy of alchymists, when, after long travail, toil and expense, they see in their furnaces the transmutation. Then is it that every member doth prepare itself, and strive anew to purify and to refine this treasure. The kidneys, through the emulgent veins, draw that aquosity from thence, which you call urine, and there send it away through the ureters to be slipped downwards; where, in a lower receptacle and proper for it, to wit, the bladder, it is kept, and stayeth there until an opportunity to void it out in his due time. The spleen draweth from the blood its terrestrial part, viz: the grounds, lees, or thick substance settled in the bottom thereof, which you term melancholy. The bottle of the gall subtracts from thence all the superfluous choler; whence it is brought to another shop or work-house to be yet better purified and fined, that is, the heart, which by its agitation of diastolic and systolic motions so neatly subtiliseth and inflames it, that in the right side ventricle it is brought to perfection, and through the veins is sent to all the members. Each parcel of the body draws it then unto itself, and after its own fashion is cherished and alimented by it. Feet, hands, thighs, arms, eyes, ears, back, breasts, yea, all; and then it is, that who before were lenders, now become debtors. The heart doth in its left side ventricle so thinnify the blood, that it thereby obtains the name of spiritual; which being sent through the arteries to all the members of the body, serveth to warm and winnow the other blood which runneth through the veins. The lights [lungs] never cease with its lappets and bellows to cool and refresh it; in acknowledgment of which good the heart, through the arterial vein, imparts unto it the choicest of its blood. At last it is made so fine and subtle within the rete mirabile [the 'wonderful net' of small arteries and veins], that thereafter those animal spirits are framed and composed of it; by means whereof the imagination, discourse, judgment, resolution, deliberation, ratiocination, and memory have their rise, actings and operation.

After Rabelais came the Elizabethans, typified by Shakespeare, for whom the liver, brain and heart were still sovereign thrones. The liver was the source of blood, the courageous humour, and consequently cowards were lily-livered. When courage left, the conduits of the blood froze up. These conduits were the veins which ran through the gates and alleys of the body. The arteries (or 'artiers' as Marlowe called them, making a more pleasant word to say) were less important, forming only a transmitting system for the spirits of the body.

Robert Burton in his *Anatomy of Melancholy*, written a hundred years after Rabelais and fifteen hundred after Galen, was still not questioning the old doctrines in 1621:

A humour is a liquid or fluent part of the body ... Crato out of Hippocrates will have all four to be juice ... without which no living creature can be sustained: which four, though they be comprehended in the mass of *blood*, yet they have their several affections, by which they are distinguished from one another ...

Blood is a hot, sweet, temperate, red humour, prepared in the *meseraick* veins, and made of the most temperate parts of the *chylus* in the liver, whose office is to nourish the whole body, to give it strength and colour, being dispersed by the veins through every part of it. And from it *spirits* are first begotten in the heart, which afterwards by the *arteries* are communicated to the other parts.

Pituita, or phlegm, is a cold and moist humour, begotten of the colder parts of the *chylus* (or white juice coming out of the meat digested in the stomack) in the liver; his office is to nourish and moisten the members of the body which, as the tongue, are moved, that they be not over dry.

Choler is hot and dry, bitter, begotten of the hotter parts of the *chylus*, and gathered to the gall; it helps the natural heat and senses, and serves to the expelling of excrements.

Melancholy, cold and dry, thick, black, and sour, begotten of the more faeculent part of nourishment, and purged from the spleen, is a bridle to the other two hot humours, *blood* and *choler*, preserving them in the blood, and nourishing the bones. These four humours have some analogy with the four elements, and to the four ages in man ... Spirit is a most subtle vapour, which is expressed from the *blood*, and the instrument of the soul, to perform all his actions; a common tie or *medium* betwixt the body and the soul, as some will have it; or, as Paracelsus, a fourth soul of itself. Melancthon holds the foundation of these spirits to be the *heart*; begotten there, and afterwards conveyed to the brain, they take another nature to them. Of these spirits there be three kinds, according to the three principal parts, *brain, heart, liver*; *natural, vital, animal*. The *natural* are begotten in the *liver*, and thence dispersed through the veins, to perform those natural actions. The *vital spirits* are made in the heart of the *natural*, which by the arteries are transported to all the other parts: if these spirits cease, then life ceaseth, as in a *syncope* or swooning. The animal spirits formed of the *vital*, brought up to the brain, and diffused by the nerves to the subordinate members, give sense and motion to them all.

The discovery of the circulation of the blood

The supposed affinities between the humours and the elements, and other theoretical relationships and analogies between the structure of the human body and the structure of the external world, were thus expounded by ancient civilizations, and they lasted until the beginning of the modern scientific era. As information accumulated, however, the forcing of physiological and cosmological data into the same mould became difficult. In the twelfth century A.D., Hildegard of Bingen, an abbess who interpreted her migraine auras (pictures of which survive) as divine visions, and who became known as 'the Sibyl of the Rhine', wrote reasonably convincing accounts of the parallelism between the microcosm and the macrocosm. Even in the early sixteenth century the alchemist Paracelsus held a similar view. But by that time, modern ideas about the solar system and the universe were rapidly gaining adherents, and it was becoming obvious that human and heavenly bodies had precious little gross structure in common. In the end the imagery which sought to contain them both became confined to non-scientific literature. For scientists today, it is only at the molecular or atomic end of the cosmic scale that structural identities between Man and the surrounding universe are at all apparent. The cosmology is still unified (or monotheistic), but it is made so by the properties of the ultimate particles which are common to all matter, living and non-living, and not by humours, elements and the music of spheres.

The weakening of medieval ideas set the stage for the Englishman William Harvey's discovery of the circulation of the blood. His work is a supreme example of a great modern 'discovery', and how it is finally made.

Since the sixteenth century, anatomists of the Italian schools had been making careful records of dissections and as a result some of the Galenical doctrines were being questioned. No pores could be found between the right and left ventricles. The heart valves had been described, and so had the valves in the veins. The fact that the blood could move from the right side of the heart into the lungs and back to the left side had been established; also, that blood did not mingle with air, so much as come into very close contact with it when it ran into small blood vessels near the air spaces. Harvey was sympathetic to the views of Aristotle and Galen just so long as these stood up to observation or experiment and were compatible with a mechanistic view of the heart. But he was very impatient when they failed these tests, as his style of writing showed. 'But dammit', he says, 'there are no pores' (*Sed mehercule porositates nullae sunt*), and 'Good God! How can the valves hinder the return of air, and not of blood?' (*Deus bone! Quomodo tricuspides impediunt aeris regressum et non sanguinis?*)

Harvey's work and argument went like this: It is evident from anatomical structure and from observing the hearts of living animals that the heart is a muscular organ *analogous to a mechanical pump*. There are *no pores between the right ventricle and the left*. The valves of the right side are such that at each contraction of the muscle *the blood must pass away from the heart along the pulmonary artery* and therefore through the porous structure of the lungs, returning to the left ventricle. From here *it must pass away from the heart into the aorta* and be distributed to the body. Now the hollow space in the dead *human heart holds only so much blood*. If we assume that even a quarter of this amount is put out with each beat by the living heart, and allowing two thousand beats an hour (half the normal rate), we can see that *even in half an hour the output of the left side of the heart amounts to more than twice the total amount of blood in the body*, measured by that which can be drained from a cadaver. (He could have made it even more convincing by pointing out that in twenty-four hours the output would be eight times the weight of a man.) *Blood cannot be manufactured from the food at this rate*, as Galen would have it. Now experiments and observations show that *the blood in arteries always moves away from the heart*, spurting from the cut end nearest to the heart. And similarly *the valves in veins allow the blood to move only towards the heart*, as can easily be seen by massaging the veins of a forearm with the fingertips and showing that they refill from below and not from above. *Therefore the blood moves, and can move only in a circle*, and *there must be pores in the flesh by which it moves from the ends of the arteries to re-enter the veins*.

You can see that Harvey ends up by being forced to assume the existence of unseen pores in the flesh, having denied the presence of pores in the septum between the ventricles on the ground that they are invisible. Nevertheless, you can see too that generally he was trying to answer the question How?, not Why? And he was using quantitative measurements and likening the living body to a mechanism with a pump in it, with no appeal to the presence of intangible spirits. Strictly, he made no external 'discovery' and nobody ever has. People make these inside themselves, intuitively, in their own heads. He was adducing evidence and logical argument in favour of a hypothesis, 'that the blood in animals is moving around, and is being driven in some kind of circuit and is forever on the go'.* His 'discovery' was that the heart and its vessels are a pump and pipes, a relational form intelligible in the world of machines, no longer spiritually transcendent, no longer defying reason.

Harvey's kind of evidence and argument soon convinced the savants of his time. Since the Renaissance, they had been cultivating a habit of scepticism and of questioning such traditional beliefs as did not stand up to experimental tests.

But, perhaps not unexpectedly, his findings also convinced the few remaining alchemists who represented the beleaguered intellectual stronghold in Europe of the microcosm-macrocosm theory of Man and the universe. Some of them were still the straggling followers of Philippus Aureolus Theophrastus Bombast von Hohenheim der heiligen Schrift Professor, der freien Kuenste und beider Arznei Doctor, Medicus et Germaniae Philosophus, Monarcha medicorum et Mysteriarcha, chemicorum princeps, Helvetius Eremita: Paracelsus for short. He had taught that all matter was animated by spirits, sylphs, pixies and salamanders, which inhabited air, water, earth and fire respectively. By this time the alchemists were a strange little band of diehards, rapidly becoming diluted by quack astrologers, Rosicrucians, neurotic mystics and by those people found in every generation who just prefer to write of perverse, rather than of received knowledge. But these men saw in Harvey's 'discovery' of the circulation an extension and confirmation of their own ideas of the excellent perfection of circular motion (a doctrine that went back to Aristotle), of the Zodiac, of the movements of the planets, of the squaring of the circle, and of the central positions of gold, the heart and the sun; also of their ideas of the analogies (which Harvey himself mentioned with reference to Aristotle) between circulation of the blood under the action of the heart and meteorological distillation of earth's water under the sun in an endless natural circle of mist, cloud, raindrop, stream, river, ocean, mist.

Four years after Harvey died, Malpighi observed the capillary blood vessels with the aid of the microscope, and the 'discovery' was nearly

---

* 'Necessarium est concludere circulari quodam motu in circuitu agitari in animalibus sanguinem, et esse in perpetuo motu.'

complete. 'Nearly', because there were still one hundred and fifty years to pass before Lavoisier realized that oxygen supported life in the same way as it supported combustion. Then the all-important purpose of the circulation of the blood steadily became apparent and formed the basis for all subsequent understanding of physiology, for it was seen how the internal circular transport system of the body subserved the life of every organ, every tissue, every cell.

Enthusiastic leeches

William Harvey died in 1657. His new knowledge had disproved Galen's traditional views about the movements of the blood. But it did not shake out of physicians' heads the old Hippocratic doctrine of the four humours; it merely tended to make blood still more important among them.

Humoral theories of disease lead naturally to the conclusion that certain symptoms must be caused by local accumulations of one humour or another. A medical tradition that believes in active interference with the processes of the body will then try to bring relief by shifting, chasing and draining humours. And this means bloodletting.

Since Hippocrates, phlegm, the cold humour, had been thought to be the commonest producer of disease. When it discharged from the nose, there was a 'cold in the head'. If it was coughed from the lungs, there was a 'cold in the chest', and if it was vomited, a 'chill on the liver'. A cloudy urine meant a 'chill on the kidneys'. When it was seen coming from an inflamed wound as 'pus', this came to be regarded as 'laudable', either because excesses were discharging or because it was nobly counteracting the hot humour, choler.

Choler was yellow and was therefore thought to be in bile and urine, but, as we shall see, it was also thought to be blood serum itself. It was regarded as a main cause of inflammation and fever. If clotting blood taken from a patient (Latin *pati*, to suffer) showed a visible glairy surface-layer of yellow serum (as do many bloods taken from sick people), this was taken for choler and evidence of the blood being 'overheated'. So cooling medicines were given. Yellow foods, particularly egg-yolk and honey, were thought to contain choler. So they were given for 'colds' but forbidden in 'fevers'. Queasy children looked yellowish or vomited bile; they were all 'bilious'.

Food became blood in the liver. Therefore (some said) too much food would produce too much blood or 'plethora'. The arguments were easy to make. Hot poultices and irritants 'drew'. Bandages and 'compresses' held in. Cold battled with hot, thick with thin. And drawing blood off was a great way of shifting humours this way or that, according to one's theories.

In considering the widespread practice of blood-letting, one must also remember that it was a dramatic procedure which demonstrated to everyone concerned — patient, relatives and the physician himself — that 'something was being done'. In the past, one of the doctor's moral failures has been to make too little effort to educate the public generally in how 'doing something' is often unnecessary and irrational, even when the patient himself is demanding significant intervention.

Nevertheless, there are indeed a few clinical situations where blood-letting (phlebotomy or venesection, literally 'vein cutting') can give dramatic but temporary relief. It is occasionally employed today in, for instance, congestive heart failure where blood accumulates on the venous side of the circulation, and in polycythaemia and haemo-chromatosis; in all of these it will make the patient 'feel' better as well as improving his condition objectively. As a matter of fact many healthy blood donors experience a certain feeling of well-being after a pint (half a litre) of blood has been drawn from them. It would seem that occasionally satisfactory treatments of 'plethora', together with the humoral theories, were in the past quite enough to justify the almost universal practice of blood-letting and doctors becoming known as 'leeches'. Blood-letting flourished from the dawn of medicine to the middle of the nineteenth century, endorsed by almost every school in turn, including that of Hippocrates, even though the latter was primarily in favour of the healing power of nature doing its job without interference.

In ordinary blood-letting a band was wound around the arm sufficiently tightly to make the veins of the forearm swell with accumulated blood. A small lancet (a fine, sharp blade) was used to nick the skin and the vein, and the blood would run out and be caught in a dish held under the arm.

Guy Patin, Dean of the Faculty of Medicine of Paris in the seventeenth century and a fierce opponent of Harvey's doctrine, believed strongly in blood-letting:

There is no remedy in the world which works as many miracles as bleeding. Our Parisians ordinarily take little exercise, drink and eat much, and become very plethoric. In this condition they are hardly ever relieved of whatever sickness befalls them if blood-letting does not proceed powerfully and copiously, nevertheless if the sickness is acute one does not see the effect as soon as from purgation. About the year 1633, M. Cousinot, who is today first physician to the King, was attacked by a rude and violent rheumatism, for which he was bled sixty-four times in eight months, by order of his father, and of M. Bouvard, his father-in-law. After having been bled so many times they commenced to purge him, by which he was much relieved, and in the end recovered. The idiots who do not understand our profession imagine that there is nothing to do but to purge, but they deceive themselves because if bleeding copiously had not preceded it, to repress the impetuosity of the vagabond humor, to empty the great vessels and to chastise the intemperance of the liver which produced the serum, the purgation would have been useless. Another time I treated in this city a young gentleman of seven years, who fell into a pleurisy by over-heating himself when playing tennis, having also received in the game a stroke on the foot on the right side, which provoked the most grand fluxion. His tutor hated blood-letting very much and I could only oppose to this hatred a good counsel, which was to call two of our ancients, M. Seguin and M. Cousinot. He was bled thirteen times and was cured in fifteen days, as if by a miracle, even the tutor was converted by it.

Patin's maxim was '*Marcher la saignée devant la purge!*' He believed in derivative bleeding: drawing blood from the same side as the symptoms were located, as taught by Hippocrates. He was bitterly against the Arabic practice of 'revulsive' bleeding where blood was drawn from the opposite side. It was Patin's habit to castigate this 'miserable Arabesque pharmacy', and there was indeed a very widespread controversy over the question at the time. When his father-in-law was nearly eighty years old, Patin had him bled eight times from the arms:

He is a fat and full-blooded man. He had an inflammation of the lungs with delirium, and, in addition, stone in the kidneys and bladder. After the bleeding I had him well purged four times with senna and syrup of pale roses, by which he has been so marvellously relieved that it is miraculous, and he seems rejuvenated. Many people would not have believed it and would believe rather some fable of a julep cordial. He shows me much contentment but although he is very rich he gives no more than a statue. Old age and avarice are always in good intelligence with one another. Such men resemble pigs which leave all in dying, but are only good for anything after they are dead because they are good for nothing during their life. It is necessary to have patience, I will not neglect to take good care of him. God has given me the means to do without the wealth of others, and live content till now without ever thinking evil.

On other occasions he had his aged mother bled **four** times for pleurisy, and himself seven times for a bad cold. Then:

I had a bad toothache yesterday, which obliged me to have myself bled from the same side [as the pain]. The pain stopped all at once, as by a kind of enchantment, and I slept all night. This morning the pain began a little again. I had the other arm bled and was cured right away. I am, thank God, without pain. I think that these two bleedings will serve to enable me to purge myself surely, which I shall do next week, if I have the leisure for it.*

From the time of Galen the practice of blood-letting was elaborate. The part of the body where a vein was opened was determined not only by the supposed site of the accumulation of the bloody humour but by the astrological state of the heavens. To complicate things more, anatomical knowledge was inaccurate and confused; it was, for instance, believed that the third finger of the left hand—the 'leech' finger— contained a vessel leading directly to the heart, and that by bleeding this finger the left side of the heart would be relieved. There is no anatomical basis for it—as was pointed out in rich detail by Sir Thomas Browne in his *Pseudodoxia Epidemica* or 'Vulgar Errors' in 1646.

Bloody humours

At all times, as we have seen, the medical arguments for blood-letting have been supported by humoral or plethoric theories of the body, but it seems the practice was most strongly justified by a common observation which apparently indicated quite plainly that the three other humours were mixed in with the blood. If someone was bled into a glass dish, the red cells of their blood would sometimes begin to settle to the bottom with unusual speed, especially if they were sick. The redness would fade from the top, leaving a straw-coloured liquid. If clotting then occurred (and it always takes at least a few minutes), the upper part of the clot would be pale (it is often described as 'chicken-fat clot') and would exude pale-yellow serum as it contracted. The part lower down, consisting of red cells, would be scarlet, and the bottom layer of all (viewed through the glass or inspected by turning over the slab of clot in a blood-letter's bowl) a very much darker red, because its haemoglobin was farthest away from the oxygen of the air. Thus there was, from top to bottom, yellow serum, pale clot, red clot, black clot. These were taken to be choler, phlegm, blood and melancholy, all separating and thus proving that the blood in the body was a mixture of the four humours. The humoralists believed that blood from a man of melancholic temperament would show an excess of the black layer, and so on. Shakespeare's King John says:

* As quoted in F. R. Packland, 'Guy Patin and the Medical Profession in the Seventeenth Century', *Annals of Medical History*, vol. IV, no. 1 (New York, 1922), pp. 136, 215 and 357.

Varieties of spider, with detail of the mandibles. 'The Cobweb of
it being layd on doth stanch bloud.'

> Or if that surly spirit melancholy
> Had baked thy blood and made it heavy thick
> Which else runs trickling up and down the veins ...

Most people today have come across blood, liver bile and nose or throat phlegm (mucus) in ordinary experience.* But 'black bile' (melancholy) may be less familiar. It was supposed to come from the spleen which, when cut, is a very dark plum colour, and in fact the spleen of someone who has chronic malaria (common among Mediterranean peoples in classical times) is quite black because of the malarial pigment accumulated by its scavenger cells. Acute malaria sometimes destroys so many red cells at once that even the urine is darkened by excessive release of pigments. This is classically known as 'black-water fever' and was considered to be another apparent instance of melancholy.

But black bile was more commonly seen in the form of vomited, partly digested blood, which is now customarily described to medical students as looking like coffee grounds. When there is bleeding into the stomach — a not uncommon event — the blood pigment is rendered very dark brown by the acid gastric juice; but the Hippocratic school, noting the black vomit which was produced, reckoned that melancholy, the depressive humour, had got into the stomach from the nearby spleen — though in fact, no passage connects the two organs. If an internal haemorrhage into the stomach or gut is not vomited but passes on down the bowel, it makes the motions black and tarry: another fairly common medical sign which would have seemed to indicate the presence of black bile.

Phlegm was reckoned by many to be the greatest disease-producer, for not only did it seem to accumulate as pus and issue from various orifices of the body in sickness, but it also seemed to be present in excessive amounts in the blood of those who were acutely ill. This could have been attributable to either the exceptionally rapid sedimentation of red cells in anaemia or other diseases which leads to a larger 'chicken-fat' top to the clot, or to the extra numbers of white cells in the blood in cases of infection and pus formation. White cells do not sediment as rapidly as red cells and therefore they form a whitish layer on top in a blood 'specimen'; such a layer may be very apparent in infections, and would reinforce the notion that a disorder of 'phlegm' was involved.

Applying leeches and cupping were variations upon blood-letting. Cupping consisted of dropping some lighted material into a hollow cup or horn and then putting the greased open end firmly on to freshly scarified skin (or on to a suppurating boil). The suction created by the

---

* The yellow pigment in serum is actually the same as that which colours liver bile, so in a way the humoralists were right in their belief that blood contained choler.

7

burning up of oxygen in the cup drew blood or fluid through any break in the skin.

Such practices do little harm to healthy people who can restore lost blood quite quickly by growing new red cells. But many of those who were bled in the old days were already sick. If they were anaemic, blood-letting would have made them more so. If it were repeated, day after day, at times and from areas of the body dictated by astrological calculation, it would produce pallor and weakness in all but the most healthy person. It was not realized that a red appearance might indicate something other than a general congestive or plethoric state of the circulation; that people with fever were only hot and flushed and that they badly needed all their body substance; that those with inflamed limbs or other parts were merely showing a natural reaction which is essentially a healing process. They needed their blood, according to modern medical teaching. But the humoral theory, or that of plethora, made no distinctions; and it could be argued from either theory that active treatment of disease required that the humours be shifted around.

It was common to advise bleeding in the spring and autumn, irrespective of sickness, and certain orders of monks kept this tradition until quite recently. Many people regularly took purging medicines made from fresh herbs to 'clean the blood' in springtime. These remedies might have contained iron and perhaps Vitamin C, and any real good they did probably had more relation to the nutritional relief of scurvy and anaemia caused by a poor winter diet after an inadequate harvest, than to any adjustment of the humours by purging.

Similar crude arguments for giving laxatives to children have lasted in some households up to the present day. Other attitudes based on the Doctrine of Sympathies ('like cures like') are perhaps dying out with our grandparents, but they go back to the alchemists. A familiar one, for example, was the mistaken belief that red flannel worn next to the skin would prevent fever or drive it away: if there was redness there already, then the redness of fever supposedly could not appear.

A hundred years ago the doctrine of the four humours and of plethora finally gave way to the view of the great German pathologist Virchow and others that cells were of more fundamental importance than extracellular fluids, but there is a legacy of popular idiom where the humours still survive. The idea that in health they are balanced makes the normal, healthy man 'good-humoured' or 'good-tempered'. 'Tempering' implies a proper mixing, or 'complexion', of one with another in natural harmony. On the other hand a man may pass into 'distemper' or 'ill-humour', or he will be 'sanguine', 'choleric', 'melancholic' or 'phlegmatic'.

Ben Jonson wrote in *Every Man Out of His Humor* (1599):

Why *Humor* (as 'tis ens) we thus define it
To be a qualitie of aire or water,
And in it selfe holds these two properties,
Moisture and Fluxure: As for demonstration,
Poure water on this floore, 'twill wet and runne,
Likewise the aire (forc't through a horne or trumpet)
Flowes instantly away, and leaves behind
A kind of dew; and hence we doe conclude,
That what soe're hath fluxure and humiditie,
As wanting power to containe it selfe,
Is *Humor*: so in every human bodie
The choller, melancholy, flegme and bloud,
By reason that they flow continually
In some one part, and are not continent,
Receive the name of Humors. Now thus farre
It may by Metaphore applie it selfe
Unto the generall disposition,
As when some one peculiar qualitie
Doth so possesse a man, that it doth draw
All his affects, his spirits, and his powers
In their confluctions all to runne one way,
This may be truly said to be a Humor ...

Shakespeare constantly used phrases which helped to contribute to the general drift of the word 'humour', until it came to mean 'whim occasioned by one's condition'; then its meaning shifted through 'caprice' and 'fancy' to the present one, 'the cultivation of mirthful or ludicrous ideas' (though 'humid' still means 'moist').

If 'sanguine' was always a respectable word it is hard to see why 'bloody' should not have been too. The explanation that it is a version of 'By Our Lady' or ''sblood' (for 'God's blood') has no strong support from the etymologists. Probably 'bloody' originally meant strong, masculine, violent — like a young blood among the landed gentry. Then with the rise of the urban middle classes in nineteenth-century England, the cult of delicacy amongst 'ladies' gradually prohibited its use in the drawing-room, and indoors it became low English. Outside, it has never lost its popularity, particularly among both sexes of the horse-owning classes, and it has always been quite respectably used in Ireland. Today, with the protracted breakdown of certain aspects of English class-distinction, it has come back into general use. Now it is a useful indication that a well-meant word or phrase is coming next in the sentence. Too bloody many people today dilute the sense of their words by prefacing or postscripting every bloody thing they say with a tentative 'you know ... ', 'sort of ... ' or 'I mean ... ', all of which should be kept for occasions when there is no synonym or neologism for what is meant — the only times when a qualified approximation is good usage. The classical Greeks went to great trouble in the other direction to create little emphasizing syllables which they added to their sentences as required. When we have bloody good reasons for making something vivid and real to our hearers, we too should emphasize it by bloody well saying 'bloody', and more.

CHAPTER FIVE

One Man's Blood

All the cells of a human body grow originally from a single cell – the fertilized egg-cell in a uterus. A hen, wrote Samuel Butler (author of *Erewhon*), is only an egg's way of making another egg. It is the same with humans. The human egg-cell divides, the resulting cells divide, again and again, many times. They manipulate food and oxygen and water, until their total mass becomes the bundle of tissues which is successively an embryo, an infant, a child, an adult. Different tissues have different rates of cell 'turnover'. Some parts of the body, once they have grown to final size, do not make any new cells during their subsequent lifetime (even if damaged, when they heal with a scar). Other parts have cells which regularly die off and are replaced by new ones dividing from the remaining stock. This stock is sometimes the functioning cell-mass of an organ itself, as in the liver where cells which die in the course of duty are replaced by some of their adjacent surviving comrades splitting into two. Other organs have an assembly-line system where a set of stem-cells divides all the time to produce a constant stream of new cells which do their work for a period, and then wear out and perish. The skin cells and the blood cells are examples of this last kind. Thus the skin, the liver and the blood are parts which can quite readily repair themselves. The brain, the kidney, and the heart as we shall see, have much greater difficulty.

Jelly in a box

In the human embryo, rudimentary blood appears at a very early stage in the wall of the part which would be the yolk sac in a non-placental species. The same area gives rise to the wall of the gut, of which the liver and spleen are later outgrowths. Relationships existing between the liver and the spleen and the blood-cell-forming system, and also the circulatory plan of the portal system, are easier to understand when it is known that these parts have the same embryonal origin in the intestinal wall.

The first embryonal blood appears in small patches which hollow out, fill with fluid, and become lined with cells which multiply and then become detached and float free. The cytoplasm of the floating cells manufactures haemoglobin, and so they turn red.

The hollowed-out patches become tubular and link up to make a circuit. Part of the circuit becomes contractile. In the third week of a human pregnancy there is the first flutter of a beating heart. Blood begins to move.

Fishes, frogs and reptiles have red cells which remain nucleated. Non-nucleated cells can seldom divide to form daughter cells, because as a rule all the inherited 'instructions' for cell formation and continuity are in the nucleus. But the circulating nucleated red cells in these animals can divide and do so. In a human embryo it is at first the same as in a fish, frog or lizard, but soon some red cells without nuclei begin to appear—a few at six weeks, one-tenth of the total at eight weeks. In an eleven-week human embryo all the circulating red cells are being produced in non-nucleated form from a fixed lining layer of immature dividing nucleated cells, which make haemoglobin as they grow, extrude their nuclei, and drift off as soon as they mature. All mammals have red cells of this kind.

Such cells have become very highly specialized, mere bags of haemoglobin, and have lost all capacity for multiplication by cell division. In a certain sense their 'maturation' is not so much a growing-up as a kind of degeneration. A useful term for it is 'differentiation'—they are becoming different from any other type of cell. (Perhaps one should not use the name 'cell' for an item without a nucleus. 'Red corpuscle' is a traditional designation, and dates from the dawn of microscopy, long before the functional concept of the cell had been established.)

During the third month of human foetal life the blood-cell-producing tissue has become concentrated in the blood spaces of the deep-set liver, spleen and kidney, through which the circulation moves sluggishly. Up to this time there are only a few scavenging white cells in the circulation. These migrate into the blood from the general solid parts of the embryo to take an occasional ride around. The lymphocytes move in from the surface lining of the fishy gill-clefts which are still present in the embryo at this stage. In the fifth month human blood formation moves to the bone marrow.

From an engineer's viewpoint a hollow rod is stronger than a solid one of equal diameter. And so the prime reason for the hollowness of long bones is to give maximum skeletonic support with minimum weight. Nevertheless the hollows themselves are useful: they accommodate the marrow—bloody jelly—in a rigid box. It is probably the perfect biological situation for so delicate a structure as a soft slush of multiplying cells which must not drift off into the passing blood until they are fully formed. Colonies of blood cells persisting in organs like the adult kidney, liver or spleen, capable of being compressed by the movements of the rest of the body, could result in primitive cells being cast off before they were ready.

Red and white cells

When red-cell formation becomes established in the bone marrow of the foetus, the cells that give rise to the phagocytic white blood cells move in too, and their proportion increases. Soon the white-cell-forming cells overtake the red-cell-forming cells until there are three or four times as many. Then these proportions are maintained, more or less, throughout healthy adult life. By the time a baby is born, the cellular marrow of the bones occupies a total volume equal to that of the liver.

The average adult human body has about ten pints — say five litres — of circulating blood: about a pint for every stone of body weight, or one litre per eleven kilograms. Blood-cell numbers are usually expressed as the number per cubic millimetre of blood. A cubic millimetre is an imaginary small box with each side as long as the diameter of the head of a pin. In this volume there are usually between four and six million red blood cells. A single human red cell is small: smaller than most other cells. It takes one hundred and fifty of them, their broadest diameters touching, to straddle the head of the pin. This makes them seem very small and very numerous, yet if you lived in the minute world of plasma macromolecules they would be like enormous blundering bags of jelly and iron, drifting like heavy balloons in soup, with gases and chemicals fizzing and wheezing in and out of their surface membranes. There are about 25 million million of them in each human body. Each one lasts for one hundred days, or a little more, before being selectively destroyed in the spleen.

This means that every second about three million of them are being removed and replaced! Tick ... tock ... the tick of a grandfather clock, and you, you have made three million red cells. Each one containing about 300 million haemoglobin molecules. How clever you must be. And such a quick worker. Now each of the 300 million haemoglobin molecules in each of your red cells is able to catch and carry four molecules of oxygen, which adds up to more than 1,000 million oxygen molecules picked up per cell as it circulates through your lungs.

It follows that as you sit reading this, each beat of your heart (putting out, say, a quarter pint of blood) is sending more than 500,000,000,000,000,000,000,000 (over 500 British trillions) of haemoglobin-bound oxygen molecules out to your body. It seems a lot. But if your breathing should stop, which would soon prevent oxygen molecules being taken up in the lungs, you will find that you have only three or four minutes' supply of oxygen within you to maintain a hard-living organ like your brain. In fact if I cut off its supply by compressing the carotid (literally the 'throttling', compare 'garotte') arteries in your neck, you will go unconscious within seconds. Because, clever and haemoglobinized though you may be, your precious blood can still carry about eight times as much food like sugar or amino-acids as it can oxygen, and cells need equal quantities of these sorts of things for ordinary survival. Therefore oxygen starvation is always nearer than any other kind.

Numbers of the order of billions and trillions have little meaning because they are outside the bounds of ordinary experience. What's a trillion? A word—and a confusing one when the Americans use it in a different sense from the British. Magnitudes can be conveniently thought of in steps. Electrons, atoms, molecules, genes, chromosomes, cells, people, planets, solar systems, galaxies, universes: here is an arbitrary cosmic tonic sol-fa we can use to play the celestial and human concords that men have listened for since Pythagoras began to guess at them. Placed in this sequence, there are very roughly the same-sized intervals between the different orders of magnitude, but the important point is that the imaginative processes or sets of mental rules required to 'describe' each 'world' can become distorted if applied to a neighbouring one instead. The world of the atom is utterly different from the world of a man. Much the same is true of time and temperature scales. The worlds at absolute-zero temperature, and at a million degrees centigrade, are totally unlike one another. Considerations of this kind can show how absurdly particular are our own everyday bodily experiences and sensations in terms of size, duration and thermal activity, and consequently how improper it is to take analogies from our 'world' and use them to generalize about other existences up or down from us on the cosmic scales. But bridges can be made from world to world, usually with mathematics.

White cells are up to twice the size of red cells and there are fewer of them in the circulating blood, about 5,000 to 10,000 per cubic milli-metre. The life span of an ordinary phagocytic white cell is probably a matter of hours, compared with the red cells' three to four months, and so it needs to be replaced more often. This, together with the fact that many white cells do not appear in blood-counts because they are wandering in spaces outside the bloodstream, helps to explain why there is quantitatively more white-cell-forming than red-cell-forming tissue in the marrow. But it is mainly the fast-moving polymorpho-nuclear white cells which grow there. The slower-moving mononuclear ones grow mainly in other parts of the scavenging system of the body, as well as in the spleen. Lymphocytes grow in the bone marrow, though at a later stage, influenced by the thymus gland, they may develop further in the lymph nodes, in the tonsils and adenoids, in the wall of the gut and in areas of chronic infection.

There is one other formed structure in the circulating blood—the platelet. Platelets, as we have already noted, are made in the bone marrow from the frilly edges of giant cells: fragments are shed into the flowing blood like jelly pushed through a wire sieve into a torrent. The normal number of platelets is between 150,000 and 500,000 per cubic millimetre, and they are very small: about one-tenth to one-fifth the diameter of a red cell.

Normal

The question of a 'normal' number for a body measurement is a difficult one. Who is 'normal'? Humans are very diverse.

A common convention is that the normal range covers 95 per cent of healthy people. Then one person in twenty walking the streets and feeling healthy will be 'abnormal' by definition. Indeed there is such natural variation among all humans that it is very difficult to define precisely the altered state one calls 'disease'.

For instance the blood-cell count per cubic millimetre can vary, not always because the total number of cells has changed, but according to the concentration of the circulating blood. If water moves from the tissues into the circulation, the total blood volume is increased and the red-cell count per cubic millimetre falls. Small variations caused by this kind of change occur daily. Nevertheless a red-cell count below four million and above six million per cubic millimetre is an indication that something unusual and probably 'unhealthy' is happening.

Every animal body lives in a hostile environment and is always in a state of siege, surrounded by germs. The white cells are part of our mobile defence system, and they increase in numbers when stimulated by the entry of foreign material. The numbers of white cells in the human blood will therefore fluctuate as they respond to one challenge after another, and as they move to and from the bloodstream and the tissues. Small variations will occur even with a walk in the cold or after a meal of meat, and in most people the white-cell count increases every afternoon, apparently related to nothing more than the time of day. For all such reasons the 'normal' white count in healthy people is given a wide range—from 4,000 to 11,000 per cubic millimetre, though it does not ordinarily vary as much as this in one individual.

A main stimulus to white-cell production and movement is microbial infection. When germs enter the body and multiply, their poisons activate the white-cell-forming tissue in the bone marrow, making it divide rapidly, and a stream of new white cells enters the bloodstream. Consequently a marked increase in the number of white cells in the blood is a prime indication of bacterial infection somewhere.

Lack of oxygen is the condition which results in extra red cells being produced. Certain parts of the body (the kidney is one), on not receiving their accustomed amount of oxygen from the blood, release a soluble substance which is carried in the bloodstream to the bone marrow and stimulates more activity in the red-cell-producing tissues. This means more circulating red cells and therefore more haemoglobin to catch and carry oxygen. Consequently, people living in high mountain villages where the oxygen is thin have greater red-cell counts than their cousins in the valleys far below. Poor lung function leading to inadequate oxygenation of the blood in the lungs may have the same effect.

The haemoglobin in the red cells can readily be measured, and in healthy people the amount is simply related to the number of red cells present, because each one is packed tight with it. But in anaemic people haemoglobin may be reduced disproportionately if the blood cells are short of the means to make it. Iron is the essential ingredient, a physiologically violent metal which the body desperately needs, hoards, binds, uses over and over again, but daren't have too much of.

A black eye

When haemoglobin molecules are eventually released from a worn-out red cell, the iron is picked out of them. Protein is also removed. What remains is still a pigment, but no longer red. It eventually turns yellow, after which it is discharged through the liver in the bile. The colour changes are nicely seen in a black eye.

The hard protective bone around the human eye socket acts as an unyielding base when a blow crushes the overlying skin. Small blood vessels are nipped and broken. Blood streams into the tissue spaces, forming a 'bruise'. The red cells quickly lose their oxygen to the surrounding tissues. Their haemoglobin consequently turns deep blue, and this colour is seen through the skin. After a day or two, wandering scavenger cells begin to pick up and digest some of the displaced red cells, which have by now been so long out of circulation that their surfaces have degenerated and the scavengers can identify them as fair game. The iron is removed from the haemoglobin and the remaining molecule is yellow. Yellow and blue together make green. A day or two more and the blue has faded, so that the green turns to yellow. This suffuses the skin for a while, then fades through jaundiced peach as normal pink returns. Any bruise or other kind of bleeding under the skin goes through the same phases.

Raw beef steak applied to cure a black eye? Better eaten — beef is expensive these days, and the treatment is a piece of traditional homoeopathic magic: raw beef, raw-looking eye — like cures like. But if you must use it, do so; it is the sort of treatment Hippocrates would have approved, for it is external, and harmless. In a superstitious community it satisfies, diverts proposals for more serious interference, and allows the healing power of nature to run its course.

The blood testers

A sample of blood is easily obtained by putting a hollow needle, attached to a syringe, into a vein that has been made to swell with blood by a light tourniquet, which obstructs it between the sampling point and the heart. Arterial blood can also be taken, but without any tourniquet because the pressure inside is naturally high enough to keep the vessel tightly filled. In infants, whose veins and arteries are very small, blood can be taken from the large venous pool of blood at the top of the head by putting a needle between the small skull-plates which have not yet fused together.

As well as the methods already mentioned, there are many hundreds of other ways in which blood can be examined. The haematologist looks at the cells, the serologist at the antibodies, the clinical chemist at the molecules, the bacteriologist at the germs which may be in it. Their methods vary.

In order to count its cells and platelets, freshly drawn blood is quickly mixed with substances which prevent it from clotting. Then it is carefully diluted in a measuring-tube, so that the cells become separated from one another sufficiently to be seen individually under the microscope; in untreated blood they would pack so thickly together as to look like a granular red mass. The diluted sample is then run under a slit-like space between two horizontal pieces of flat glass. The exact depth of this slit-space is known. The base of the flat compartment is already etched with squares in a tartan pattern. The exact measurements of these squares are also known, and so their area multiplied by the depth of the space will give a known volume. By using a microscope one can count the number of cells in the squares and thus in known volumes, and by allowing for the dilution, one can then calculate how many there must have been in the original blood sample. Although there is nothing complicated about this, it takes time doing it by eye. Big laboratories have therefore adopted electronic methods, where cells are counted at remarkable speeds (thousands per second) as they flow past microscopic electrical 'eyes' or 'feelers'.

Haemoglobin pigment, being coloured, can be matched against coloured-glass standards of known density. This can be done by eye, but photo-electric techniques are common here too.

Have you ever thought how much simpler diagnostic medicine would be if most of the normal body components were of different colours? As it is, we have only red haemoglobin and yellow bile, though the skill of the chemist has produced many 'colour reactions' which facilitate chemical measurement of body constituents in the laboratory. But if the secretions of various glands had different hues in their own right, and if all the different internal organs and tissues were obligingly coloured like the strands of an electrician's cable or the painted pipes in an engine room, things would become much simpler for the doctor. (Radioactive tagging of different organs brings us a little nearer this state of affairs.)

Apart from counting the blood cells, haematologists also take a look at their shapes and appearances. Red cells can be measured in volume and diameter, and their shapes assessed by the eye. But white cells, having no haemoglobin, are colourless and must be artificially stained for their details to reveal themselves. The art of such staining arose in the nineteenth century when the leading microscopists included many Germans: it happened that both the manufacture of optical instruments and also the dye-stuff industry were highly developed in their country. They found, by trial and error, that some dyes had a special affinity for certain parts of both cells and bacteria, which then became more clearly visible under the microscope. So the German nation led the world in the describing of stained cells and microbes. But the implications turned out to be even more far-reaching. It was found that particular dyes had such a chemical affinity for certain microbes that the living germs were specifically killed by them; and a line of research developed which led to the making of substances which could be used as antiseptics, and then to protective drugs such as the sulphonamides. That is why you can perhaps remember the days when the cut on your knee or the spots on your face were painted bright yellow — or violet, or green, or fiery red — when you went to the doctor. The colours were impressive, but there was scientific thought, not witchcraft, behind them. As one might suppose, as time went on these desirable antiseptic activities of the dyes proved to be fundamentally associated not with their colours but with the known chemical combinations which they made with the germs, and so today's antiseptics which have succeeded them are not necessarily garish.

Before being stained, wet blood is spread as a thin film which quickly dries on a flat glass slide. The film is made thin enough for the cells to be strewn out separately from one another in the layer of plasma. As the water evaporates from the plasma the protein sets like a glue, holding the cells firm and flat against the glass. Then the slide is heated or put into strong alcohol, which alters the proteins of both the plasma and the cells so that they become 'fixed'; this means that from then on they will not dissolve or float away if put into a watery solution again. (Boiling egg-white, for example, or adding alcohol to it, will 'fix' it and make it insoluble in the same way.) Fixation of the blood film is important because watery preparations of dyes may be used for staining.

A commonly used staining method turns the nucleus of the cell blue and the rest pink. Stained in this way the differences between polymorphonuclear, mononuclear and lymphocytic cells become obvious, and the stainable properties of granules in certain of their cytoplasms allow further categories to be made. Then all types can be counted and expressed as percentages of each kind present, and can be related to the total white cells counted in a liquid blood-sample at the same time. This will show whether or not each cell type is present in the blood in absolutely abnormal numbers, which is not necessarily indicated by their relative percentages in the dried film.

Immaturity of the circulating white cells can be deduced from the stained appearances of their nuclei. The presence of immature white cells in the blood shows that they are being released prematurely from the marrow. It is not necessarily a serious matter, medically speaking, if a few primitive white cells are present, but if immature nucleated red cells appear in the human bloodstream this commonly indicates a major disturbance in the bone marrow. Very young, but not immature red cells just released into the circulation have a stainable network or 'reticulum' indicating the recent presence of a nucleus. These are 'reticulocytes' and their presence indicates an abnormally high rate of red-cell production by the marrow.

Samples of bone marrow can be had almost as readily as blood. A needle is put into the breastbone or another hollow bone that lies close under the skin surface (local anaesthetic prevents any serious discomfort), and the marrow, which has a pasty consistency, is drawn into a syringe. A stained film of bone marrow normally shows primitive red and white cells in all stages of development. The maturation of a red cell has three main features: the cell starts large and becomes smaller; the nucleus becomes dense and disappears; and haemoglobin appears in the cytoplasm. Departures from the normal sequence can be appreciated visually under the microscope by a trained person; for instance, the irregularities caused by a lack of vitamin B_{12}, or the presence of excessive numbers of the white-cell series indicating leukaemia, are both very characteristic.

Here are some examples of other ways of examining blood in a haematology laboratory: by centrifuging a given amount of blood until all its cells are packed tightly together at the bottom of a straight glass tube so that one can measure what proportion of the whole this 'packed cell volume' may be (normally it is just less than half); by treating unfixed living cells with coloured chemicals that actually take part in the life activities inside the cells and thus visibly indicate their condition (this is known as cytochemistry or histochemistry); by putting red cells into various weak solutions of salt in order to measure the extent to which they can withstand osmotic swelling and bursting (osmotic fragility testing); by chemically or biologically measuring the amounts of bile pigments, iron, proteins, enzymes and vitamins in the plasma; by looking for abnormal pigmented breakdown-products of haemoglobin with a spectroscope; by separating protein molecules on a wet paper strip or column of clay, along which an electric current may be flowing (chromatography and electrophoresis); and by estimating the levels of the known clotting 'factors'.

The blood sedimentation rate

Perhaps the commonest test of all is the 'blood sedimentation rate'. This is useful, and reminiscent of the physicians of the past two thousand years who would look at blood or urine standing in a glass to see which way its humours would separate. The sedimentation test consists simply in watching a column of blood, which has been prevented from clotting, standing in a vertical tube. The red cells settle down to the bottom. The faster they settle, the sicker the patient (with a few exceptions such as pregnancy). Absurd? No—more or less true.

The explanation is that normal red cells are like coin-shaped flakes of jelly, and are slightly heavier than the plasma in which they are suspended. When blood stands still, they will very gently settle to the lowest part of their container. They settle slowly because each individual one falls like a light disc in syrup, and there is maximum resistance to its fall because of its large surface area. Now, in healthy blood all the red cells carry a similar small negative electric charge. Bodies with the same electric charge repel, and so the cells tend to remain apart from one another. These charges on the red cells can be weakened or neutralized by abnormal protein becoming stuck to the cell surfaces, or by the appearance in the blood plasma of an excess of large-molecule proteins either deriving from tissue breakdown somewhere in the body or the result of an infection and the release of foreign material into the bloodstream. When this happens, the red cells in non-flowing blood tend to stick together by their maximum-contact surfaces, which means that they become arranged like piles of coins or dinner plates—called 'rouleaux' by the haematologists.

These adhering collections offer less surface resistance when falling through the plasma, and therefore in the test they settle more quickly. Rapid sedimentation accompanies all diseases which involve tissue breakdown or the entry of foreign or abnormal proteins into the blood. This will include a wide variety of chronic inflammations, toxic infections, operations, fractures, blockages of blood vessels, and disorders of the cell system which normally manufactures the plasma proteins. The test is therefore 'non-specific' in that it indicates an abnormal situation without showing precisely what is wrong; but other valuable medical signs such as the presence of fever, or an increase in the number of circulating white cells, have just the same shortcoming.

Radioactive labels can be used to trace the movements or quantities of blood components; for example, circulating red cells have an affinity for chromium. A blood sample removed from a patient is tagged with an appropriate radioactive substance, chosen for the mildness and short-lived nature of the radiation it emits, so that it will not endanger the recipient. Then the blood is put back into the patient's circulation and its behaviour is monitored with instruments that scan the body for radiation. The scanning instruments are extremely sensitive, and only the merest traces of these radioactive labels need to be used. In this way one can assess the total blood volume, the total mass of red cells and the survival times of red cells or platelets in the circulation; and one can note particular organs, such as the spleen, in which they are being trapped or destroyed.

Biochemically, these radioactive elements behave exactly like their non-radioactive counterparts. Radioactive iron administered by mouth can give information on the absorption of iron from food. Vitamin B_{12} labelled with radioactive cobalt can be used to differentiate the types of anaemia related to lack of this vitamin. Radioactive phosphorus is rapidly taken up by bone; radioactive iodine by the thyroid gland. Radioactive sodium, potassium, chlorine, bromine and calcium can be used to measure irregularities in the movements of these substances between the tissues and the blood plasma. Sometimes a radioactive element can be attached to a substance which has a special affinity for particular tissues and so becomes concentrated in them.

A wide variety of radioactive chemicals is now becoming available for outlining most organs and for identifying diseased parts of the body, with the use of scanning machines, which are a type of camera. Sometimes a display of an organ's blood supply is obtained, or a shadow showing interruptions in the blood supply.

Blood-clotting

The great biological advantage of blood is that it is a mobile, flowing tissue. But an inevitable disadvantage of a fluid is that it can be spilled. Something has to counter this. After all, a faulty washer in a tap, or a leaking joint in a pipe, would quickly deplete a tank which held only about a gallon and a quarter (say 5 litres) of water. As it is, our blood can and often does flow out from small blood vessels broken in cuts or abrasions, but we are not drained dry: the flow stops. The sealing mechanism is partly an arrangement whereby after a few minutes the living ends of our blood vessels go into a contractile spasm which greatly reduces or stops the leak, and partly the result of blood-clotting.

The human blood-clotting system — a series of chemical triggers, each of which has to be pulled before the next one can work, with neutralizers set around — can be likened to a widely dispersed task force which has a dangerous job to do. It works with great rapidity and effectiveness but only in the precise situations where it is required. A complex system of multiple keys, short-lived primers, essential sequences, dependent cascades and widespread neutralizers ensures that duties are not exceeded. It is reminiscent of a fail-safe system for firing particularly dangerous military weapons. Perhaps a study of the intercontinental missile system by blood-clot scientists, and of bleeding and blood-clotting by the missile people, would be salutary for both.

A clot consists of platelets and blood cells, tangled in a fibrous jelly produced by the precipitation of a long-molecule protein (fibrinogen), which is normally dissolved in the plasma. Fibrinogen becomes congealed when an enzyme (thrombin) splits, or 'digests', little pieces off the ends of its molecules, exposing parts which then click together into straggling rafts and bundles (fibrin). The clot shrinks, and the plasma in it oozes out and is called serum. Serum is therefore plasma which has lost its fibrinogen because of clotting.

Thrombin cannot ordinarily be present in active form in the circulating blood because this would immediately convert all the fibrinogen into fibrin and clot up all the vessels. So thrombin circulates in an inactive form, prothrombin. Prothrombin is activated to thrombin by a plasma enzymic activity (usually referred to as 'prothrombinase') which splits a piece off it, exposing active parts, just as thrombin does with fibrinogen. Prothrombinase activity can be generated by several different agencies.

Shed blood immediately comes in contact with tissues and surfaces quite different from the natural linings of the blood vessels. Blood platelets immediately stick to the unfamiliar coverings of broken or strange cells outside the vessels, and certain other soluble surface-sensitive substances in the plasma are at the same time altered. These stimulate the platelets to burst and liberate material which combines with at least two other soluble plasma proteins to become pro-thrombinase. There are other 'factors' in the plasma, among them anti-haemophilic globulin and 'Christmas' factors, which accelerate the actions of prothrombinase or prothrombin. Up to this stage the process takes about three minutes, but the final stage, once prothrombin has been activated to thrombin, takes only a few seconds more. Another variety of prothrombinase is released ready-made from crushed tissue cells, so local laceration will accelerate the clotting process by shortening the time required for activation of thrombin from plasma constituents. The presence of dissolved calcium is essential for most of these stages in the clotting reaction. During clotting, some of the substances which take part seem to be used up. Others are steadily inactivated by specific natural anti-clotting factors.

Paradoxically, nearly all of these clotting 'factors' were originally 'discovered' by examining the bloods of sick bleeding people who

Leeches, natural size. The background depicts fire and the grave,
two other things which, according to the Book of Proverbs, cannot
be satisfied.

turned out to lack one or other of them. The term 'factor' is used because it is not very clear what many of them actually are in chemical or molecular terms. The only visible part of the clotting reaction (in a test tube, say) is the appearing of the fibrin clot. Most investigators of clotting used little more apparatus than a stop-watch to measure the rate at which a clot would appear in various experimental mixtures of plasma in small glass test tubes. They could halt the process by adding a chemical binder of calcium, and could restart it at will with a calcium salt. Blood-clotting research has been slow because the basic chemistry of nearly all stages of the blood-clotting reaction is not yet understood, and no relevant chemical colour reactions have been discovered which would allow the investigations to be accurately adapted to photometric instruments in any simple way.

The ordinary remedies for local bleeding are compression, elevation of the part, which reduces the blood pressure, and local chilling, which brings about reflex nervous contraction of small blood vessels. When it is the nose which is bleeding (as so often it is) these are less applicable to the site, but the traditional piece of ice (or a large, cold key) on the back of the neck may work, for this treatment, though doubtless based originally on some theory that it cooled a hot humour, can be backed by a physiological observation that it makes the small nasal blood vessels contract.

Epistaxis, the time-honoured medical name for a nasal haemorrhage, means a 'flowing from above' and also refers to ancient notions of 'plethora', that the body can become too full of blood. Actually, the lining of the parts just inside the normal nose is wet and hot, to moisten and warm the air as it is breathed. There is also a constant secretion of viscous mucus which traps dust particles, cleaning the air before it goes on to the lungs. These functions, particularly the warming, require a rich blood-supply close under the lining membrane which is like hot, red plush. Sometimes a trivial blood vessel in the area breaks and bleeds for a while. Nose bleeding is as simple as that.

Some traditional household styptics, such as are used on oozing cuts on the face after a shave (but not for a nose bleed!), are chemical agents: namely, silver nitrate, tannic acid, alum, or salts of iron or aluminium. Used externally, they are harmless, and effective only on small grazed areas of capillary oozing. They lightly coagulate the area by agglutinating the plasma proteins and cells into an irregular kind of clot. Such agents can be dangerous if applied to any internal surface of the body or to large wounds, where they may be absorbed in significant amounts.

But Granny's traditional remedy for a bleeding skin surface was the application of cobweb. Perhaps this originally came into use because blood newly clotting in a gaping wound shows sticky fibrin threads

8

which on dressings or in the gap of the wound look like the strands of a spider's web, and so if there's some web there already, it could seem worth it to add a bit more on the good old principle that like should cure like. This cobweb tradition is still found in rural European communities and goes back a long way.

CHAPTER SIX

Granny, Miracles, Dreams

Apart from Galen's medical treatises, the books of remedies of Dioscorides, a Greek surgeon in Nero's army, were considered essential reading for physicians in the Middle Ages. Dioscorides says of the spider that 'The Cobweb of it being layd on doth stanch bloud'. Let us look at this scientifically. It *might* be true.

Why not?

Why might it be true? Well, web silk is made of protein and comes from small glands at the back end of the spider. Some of the spider's biological relatives also have glands at their back ends, but they have them for producing stinging venom, not silk. Such venoms are strongly reactive proteins. A widespread property of venoms generally is that they can affect the human blood-coagulation mechanisms or the local behaviour of small blood vessels. If the spider's web is an evolutionary analogue of arthropod venom, why should it not be able to 'stanch bloud'? Thus might an experimental biologist muse about it.

Answering, literally, the question 'Why not?' is different from asserting or proving that a supposition is true. But, contrary to what is often believed, asking not 'Why?' but 'Why not?' is the commonest way of making progress in experimental science, and the answer comes in the form 'Because crucial experiments have more than once shown that it isn't'. The scientist himself is not supposed to answer the question. Nature, the experimental outcome properly observed, answers it. Measurement, description, naming, classification and analysis are preliminaries to scientific investigation: when Francis Bacon put forward this idea in the early seventeenth century it represented an entirely new way of looking into things.

Today there are simple ways of putting the question 'Why not?' First you think out alternative hypotheses, and then you set up crucial experiments which are capable of showing clearly why all the alternative hypotheses but one 'are not'. This one is then taken as the received scientific account of the situation until somebody is able to refine it to some new and previously unimagined, more particular alternative, or until it is shown that a formerly acceptable hypothesis contains an untested assumption that nobody at the time thought of questioning.

115

The word 'hypothesis' only means something that is 'put under': the foundation for a belief. The word 'supposition' is exactly the same. In science an effective 'working hypothesis' and its alternatives must be capable of being denied by experiment. Hypotheses which cannot be tested in this way are not as a rule worth thinking about, unless they provide general explanations of processes which cannot be repeated because of remoteness in time or space, such as the hypothesis of evolution, whose validity certainly cannot generally be tested in this way.

If you have any scientist friends who have been impressing you with their research, try marching into their laboratories and saying, 'Sir, what hypothesis is this experiment capable of denying?', or 'Sir, what crucial experiment do you propose to use to test that hypothesis?' If they get red and confused, you will know that they are messing about, a human activity that is as common among researchers as anyone else — only it is harder for the ordinary mortal to catch them out at it. But don't be too hard on them. They may well be up against certain special problems, some of which involve what might seem to you at first sight quite simple areas of human biology.

Such as our cobweb problem. To begin with we can allow the alternative hypotheses to be: (1) Cobwebs are effective in staunching bleeding, and (2) cobwebs are *not* effective in staunching bleeding. Now we must ask why one of them is incorrect. This assumes that we agree on what is meant by 'cobwebs' (situation? species of spider? age of web?); 'effective' (more quickly than when cobweb is not used? — but since it cannot be used and not used at the same time, how can we be sure that a comparison of different occasions is valid?); 'bleeding' (what size wounds? when, where and how made? on man, rabbit, rat, mouse, bird, monkey, lizard, beetroot?). However, assuming agreement on these things, surely the experiment itself, the appeal to nature, is simple enough?

Experimental investigation

All right. You're a doctor. You think it's time you did some medical research, like the other doctors. You take six people on whom minor surgical operations are being performed. You apply cobwebs to their wounds. You time the duration of bleeding with stop-watches and reckon up the results: 108, 103, 92, 88, 112, 125 secs. The average of the six observations is 104·6 secs. You will want something to compare them with, in order to satisfy your critics that not only did these patients stop bleeding but they stopped bleeding sooner.

All right. Take six others, give them no cobweb treatment for similar wounds, and again time the duration of bleeding: 299, 188, 224, 195, 291, 330 secs. This time the average comes to 254·5 secs. Good!

Now your critics will point to a difficulty. Even though you may have matched the two sets of six patients by age, sex, and so on, they will still be different sets of six people and will not have quite identical wounds or constitutions. The comparison is therefore not perfectly 'controlled', and the difference may well be just chance variation. Bother!

All right, take another set of patients, apply cobwebs to part of their wounds and watch both the treated and the untreated part; in this way, these people can 'be their own controls'. You find that their treated parts stop bleeding in an average of 124·3 secs. and their untreated parts in 231·8 secs. Very good.

But quickly other critics appear. Have you obtained your patients' permission to play about with their bodies like this? Even if you have, are you morally justified? Are you going to use other established methods of arresting haemorrhage at the same time, or not? An interesting dilemma now appears: if by this time you have come to think that cobweb treatment is effective, how then can you justify withholding it in any way from a patient who is bleeding? On the other hand if you are beginning to believe it isn't effective, how can you justify applying it to any more people who are bleeding?

Well, you persevere. Your results apparently show that bleeding times are somewhat shorter when cobwebs are used. According to the conventions of science, you must now publish your results openly. Therefore you write a scientific paper, 'Arachneostasis: A Recommended Technique for Arresting Surface Haemorrhage', feeling this will be more informative in the international medical indexes than 'Dioscorides and Granny were Right After All', which had been your first choice of title. You send it to an old-established weekly medical journal, quaintly called *The Bistoury*.

After a few months the editor writes back saying that he submitted your paper to an internationally known blood-clot scientist for assessment and that some extracts of the man's report are appended. The assessor has evidently said that your paper is too long, particularly in the 'Discussion' section, where you have speculated in an interesting way on possible mechanisms underlying the action of cobweb on blood vessels, on fibrinogen and on other clotting factors. No comments at all on the scientific data in your paper. You strike out the apparently offensive paragraphs and return the manuscript to the editor. To your surprise he prints it in an early issue, with an editorial annotation by himself headed 'Dioscorides and Granny', civilly drawing attention to your work and containing some pretty quotations from polite authors of classic and medieval antiquity.

This is too much for your professional colleagues. They write by the dozen to you and to the editor pointing out variously that (1) your trial of cobwebs was biased because it was not 'blind': that is to say, you and your assistants who held the stop-watches were personally involved in the treatment and could be consciously or unconsciously cheating; (2) even if your evidence is accepted you have not shown that cotton, silk, wool, grass, seaweed, moss, bird's nest, gossamer, thistledown, glass fibre, asbestos and candyfloss would not be as effective as spider's webs; (3) your reckless attitude in applying a filthy and dangerous remedy, probably carrying tetanus spores, to helpless, wounded people is criminal and you should be struck off the medical register; or alternatively (4) your reckless attitude in deliberately withholding the ancient, proved, effective cobweb treatment from helpless, wounded people is criminal and you should be struck off the medical register. *The Bistoury* has letters and counter-letters in successive weekly issues.

Seriously frightened by the notoriety you have achieved, you hope the noise will soon die down. Just as it seems to have done so, another letter is printed which points out that 'Arachneostasis' means stopping spiders rather than stopping bleeding and is therefore a term more suitable for the work of an expert in pest control. The proper word, the letter says, is 'Arachniasmeniatrics', which means 'satisfactory doctoring by covering with spiders' webs'. Another letter appears the following week saying—nastily—that this means something quite different, namely 'self-satisfied doctoring *while* covered in spiders' webs', but that the term is still appropriate because that is what the writer reckons you have been doing. Unfortunately, he gets the last word because underneath is written in italics: *This correspondence is now closed. Ed.* With a last thread of courage you decide you will not abandon your research but that you will retire to the laboratory and do it in non-controversial test tubes.

All right. You catch some spiders. You collect the web by touching their spinnerets with a glass rod and winding it up. You also collect spun web from bushes and corners of rooms. You get a colleague to take some of your own blood, you mix it with sodium citrate to neutralize its calcium (to prevent clotting) and you separate the plasma from the cells. You hypothesize either (1) that spiders' web is an accelerator of the reactivity of prothrombinase and prothrombin, or (2) that it is not. You measure standard amounts of plasma into test tubes, add active tissue prothrombinase to some, allowing the rest to generate prothrombinase just from platelets and plasma components. You pop in some calcium chloride (enough to overcome the citrate) as you click your stop-watch, and you measure the times taken for the mixtures to clot. Then you do the same again, adding spiders' web. Here are your results, repeating each test six times:

CLOTTING TIMES OF PLASMA (in seconds)

With tissue prothrombinase		Without tissue prothrombinase	
Without web	*With web*	*Without web*	*With web*
13	12	95	110
14	12	108	95
13	14	102	102
12	13	99	100
14	12	101	108
12	14	96	94
AVERAGE 13·0	13·2	100·1	101·5

Your conclusion is that prothrombin and prothrombinase (of whatever kind) do not react together any more effectively in the presence of spiders' web; you might also argue that threads of fibrin are not produced from fibrinogen any more quickly.

You look then at another hypothesis: that spiders' web has an activity like that of human prothrombin but weaker, so that you wouldn't notice it in the presence of normal amounts of prothrombin. Now it happens that you can greatly reduce the amount of prothrombin in plasma by absorbing it on to aluminium hydroxide. You take plasma treated in this way, which has a greatly lengthened clotting time, and you add tissue prothrombinase, and spiders' web to some, to see whether the time will be shortened. Here are your results:

CLOTTING TIMES OF ABSORBED PLASMA (in seconds)

Without web	*With web*
47	42
49	50
54	52
50	48
50	47
54	50
AVERAGE 50·6	48·2

There is no gross difference between the average times. There are subtle mathematical ways of looking at small differences to see whether they are 'significant', but in biology only gross differences are convincing. So spiders' web has not been shown to have prothrombin-like or thrombin-like activity.

You think again. Spiders' web perhaps accelerates the rate of generation of plasma prothrombinase which, unlike tissue prothrombinase, has to have a few minutes to 'get going' at the beginning of the clotting process. You set up a system which measures the speed at which the various components in the plasma, including platelet material, will generate this plasma prothrombinase. Your results are shown in the form of a graph.

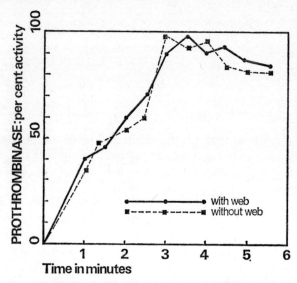

Graph showing the rate of generation of plasma prothrombinase

So, web still makes no significant difference. Repeating the experiment with extracts of spiders' web made with various solvents such as acetone, ether and chloroform, you get the same sort of results.

Therefore in spite of your clinical findings (which you have come to see were rather crude and possibly mistaken), spiders' web has no effect upon the human blood-coagulation mechanism. Is this the right conclusion? Alas, no. Not yet. There are other phases of the clotting system which could be tested and many different sets of laboratory conditions which could be tried out.

So you begin to realize that, in spite of Bacon and his successors, it is next to impossible to prove a negative in a complex biological context of this kind, unless you can tackle the real molecular physics or chemistry of the situation—and in blood-clotting that is still remote. But you conclude that in some limited though meaningful scientific ways, spiders' web has *not* been demonstrated to accelerate blood-clotting in a test tube, and that your examination of the long tradition of cobwebs for staunching wounds, however promising it seemed at the outset of the investigation, has not confirmed some powerful folk remedy reminiscent of foxglove tea. You are now obliged again, according to the morality of scientific investigation, to publish your results openly. You send a short paper on your negative findings to a journal devoted to blood-coagulation research, *Clangor Sanguinis et Haemorrhagiae*, which you are surprised to see is edited by a Tokyo professor, printed in Prague and published by a firm in Bergen-op-Zoom. Your work appears. You never hear about it again – from anyone. With relief, you end your research career, which turned out to be more trouble than you expected, and than it was worth.

These paragraphs do not recount a completely true story about the spiders' web experiments. However, the laboratory tests, though not the clinical ones, were actually performed; and the account is true enough to show some ways in which medical research is made difficult by the complex biological nature of the human body. Such an extraordinary physico-chemical structure cannot be investigated amateurishly. But medical research is also difficult because medicine itself attempts to reconcile scientific biology, social values and a concern for the welfare and dignity of the individual.

Ancient wonders

It has been found that for nearly all the plasma components of the clotting system there are corresponding antagonistic substances which can be activated in the blood after a clot has formed. One of them is fibrinolysin which dissolves fibrin, and it has its activators and precursors, much as do prothrombin or prothrombinase. Fibrinolysin plays a part in maintaining the lining of normal blood vessels; there, fibrin is being continually deposited in molecular amounts and continually removed in a dynamic equilibrium. Fibrinolysin is also active in the repair of injured vessels in which clots have formed. Apprehension can stimulate this fibrinolytic process and the bloods of many people who have died sudden violent deaths are found to be altogether fluid when examined at necropsy. In some countries it has even been possible to make extensive use of such liquid cadaver blood for transfusion. Aesthetics apart, it causes no ill effects to recipients if carefully collected under clean conditions, and can be as useful as the donations of living people.

Sometimes during surgical operations this natural clot-dissolving mechanism becomes excessively active. It can also occur as a complication of childbirth, but this is rare. Tests are set up which show firm clots of blood dissolving in glass tubes. Which brings to mind the famous miracle of the Blood of St Januarius.

Miracles are matters of evidence. By definition they are events not comprehensible in terms of regular natural causes. One therefore wants evidence that the events have occurred, and evidence that they have no commonplace causes. But you have just seen how difficult it is to prove a negative in biology. It is unlikely that we shall ever describe all the causalities of nature – not necessarily because we cannot, but

simply because we will not have time, or inclination, or even enough
writing paper to set it all down. We may manage it in physics and
chemistry, which are highly generalized subjects, but we are less likely
to in biology, which contains more 'organization' and 'information', and
still less likely to in sociology, which has even more. Given this situation, some people feel free to believe that there must be still-unknown
causes or even that some human events have occurred without such
causes.

In the heel of Italy on the Adriatic coast is the little town of Fasano,
once called Gnatia, through which the poet Horace was passing with a
few friends in the spring of 37 B.C., on their way to Brindisi to see Mark
Antony. Horace records in the first book of his *Satires* that he and his
companions were troubled by the stink of fish and fishermen at nearby
Bari, and then at Gnatia they laughed when at a local temple they were
told about a resin which would melt miraculously without being heated,
if placed on the temple's holy threshold. Horace says that such beliefs
are all right for superstitious Jews, but he knows from reading Epicurus
that the gods are too careful to bother about working miracles for
earth-bound humanity.

Pliny the Elder mentions that at Gnatia there was a rock on which
wood, being placed, broke spontaneously into flame. He refers too to
the famous fish sauce, the *garum*, which was made along the same coast.
This *garum* was originally invented by the Sybarites, a people who lived
in great luxury at Sybaris (another coastal town in southern Italy) and
who were exterminated by their neighbours in Crotone, the ascetic
Pythagoreans, almost five hundred years before Horace and his friends
were at Bari, complaining about the smell. Well-to-do Romans like
Pliny and Horace were well acquainted with the *garum*. It was in great
demand as a flavouring at their Roman dinner parties, and was made of
unlikely parts of fishes. The gills, roes and intestines were mixed with
some salt and egg-yolk, and then allowed to decompose with wine and
oil in jars. The decomposition was probably 'autolytic' or self-digestive
rather than the result of bacterial action, because the dead fish cells,
especially those of the intestine, would release active enzymes to digest
and liquefy the fish parts; also the added salt would discourage the
growth of bacteria. After a few months the contents of the jars would
then become soft and runny, and the famous *garum* could be decanted.
Gourmets who have repeated the recipe today find the result horrible.
But *de gustibus non disputandum*: we are digressing—this bit is about
miracles not sauce.

Today in Naples—also in southern Italy—an intriguing wonder is
regularly celebrated: the liquefaction of the blood of St Januarius. He
was beheaded in A.D. 305 in the persecution of Diocletian and his blood
was said to have been collected by his old governess. Although by

tradition it first liquefied in the reign of Constantine, the first known written mention is in 1389. Since then it has become widely known, and the subject of controversy and travellers' tales.

The saint's blood is kept in a small, transparent sealed bottle, with another, almost empty, beside it. The contents of the second are said to have been given to Spain long ago. The bottle containing the blood can be seen to be half full of a dark red mass which is ordinarily not fluid. The gummy seal on the top has not been removed for at least two hundred years. Both bottles are firmly fixed inside a silver reliquary with two glass faces, like an old-fashioned carriage lamp, and this is mounted with an ornament and fitted with a handle. It is kept in the treasury of the cathedral at Naples, where St Januarius (Gennaro, Janvier) is the patron saint.

On certain solemn occasions, such as the saint's feast day (September 19th), but in the relatively recent historical past up to eighteen times a year, the blood is brought into a magnificent sanctuary in the cathedral. In the presence of the public, the officials of the cult and a group of devout women known as the 'aunts of St Januarius', prayers and litanies are said, and a priest inverts the reliquary at intervals to show whether the contents are congealed. Another holds up a candle from time to time to illuminate the phials behind the glass. After anything from a few minutes to a few hours of this treatment the dark red mass may begin to flow. When it does it covers the whole of the inside of its bottle, and by transmitted light the contents appear bright red. Occasionally it fails to liquefy at all, but only about once in four years.

The evidence for a previously non-flowing red substance that begins to flow is incontrovertible; the evidence for its being blood is poor. The ecclesiastics of Naples allowed it to be tested spectroscopically many years ago, and although at least one scientist was convinced then that the spectral absorption lines he saw were characteristic of blood, there have been others, themselves Roman Catholics, who have criticized his evidence. They have pointed out that the test was subject to various errors and that at most it showed only that the phial contains traces of blood.

Of course many sceptics, too, have said that, using waxes and a red dye, a mixture can be made which will remain solid in a cool storeroom but melt when the temperature is raised a few degrees. This is quite true. You have only to think of the bottle of olive oil in the kitchen cupboard which so readily solidifies in cold weather; adding a dark red fat-soluble dye to it will give you something like blood.

Alternatively, there are thixotropic mixtures of liquids and solids which set when left alone but flow when agitated—like the hard, wet sand of the seashore which becomes liquid when you stamp on it, or those plastic paints which flow when brushed and set when still.

But one can get properly impatient with technologists who wish, without reason, to strip all the aesthetically satisfying mysteries from the traditional world we have inherited. They are to some extent missing the point and in danger of releasing themselves into an anti-culture in which everything is discounted and where scientific wisdom will have no more status than the supernatural—for it is not difficult to show that science too is based on a set of unproved axioms believed by its 'faithful'. Neither the Archbishop of Naples nor any responsible Catholic today claims in so many words that there is a miracle in the crude phenomenon of the 'blood' of St Januarius, but those who administer the cathedral carry on with its exposition. There is no real conflict with science; the two belong to different systems of thought, marginally related. In the same way the British do not claim that their Queen has any power, but they continue to give her the trappings of it; this is aesthetically satisfying to them and a part of their commitment to social stability and to their culture, and so it is administratively useful. There is logic in it, or there is no logic in it, according to your axioms.

However, it is from an aesthetic point of view that the miracle of St Januarius can be most criticized. Surely, to be agreeable it should have happened more rarely than it did? Eighteen times a year was vulgarly frequent for such a 'wonder', though indeed this has been adjusted now to a more discreet number. But, worse, there are other rival saints in Naples, and in the same vicinity, who in the recent past promoted similar miracles with less publicity. The 'bloods' of St John the Baptist, St Stephen, St Pantaleon, St Patricia and St Felix were all reputed to be at it, and there were many more in the seventeenth century, when even the milk of the Blessed Virgin herself liquefied annually on the feast of the Assumption. Even worse still, none of these phenomena can be traced back in written records before the mid-sixteenth century. Either the tourist trade has been overdoing things, or else parts of the Italian warm South are uniquely suited to supernatural haematology. Horace and his cultivated friends, passing down Italy again today, would still laugh.

But consider how much charity, hope and faith is enkindled in the hearts of the devotees when they see the miracle repeat itself. And consider how it affects their behaviour after they have left the cathedral. Scientists applauding another piece of Science announced at a scientific meeting should ask themselves exactly how their behaviour differs from that of the 'aunts of St Januarius', and whether it is wise to separate their subject from its historical sources. *Semen est sanguis Christianorum*. Science has martyrs too. And heretics. And even miracles of a sort, which as they are 'explained', reveal others requiring 'explanation'; but many miracles turn out to be simple microscopic or atomic phenomena.

For example, there is one which bacteriologists had no difficulty in explaining when it was brought to their attention. Like that at Naples, it too is concerned with 'blood'.

In the past, from time to time alarming tales were told of a strange thing happening to stored food, again in the warm South. Alexander the Great was besieging Tyre in 332 B.C. The bread of his army, when broken, contained drops of blood. His army chaplain, Aristander, thought quickly and explained to the terrified soldiers that as the blood was inside the bread, this was a sign that blood would flow from those inside the city of Tyre too. It did in the end, though the siege took seven long months.

The Bleeding Host, which appeared again and again in the Middle Ages, was sometimes thought to be the result of the stabbing of the sacramental bread by unbelieving Jews, and they were massacred in the cities where this occurred. On other occasions it was taken as miraculous evidence of the Real Presence in the Eucharist, as for example, at the Mass of Bolsena in 1263, which is graphically illustrated in one of Raphael's great frescoes in the Vatican.

In the nineteenth century, similar experiences with food came to the notice of various public authorities in Italy, in France and in Germany, and on these occasions they were investigated by scientists, who found them to be caused by a microbe that produced a red pigment. In France blood had turned up again on military bread which excited the Gallic soldiery much as it had Alexander's Macedonians two thousand years previously. But it was the Germans who, although not the first to identify the microbe, gave it the name which has caught on. They called it *Bacillus prodigiosus*, 'the portentous germ' or 'miracle microbe'.

Chromobacterium prodigiosum, as it is known today, is widespread in nature, growing rapidly at ordinary temperatures on moist starchy substances, on gelatin or in milk. Many cold foods can become contaminated with it. Mind you, there are hundreds of other varieties of similar saphrophytic germs which grow on exposed cold food but because they produce no pigment at all, they go unnoticed and nobody knows or cares. But food turning red causes great alarm and although it is harmless (in that it causes no disease), a bacteriologist once pointed out, in reference to the Bleeding Host and the resulting Jewish massacres in the Middle Ages, that this 'harmless' germ has killed more men than many others known to cause conventional disease.

This microbe miraculous is so characteristic under the microscope that bacteriologists sometimes use it today as an innocuous marker in tracing the probable route of a bacterial cross-infection moving through a hospital. They may scatter a harmless culture of it on a floor, so that it is carried into other parts of the building on people's shoes. By checking where this culture has been carried, they can get a general indication of the directions in which harmful bacteria might similarly be carried.

Dreaming of blood

So today loaves no longer bleed, because technology and science provide an 'explanation', transmuting terrifying conscious experience into intelligible relational forms. At the conscious level, this is a gain. But in the unconscious mind, which controls much important human activity, and where we can bury things—and out of which, indeed, we produce the mental components of our scientific 'discoveries'—the need for congruence between proposition and fact is not so great.

There is no general agreement on the interpretation of dreams. Dreams are fits and starts in the cogs of consciousness when these happen to be disengaged from the main gears of the working brain. One would expect the mechanism now and again to emit snatches from the experiences and personality of the person of whom it is part. And so it does. The simple gross lusts and fears, or the first things learned in babyhood, are as likely to be represented in dreams as the special worries and triumphs of the day before, and the significance accorded by doctors to dreams as clues depends greatly upon which school of psychiatric theory they follow.

There are those who believe that this or that facet of human experience is written into the memory of our whole race, so that archetypal symbols of the Father, the Mother, the Self, the Hero and so on can be recognized both in the dreams of the individual and the myths of the tribe. The White Goddess of Love and Growth, the Red Goddess of Fruition and the Black Goddess of Destruction, they march about. Others say that a dream can be 'interpreted' only in the context of exhaustive analysis of the particular dreamer's personality.

Some of those who are prepared to generalize tend to see a symbol of menstruation, or of castration, in dreams of blood or of the colour red. These are certainly two powerful and potentially terrifying symbolic phenomena. In primitive human tribes the young females would have mated regularly and would have been almost continuously pregnant or suckling their young. Thus menstruation would have ceased, or been much inhibited, for most of the time, and when it did occur it would have been more significant and disturbing than it is nowadays. Galen believed that during pregnancy special menstrual veins carried the menses to the breasts, where the blood was turned into milk.

Certainly taboos and cleansing rituals concerning menstruation are almost universal, and the psychological aura traditionally surrounding it has been one of prohibition and foreboding. In general, the tense sexual overtone which permeates our human culture relates to the high degree of interaction between conscious and subconscious behaviour which sex involves. For some people this may indeed be a source of anxiety, and be represented by blood—whether that of menstruation, childbirth or a castration wound. One famous psychiatrist interpreted the tale of Little Red Riding Hood as a disguised dream-story of a girl who had reached sexual maturity and ignored parental warnings of what could happen if she dallied with a wolf. James Joyce hinted at the same idea—a line in *Finnegans Wake* reads 'Jests and the Beastalk with a little rude hiding rod'.

The more obvious dream symbolism of blood as an indication of murderous wishes seems to be uncommon. It is said that in the dreams of those with homicidal leanings their prospective victims vanish, or do not appear at all. Unconscious fears and threatening symbolism may be factors in causing people to faint at the sight of blood, but only a psychiatrist could hope to establish this in the individual case.

In Joyce's *Ulysses*, the 'Wandering Rocks' episode is supposed to symbolize the circulation, and the construction of this part of his book represents the bloodstream. Joyce himself didn't take the correspondences too seriously, and blood is scarcely mentioned; but the movements of people, traffic and gossip through the streets of Dublin are like those of cells and dissolved macromolecules roaming a labyrinth of tubes. The impression is random purpose—a drifting disruptible relationship laced with intentions and possibilities of meetings. Analysed into minute particulars such a picture is confusing, but its total statistical impact adds up to a living system, like the bloodstream. In *Finnegans Wake* Joyce extends this method, so that the whole work becomes a 'commodius vicus of recirculation'; the last sentence leads into the first in this book of double ends joined, in a circulation not merely of the blood of Dublin's Giant, or of the River Liffey, but of the total biologico-historical situation of civilized man on earth.

Sophisticated writing as elaborate as this is more effective than the simpler direct body allegories found in earlier English literature, such as the straight anatomical symbolism used in *Microcosmos* by John Davies of Hereford, or in *Purple Island* by Phineas Fletcher. The latter is worth looking at because its extensive footnotes explain in contemporary terms the parts of the body to which the author refers. Although the poem was published a few years after Harvey's announcement of his discovery of the circulation, it gives the classical Galenical account of the movements of blood in the heart and vessels. David Person, writing on *Varieties, or a Surveigh of Rare and Excellent Matters* in 1635, compared the earth to the human body:

> ... the rocks and stones whereof are his bones; the brookes and rivers serpenting through it, the veynes and sinews conveying

moistness from their fountaines unto all the members; the hollow of our bowells and of the trunke of our bodies to the vast and spacious caverns and caves within the body of this earth.

All such pieces, ancient and modern, are literary elaborations of the old theme that the microcosm and the macrocosm have common features. There are rivers of life inside and outside, and when the outside ones turn red they may seem to be in special sympathy with those inside. But here again, as with the bleeding bread, the microscope can provide an 'explanation' which incorporates the phenomena in the consistent framework of science.

Small, red, one-celled algal plants, ordinarily found in sea-water, will sometimes multiply enormously when conditions of light, warmth and relative stagnation are favourable. This is the cause of the redness of the Red Sea: an algal 'blooming' which from time to time makes parts of the sea look brick-red. The same thing occasionally occurs in other waters throughout the world.

By different means, the River of Osiris, which is just north of Beirut in the Lebanon, also turns red. But though it may happen when the wild anemones — the flowers of Adonis — are blooming on its banks, the redness in its water is only silt washed down from the slopes of Mount Lebanon after rain, and not the blood of the Lord Adonis yearly wounded. Mighty-mouthed Milton, organ-voice of England, refers to the phenomenon in *Paradise Lost*.

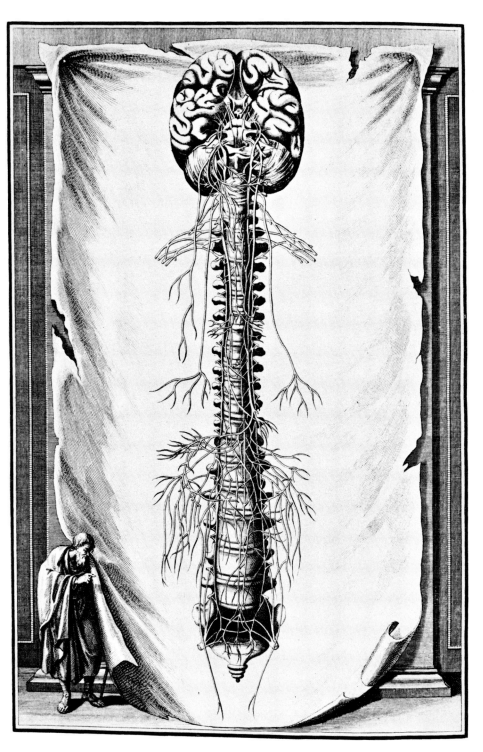

The brain, spinal cord and associated nerves

CHAPTER SEVEN

Life Codes

Although all mammal bloods look alike, in fact they are very varied. Human bloods vary between individuals—with the one exception of identical twins, whose bloods are perfectly alike. In the legend, Faust signed the compact with the devil in his own blood, which was even more characteristic of him than his signature (which could be forged). The bloods of other mammals also vary between species and between individuals, except in the case of identical twins originating from the same fertilized egg-cell (and in certain lines of laboratory animals, mice or rats for example, which have been artificially selected and inbred by brother-to-sister mating for about twenty generations, until all the stock is genetically identical, only the sex differences remaining).

It is only in recent years that this confident statement about the variations between individual bloods has become justified, and it rests upon observation of the inheritance and multiplicity of blood groups and other characters.

In the old days, surgeons, physicians, apothecaries and alchemists thought of blood as a substance which was materially the same whether it flowed under fur, feather, skin or scale. Blood was blood, one of the basic humours of life; it was red, and it clotted. Concurrently, in the curious way in which the human brain can hold incompatible beliefs without wondering at the clash, they considered that various bloods, in spite of an outward gross similarity, must somehow bear individual essences or vaguely defined potencies characteristic of their owners. The blood of a strong man, for instance, was perhaps 'stronger' than that of a weakling. The blood of a lamb was gentle. It was largely a matter of attributing personality traits and spiritual endowments which could *blend*. There was no inkling of an actual *particulate* structural dissimilarity. The tradition of Aristotle, which laid emphasis on qualities rather than on quantitative measurement, was partly responsible for this situation. It was only when the sciences of physics and chemistry produced ideas about the disposition of discrete molecules, and the linkages between them, that our present knowledge began to be developed. Then scientists could begin to guess at the great variability of personal pattern which is possible between the fleshes or between the bloods of even closely related individuals, provided they have arisen as a result of separate egg-cell fertilizations.

A copying machine

Chromosomes and genes are the elementary particles of inheritance, as molecules and atoms are the elementary particles of material form. One needs to illustrate this by analogy.

With an unlimited supply of bricks of half-a-dozen different colours, you could build many thousands of long garden walls, no two with the same brick pattern. With a modest increase in the kinds of brick — differing shapes and textures, combined with the colours — the possible variations in wall pattern would run into millions of millions of millions of different permutations, and if you wished, you could repeat a pattern. But if there was a system whereby the bricks were shuffled at random and then dealt to you one by one, so that you could not pick and choose, the chances are that you would never build the same pattern of wall twice, though you lived for aye.

Suppose that one of these imaginary walls was one brick thick and that it symbolized the pattern of the sub-microscopic structure of a speck of living material, and suppose the wall split all down its length, each brick dividing in half. This would make two walls, each one with the same pattern of bricks — the same surface mosaic. If these two walls then grew to full thickness (the bricks having an organic method of adding to their characteristic selves while keeping their relative positions in the walls), and if they should then in the same way divide and grow again and again; then you could see how the living protoplasm of one person can maintain an established personal pattern during growth.

It is difficult, perhaps, to visualize how anything very small can contain such complexity of structure, and brick walls keep the image rather large. In any case walls do not divide and grow, and this analogy risks being extended to absurdity. Let us think, then, more generally, not of walls but of linear self-replicating structures bearing characteristic sequences of particulate units.

These linear structures may be likened to the tapes on which information is coded or punched, which are fed into automatic machines, which are thereby 'instructed' what to do. Living cells contain tapes of this kind in their nuclei. These are the strap-like chromosomes, present in pairs, which can be seen uncoiled during favourable moments of cell division, always in the same numbers and lengths and shapes in the normal cells of a given species, although for most of the time they are hidden in the nuclear structure, as when tape is wound into a ball. Strung along them in tens of thousands are the information units, the genes, too small to be seen with a microscope because their organization is at the molecular level, and so-called because they can be inherited from one 'gen'eration to another. The possible numbers and variations in the molecules which make up living matter are quite capable of providing the structural complexity required to 'write down' almost any 'instruction', even one of great length, in submicroscopic space.

A chromosome maintains its genes in ordered spatial sequence, as a piece of writing or written code maintains the linear order of its words or symbols; and the genes can influence one another, just as the words in a written piece can influence one another's meaning. Each gene is itself composed of an ultra-microscopic molecular subcode, as words are composed of letters, and these molecular sequences have now been elucidated. Each gene can determine one particular chemical activity in

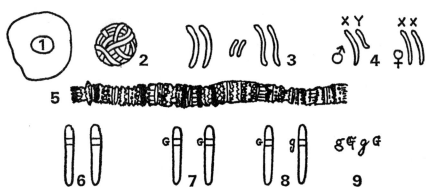

The nucleus (1) of a human cell is a chain of coded information (2), consisting of 23 *pairs* of chromosomes (3). The members of each pair are alike except in makes, where one of the pair determining sex is shorter than its partner (4). Each chromosome bears a characteristic microscopic series of genes (5). The position of a given gene on a chromosome is fixed (6); at such a position a pair of chromosomes may each have an identical gene (7) or two different ones (8). Although there may be many genes (9) determining variations in one inherited character throughout a community, each individual can inherit only two.

the intimate structure of cells and cell products, although the extent to which its influence will be expressed can depend upon the situation of a cell and the nature of other accompanying genes. The effects of all genes are fundamentally molecular and chemical, but in many cases they are reflected as identifiable morphological or gross traits of the bodies or in the cells or juices of those who inherit them.

People inherit different traits, and genes vary among people, but genes for a single variable trait are always located on one restricted particular place on each one of a particular pair of chromosomes. Therefore when there is a coterie of available genes in a population, each one of which can control a single human inherited trait in a different way, only one gene at a time can occupy the one particular slot devoted to this trait on each chromosome of a pair in one person, so that no more than either one or two of the variations can be present. In this way a choice is forced when a new organism is to be generated by sexual reproduction.

For each sex cell (sperm or egg) contributes only one outfit of chromosomes (see next page) and in the new individual they combine their two outfits to make the chromosome pairs. There will then be two slots, each holding one gene location on each chromosome of the pair in the new individual, which therefore has either two identical or two different genes capable of influencing each gene-controlled character in its inheritance. Each gene may have such an effect, or one gene may 'dominate' the other, in which case the ineffective one is said to be 'recessive'; a recessive gene can express itself only when present in double dose, one on each chromosome. The members of each human chromosome pair, except for the chromosomes which determine male sex, are alike in size, shape and allocation of gene-slots.

The physical limitations and capabilities of every species of plant and animal are determined by its genes. Man has in a certain sense transcended some of the genetic limitations on his protoplasm by self-consciously using tools to manipulate his environment, and by passing information about this from one human to another by non-genetic means. For example, as a species he has no genes that will enable him to breathe water, and so he manufactures diving equipment and tells other humans how to do so. Nevertheless, as a species he cannot transcend the final biological limitations of the surface of the earth – the biosphere – in which he lives. He cannot breed to infinite numbers or to independence of other living things.

A gene replicates itself (for cell division), or manufactures the chemical substances under its control (for cell growth or secretion), by acting as a mould or template, whereby particular molecules from the pool of food material available to the cell can come together, form into structures analogous to the sequences and patterns on the gene, and then peel off. There may then be recopying and part-copying of codes by 'messengers' at various successive sub-stages down along the line, so that basic 'information-control' by a gene may have its final effects within a cell at several chemical removes from the gene itself. It is helpful to think of these activities as analogous to printing, moulding and even to strict translation.

In this code-copying amongst the jigging molecules there are slight chances of mistakes. The chances must be small or the forms and processes of life would not be handed on as reliably as they are. But imperfect copying of molecular patterns in the genes in cell nuclei seems to explain the occurrence of two remarkable biological phenomena: the variation of species and the growth of cancers.

When an incorrectly copied gene is produced, a molecular pattern is mistaken, and the change will be passed on if the cell divides. But, as with a printer's error, the new code-word is usually 'meaningless' in its context, and a cell in which this chance mutation has occurred is likely to die as a result of the loss or distortion of chemical organization in its internal structure. But sometimes an error adds a chance pernicious 'meaning' to a code, so that the tissue now deriving from the cell has significant but wrong information and develops irregularly. Its relationship with the interests of the surrounding normal cells becomes disordered. Such mutated cells can grow to become a cancer, or—if a sex cell (egg or sperm) contains the mutant gene—to form an abnormal or monstrous offspring.

Very occasionally, however, one of these errors in the copying mechanism provides a new, more appropriate and harmonious 'instruction' with reference to the environment. If this advantageous mutation occurs in, or is passed on to, one of the sex cells, and leads to the natural selection of those who inherit it, it can 'improve' the whole species. By this means, biological species have reconciled the need for stable continuity with the need for appropriate change, and slowly they evolve down the millennia, as the fossil record shows.

Halving the message

We can now visualize the two orders of biological code-ribbons, the chromosomes and the genes; the first are relatively large vehicles for the detailed structures of the second. They mould their replicas and peel them off, during cell division or cell life-activity respectively. But a new biological individual is made by sexual reproduction—not by conventional cell division, or by ordinary cell activity, but by union. Two cells must fuse, one from each parent—a sperm-cell from the male and an egg-cell from the female—and the chromosomes and genes from each must combine in the new body's first cell, from which all its tissues will then derive. If each parent were to contribute a full repertoire of genes, the offspring would be embarrassed with double numbers, doubling again at each succeeding generation. This problem is overcome by the sex cells first undergoing a 'reduction' division when they are formed in the parental ovary or testis. They each lose half their chromosome-and-gene 'information' by discarding one chromosome of each pair. Before this is done, each pair of chromosomes shuffles its genes between one another by twisting together, crossing over and exchanging runs of gene-slots before splitting apart again into two singles. One of these passes into each resulting sex cell, which then has a different and probably unique half-set of genes taken at random from the available shuffled full set. Then when two such half-sets, one from a sperm and one from an egg, are fused, the new individual will have an altogether novel combination of basic molecular structures, although owing exactly half its bricks to mother, and half to father. However, either parent might well have failed to get some particular gene brick 'of his (or her) own' into Junior through not possessing it originally in double dose, since if possessed singly, it has only a fifty per cent chance of being included in every one of father's sperms or mother's eggs. This is what makes the differences within families, even between brother and brother and between sister and sister.

All these analogies, which threaten to confuse bricklaying, printing, moulding and card-playing had now best be abandoned.

In humans there are twenty-three pairs of strap-like chromosomes. The members of a pair, as we have seen, are matched in shape and size except for the sex pair in the male, which are dissimilar: one is the same shape and length as the two which make up the female pair, the other is much shorter. In mammals, the female sex combination is usually designated XX, and the male XY. In the testis of a male the reduction division ensures that only one of his sex chromosomes can go into each sperm-cell (along with the twenty-two from the other pairs of 'ordinary' chromosomes). The same is true of the egg-cells formed in the ovaries of the female. This results in all the egg-cells of the female having similar sex chromosomes (X); while half the sperms of the male have one kind (X) and half have the other (Y). When fusion between sperm and egg takes place the double number is restored, but the sex of the offspring depends upon which variety of sperm-cell (X or Y) happens to have won the race to fertilize the egg for, as we noted above, a matched combination (XX) will make a female, and an unmatched (XY) a male. All the ordinary adult body cells, which derive from this one original fusion of two sex cells, carry the full complement of chromosomal 'instructions' in all their nuclei. The only exception to this will be the sex cells eventually produced by the new individual, which will again have half-sets.

This implies that each one of the billions of nucleated cells which grow from the fertilized egg and which make up a normal human body carries a structural mark of the sex of the owner. And the presence of the double X chromosome can be quite readily observed in a female by microscopic examination of nuclei of cells from various parts of the body, including certain of the white cells of the blood. We have noted

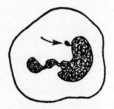

The clublike structure which represents the extra X-chromosome of a woman, as occasionally seen in a stained blood film

that the active polymorphonuclear leucocytes move in the plasma and tissue spaces by amoeboid cytoplasmic streaming. Their contortions in narrow spaces serve to massage their nuclei, which get drawn out and misshapen like strings of sausages. In a nucleus the skein of chromosomal genetic information ordinarily lies hidden in a tangle. But in some of the polymorphonuclear leucocytes of a female a small speck of densely staining nuclear material sometimes gets swung out sideways like a tiny Indian club. No such structure can be seen in a male. It is the extra doses of X-chromosome material in the female which show up as these small areas of greater density in her cell nuclei.

The growing self

Now if all ordinary body cells carry in every one of their nuclei the full gene code, or 'set of instructions', for the individual whose body they make up—how is it that these cells are not all identical in shape, size and behaviour? How is it arranged that they differ—that they are 'differentiated'? The answer is that the control exercised by the genes in their nuclei is permissive and not mandatory, so that the responses and chemical activities within a cell, though limited to the genetic capabilities it has inherited, may differ in different environments, since all these capabilities may not be realized to the same extent or even at all. Therefore the morphological differences between cells within a multicellular animal are less in their nuclei than in their cytoplasms— the jellies which make up the rest of the cells and with which they do their characteristic business of living. For example, it is not the appearance of the nucleus of a contractile muscle, but that of its cytoplasm, which distinguishes it from a covering skin cell. During bodily growth the cytoplasms of the cells of different tissues are determined not only by inherited capacities in their nuclei but also by the situations of the cells relative to one another and to their surroundings. The cytoplasm adapts itself to local conditions, increasing itself by means of subsidiary copying mechanisms so that specialized cells produce the enzymes, proteins, carbohydrates, fats and so on that responses to their local tissue environments demand, and this process of controlled adaptation produces the microscopic cell differences and characteristics of each organ. In fact the prime point about differentiation is not that a cell grows into what it does, but that it avoids developing those potentialities which are not appropriate to the tissue environment in which it finds itself.

A light-microscope cannot distinguish molecular structure. But as it happens, there is a simple way (requiring little apparatus) of determining whether or not certain molecular patterns are present on red-cell surfaces—by blood-grouping. The blood groups relate to the science of immunology, which leads directly to the fascinating question, What is self, biologically speaking?

I know that I am. You know that you are. The statements have meaning because we are self-conscious. But our ordinary cells are not conscious; how then do they 'know' how to 'behave' in 'our' interests? ('Purposive' language again.) The question is not fanciful for there are circumstances where cells of other species may 'infect', or come into, 'one's' self.

The science of immunology began by considering the mechanism by which one became 'immune' to infectious disease: how one acquired resistance to the entry into one's 'own' private biological territory of certain 'foreign' living matter. Such an entry can be made by a parasite. The name parasite may conjure up thoughts of worms and flukes, but these are relatively large creatures. By far the commonest parasites are microbes, mainly bacteria and viruses. Parasitism exists because many forms of animal life have some reserves of energy and food and tissue to meet unexpected challenges, and this reserve capacity becomes prone to exploitation by simpler organisms, which seek to mesh their smaller cogs with those of the larger machine and have them turned 'for free' for as long as possible.

If a parasite steals too much energy it will kill its host. Then it is a silly parasite and not doing well biologically. The best way to retain a steady supply of golden eggs is not to kill the goose that lays them. Therefore 'well-adapted' parasites are those which have arrived at a nice balanced relationship with their hosts, and this is why most common infectious diseases of which humanity has long experience are not widely fatal.

Hosts, particularly vertebrate hosts, though they may be taken unawares, do not remain passive when parasitized. They have a mechanism for 'recognizing' foreign living matter, for neutralizing it and for keeping it out thereafter. This recognition and elimination takes a few weeks and has led to some of our parasitic microbes adopting an island-hopping way of life: they can inhabit our bodies only during their short initial period of freedom—before our resistance develops—in which time they may cause some temporary damage to our tissues (i.e. they produce 'infectious disease'); but then they or their descendants have to move on into another susceptible host, if they can find one. Their 'object' of course is not to cause disease in us; it is only to live. Parasites have different ways of making an entry into a human. Some grow, wriggle or swim through cracks in the skin or through the soft wet lining membranes of the throat, the lung, the gut or the sexual parts. Others allow themselves to be injected by a biting insect.

A host's biological recognition of the non-self nature of the parasitic material, and his development of specific resistance towards its re-entry, are important parts of the story of blood, for the white cells and plasma are agencies of the specific immunological reaction.

Take an example. Having 'had' typhoid fever once, and survived, you do not 'get' it again. You become immune, but your protection is only against the typhoid germs—not against diphtheria, or yellow fever, or measles, and so on, unless you have 'had' them too.

The entry of the typhoid microbes would have stimulated certain of your lymphocytes (page 139) to divide rapidly and then to manufacture anti-typhoid 'antibodies' within ten to twenty days. An antibody is a globulin. Globulins are a particular class of soluble protein molecules which can be formed in a near infinite variety of patterns that fit to particular targets. Antibodies are set free into the circulating blood plasma and thus distributed throughout the body. In typhoid fever an anti-typhoid antibody molecule will 'fit' or stick into a typhoid microbe like a specific key turning in a lock. The precise part of the microbe to which the antibody fits is called its antigen. It is the antigenic parts of the molecules of the typhoid germs that are 'recognized' as biologically foreign, and which provide the original stimulus to the production of specific antibody. Antigens vary in their 'antigenicity', some stimulating the antibody response more quickly or more intensively than others.

The typhoid microbe is altered by the attachment of antibody, and this alteration leads to the disablement of the germ and to its elimination by the body's scavengers. Thereafter, surpluses of anti-typhoid antibodies in the blood plasma and of the cell lines which can produce them, remain as a legacy of the disease and fade only slowly. Hence the persistent immunity afterwards (the rates of subsequent fading are different after different kinds of infection), and the increased capacity to make more antibody of the same kind very quickly if any more typhoid germs should ever get in.

The 'lock-and-key' specific production of antibodies—typhoid microbes stimulating only anti-typhoid 'keys' which turn only in typhoid 'locks'; diphtheria only anti-diphtheria and so on—is yet another biological complementary-pattern mechanism. Its relationship to the genetic copying systems in the nuclei and cytoplasms of cells is not yet clear.

Antibodies are detected in the laboratory by observing serums (i.e. blood plasmas from which the fibrinogen has been removed by clotting). Those which contain antibodies will agglutinate, precipitate, neutralize, dissolve, absorb or otherwise alter the antigens towards which they bear complementary activity.

Antibodies are made, transported and liberated by a group of inter-related cells that includes the scavengers and lymphocytes of the blood-stream. These cells engulf, break down and remove any irregular material which they encounter during their constant journeyings through the body. 'Irregular material' includes dead and dying self cells from any tissue (which is most tissues) in which cells are normally and regularly replaced; and also foreign bacteria, parasites and any other non-self material whether natural or artificial. But although the scavengers clean up everything, they ordinarily go on to make specific antibody molecules only against the non-self structures. Now the scavenging cells themselves belong to a differentiated tissue system. Their cytoplasm is very unlike that of, say, a liver cell or a lung cell; therefore one might quite reasonably think that much of the bio-chemical material found in the cells of those organs, even though it is 'self', is 'foreign' to them. However it is not, and so one must wonder at the mechanism by which cells normally avoid making 'auto-antibodies' against their own 'comrades'.

Up to a couple of decades ago immunologists had been contenting themselves for two generations with what they reckoned to be the 'self-evident' principle of *Horror autotoxicus*—that such fratricide was 'obviously' abhorrent to the organism. Latinizing the problem seemed to stifle further speculation, until the whole question—What is self, biologically speaking?—was reopened by the Australian immuno-logist Burnet. It is now believed that the antibody-forming mechanism of a mammal does not become fully effective against foreign material until after the final differentiation of embryonal tissues which is some-where very roughly round about the time of birth. Before that time the scavenger cells do indeed take in and break down all waste material, which is almost entirely made up of 'self cells' of developing tissues, but antibodies are not made. The patterns of the differentiated cytoplasms of the self (muscle, liver, etc, which we have discussed above) seem at this early stage to become the permanent friends of the cells of the scavenging system. This 'tolerance' by the scavenging cells may be just a matter of quantity: maybe they will tolerate anything that either was there before them or is in larger bulk (you will recall that scavengers appear in the human foetus at the third month). The interesting thing is that the same mechanism will also work in regard to any material of non-self origin which may irregularly find its way into the embryo, either naturally or as part of a medical or scientific procedure. This latter observation seems to confirm the present belief that tolerance of self is specifically acquired during embryonal development, for if such tolerance were genetically built in from the beginning, then non-self material artificially or inadvertently introduced into the embryo would not be expected to have its specific molecular patterns included in the tolerated range.

Antibodies

But, given the necessity to avoid making antibodies against self, and given then the need of the antibody-forming system to wait until all the minor self-patterns have become established before it can with safety recognize not-self, it might still be asked, Why not make a complete full-strength set of anti-not-self antibodies at this point, and be permanently immune from all parasitic disease? The answer is that this would be physically impossible, so numerous are the permutations of molecular antigenic patterns in which the foreign living material can arrive. It is just not possible for one person's circulating blood plasma to contain, always at effective strength, a complete set of all the anti-not-self antibodies which might be needed in a lifetime. At the same time it is possible, as we shall see, to keep a set of patterns available, and to choose the appropriate one, grow cells containing it and make appropriate antibody as required. This is the more economical and flexible alternative, and a manufacturing function of the cytoplasm of the lymphocyte group of cells.

Lymphocytes have a life of some months in the body and are re-placed by division. Their capacity to make antibodies of a particular kind may last for years. The patterns, moulds or templates from which these are made must therefore themselves be persistent or self-copying, the information passing on to daughter cells at each division, so that once the capacity to make a particular antibody is acquired it can be retained by a particular line of cells. This would explain why microbial disease in mammals is commonly followed by 'immunological memory' of the occasion, giving relative 'immunity' towards subsequent further 'attacks'. The precise cellular molecular mechanisms of antigen recognition, and of initiation and maintenance of antibody production, are currently the subjects of vigorous investigation by scientists.

The lymphocyte system of cells is involved, and also that curious neck structure, the thymus gland, from which at least some lines of lymphocytes originally derive in the early embryo before taking up residence in the spleen, bone marrow, lymph nodes and so on. In the adult, some circulating lymphocytes are influenced by a visit to the thymus—as though to an ancient family shrine—while the appendix, certain lymphocytic patches on the small intestine, and the tonsils and adenoids (all of which are organs made up of intimate associations of surface or lining cells and lymphocytic tissue) probably have a 'thymus-like' influence on other lines of lymphocytes.

The thymus is a structure that develops in the embryo from cells lining the pharynx or primitive 'throat'. We may conjecture that its tissue has specialized cytoplasmic 'information' mechanisms for 'recognizing' foreign or non-self items in what the fore end or throat encounters in the food and in the surroundings. After all, in the most primitive organisms, consisting of simple cell layers, the main burden of defence must fall on those cells which have first contact with the outside world. We more elaborate animals retain this basic life mechanism: even though we now require internal defence, the function is carried out by specialized cell types which are distributed by the bloodstream and originally derive from 'surface' structures like the thymus.

The numerous circulating lymphocytes in our bodies conduct a constant patrol or surveillance through almost every part, working alongside the scavengers, drifting through crannies and nooks, touching and contacting everything they 'find'. It is thought that there must be a random mutating or scrambling mechanism in their cytoplasms which results in billions of these uncommitted lymphocytes each having a different set of molecular surface patterns. When a single wandering lymphocyte with an appropriate surface configuration of molecules comes into contact with a piece of material (i.e. an antigen) which has a corresponding complementary pattern, that lymphocyte is specifically stimulated to migrate to an antibody-forming area (such as a lymph gland). There it will produce numerous daughter cells, most of them actively producing an appropriate antibody specifically active against the antigenic material which was contacted by the original appropriately patterned wandering lymphocyte. The concentration of this antibody then builds up rapidly. Some lymphocytes give rise to yet more daughter cells, maintaining the specific antibody-producing line.

Eventually a stage is reached when no more of the particular antigen is entering the body. Then the descendants of the relevant line of lymphocytes remain drifting around on 'surveillance duty', producing others like themselves, for months, even for many years. In the continued absence of the same antigen, the numbers of such cells will eventually begin to fade away year by year; but for a very long time after the original antigenic encounter there will be more of these specifically patterned cells on patrol than there were at the body's first experience of the antigen.

Therefore specific lymphocyte activity, and consequently specific antibody production, is much more promptly set up at a second or subsequent occasion. If, as is usual, the antigen is part of an invading germ (say the typhoid germ), you can see why many infectious diseases are 'had' only once in a lifetime. On the second attempt by members of the same group to invade—even after many years—the germs meet with so brisk an antibody response they do not succeed.

The overall body surveillance conducted by the drifting traffic of lymphocytes grows weaker as the body ages, and so does that of the thymus gland. It is thought by some scientists that this lymphocyte surveillance system guards not only against infection but against the development of internal cellular irregularities such as cancer. This would explain why resistance to cancer fades with increasing age, for, generally speaking, it is a disease of the over-sixties. However, it might also be that successive cell mutations, which are rare, require a lifetime to build up into a cancer.

Specific antibody is made in different forms, probably by different cell lines. That is to say, the specific 'key' pattern of the antibody that is to fit the molecular 'lock' of the antigen may be the same, but the adjacent molecular 'carrier' of the key pattern can differ—as though keys to the same lock come with a selection of different handles—and the different types are designed to act in different situations. One type of soluble plasma antibody—a kind of immediate mopper-up of antigen—can be produced by lymphocytes very quickly, but it is unstable, it doesn't last long. The more usual kind (the so-called 'classical' antibody) is produced by lymphocytes more slowly, but it lasts much longer after its release into the circulating plasma. This type is particularly effective against viral antigens. Another kind passes from the plasma into the secretions of the body, such as the nasal secretions and the juices of the stomach and gut, and it resists being digested by the intestinal juices. Another type readily binds to cell surfaces, and while protective, is also responsible for many allergic reactions to antigens. And there is evidently also a type which is not released by the lymphocytes at all, but remains firmly attached to thymus-dependent lymphocytes. Some immune reactions (such as graft rejection and resistance to chronic infections like tuberculosis) are mediated through the action of this type of lymphocyte-bound antibody, and not through soluble antibodies in plasma or other body fluids.

Why so many different kinds? In the last ten million years Man has become a close-living, dense-community species, which lays him open to exploitation by parasitic germs—in fact to 'infectious' disease. He therefore makes these antibody all-sorts, each protecting a different situation in the body.

Making antibody is an activity comparable to cellular differentiation, where individual comment upon the contemporary environment is the job of cytoplasm under guidance of the genes. Another series of molecular complementary-pattern arrangements is obviously involved. Somewhere there are more 'messengers', 'copiers', 'translators', 'printers', 'photographers', 'locksmiths', 'moulders' or 'cipher clerks'; but we do not yet know which submicroscopic cell structures do these jobs.

Mind and matter

This discussion, which touches on order, information and recognition within and among cells, has involved analogies with rational methods of recording and appreciating instructions and information. A thoughtful reader will be wondering whether there must not be similar material mechanisms in the brain, a basis for rationality itself, perhaps involving some more complex interactivities of cells. To find the answer one must decide whether mind and matter can be separated. If they can, then the mind is a ghost, to which miraculous powers outside the present scope of biology can be ascribed, and there is therefore little point in discussing it in restricted material terms. But there is no need for a ghost if ordinary consciousness is inseparable from brain. There is no scientific evidence that it can be, any more than that the force of gravity can be separated from matter.

Thoughts, inferences, perceptions, valuations, memories, comparisons, judgements, speculations and the rest are probably electric and chemical patterns persisting in channels in the brain, so that information codes become established in the form of three-dimensional permutations of mazes of branching and interconnected circuits in parallel and series, combined with figured molecular nodes and traces set up in the cytoplasms of brain cells or in the supporting glue in which they are embedded.

But, you say, surely there is something more? Where is the 'I am'? Honestly, I see no difficulty in accepting an axiom that the *you* which you talk about is actually a private collection of cerebral physico-chemical patterns and micro-movements. There is 'you' in your brain. There is an external 'non-you' world more or less outside your brain. I see nothing alarming or degrading in the idea of your consciousness being composed of ordered matter, some of it in motion. It can, if you wish, be a matter of personal pride that there are no collections of material on earth which can so readily transmit information from one to another across intervals of space, and forward in time, as can human brains using verbal, written or other symbols, immediately released or recorded for the future. The amount of information ordered and coded in a brain may not be large by cosmic standards, but the fact that so much of it can be deliberately passed across to other brains by non-genetic methods makes the situation biologically remarkable on this planet at least. There may be living material in other parts of the universe which has reached this stage or surpassed it, but it is a remote possibility. So from the point of view of biological connoisseurship, apart from instincts of self-preservation, we should try by all means to preserve our species into the future. It would be a pity if we weren't in that, for there may be non-earth intelligences to meet. Our major policy should be (and at present is) to increase the ratio between the amount of ordered information stored in our central nervous systems and that corresponding order which we presume exists in the world outside them.

The number of nerve cells in the brain is about ten thousand million, and each one has electro-chemical links with up to ten thousand of its fellows. Therefore the variety and permutations of these linkings must be very large. By contrast, an elaborate electronic computer has at present about one hundred thousand units, and so far there are only five ways in which each one can be interconnected with its fellows.

Consciousness, or self-awareness, may be a property which develops in an information-coding structure when it has more than a certain critical number of interacting units. If this is true, computers one hundred thousand times as elaborate as those presently in use may well become 'conscious', if we can ever build them.

But I think I can hear you persisting in an objection that thoughts are more than pullulating electro-chemical events, because you can feel them or be aware of them, and the experience is not one of electricity or chemistry but something unique and different. I disagree. What does electro-chemistry 'feel like'? Why should patterns of molecules and moving electrons not 'feel like', in fact 'be', thoughts?

In the growing child the ability to perceive develops through the setting up of brain circuits and patterns following the receipt of patterned nerve impulses from the sense organs. Such patterns, once received with sufficient repetition, resonate and persist so that they can thereafter be picked up again by other parts of the brain without further sense experience. They are now memory circuits and printings. Concepts can form through these being repeated and linked to form new permutations in other parts of the brain, which in that sense 'sees' them with an inner eye, but in no more mysterious a way than the visual centre receives impulses which are called 'sight' and which have only a coded relationship with the external light waves that excite the retina. Awareness or self-consciousness is the activity of large numbers of circuits, which in turn have taken their patterns from lower parts of the brain more directly connected than they to information channels running in through sense organs in contact with the outside environment. When you close your eyes vision is lost, but the power to visualize remains in the memory chains. When you sleep the parts of the brain which are able to form patterns related to its own working are temporarily out of action, but the underlying circuits are as much still there as those in a working radio from which the sounding unit has been temporarily disconnected.

The number of brain cells does not normally increase after birth. Constant growth would involve rearrangement or distortion of the circuits and of the established molecular patterns, and this is exactly what happens when a brain tumour grows or when the brain is injured, causing confusion, hallucinations or unconsciousness.

It may still be argued, though, that because mental consciousness has the power to select thoughts for attention, there must be an overall 'will'. But not if one visualizes consciousness as a persistent electric activity with a wavering component emanating from one or more areas of discharge, which receives copies of the information coming in from outside, flicks through already established circuits to pick up harmonies and associations, memories and half-memories, puns and *déja vus*, and which has perhaps a scattered series of stimulation points that fire randomly now and again, so that the sum of the activity in the most elaborate centres has just sufficient instability to prevent it ever becoming wholly automatic or repetitive—ln fact sufficient to allow some 'choice'. Seen in this way, there is a constant possibility in each individual brain of greater and greater degrees of unique pattern of association being made and fed back to the memory circuits as long as the nerve cells live, and so 'original' thought and 'personality' can develop.

The sum total of conscious electro-chemical activity within your brain can with all good reason and convenience be called a private person. The samples of information which enter your skull from outside have presumably been derived from ordered material or events in the external world, which in this sense may include everything from parts of your own body (including the brain itself) to the stars in distant galaxies.

The stars in the sky are complex events; they produce light waves which activate the eyes in such a way that after a series of re-codings a related pattern in the form of a physio-chemical permutation is set up in the brain. The brain pattern bears no greater physical similarities to the star patterns than written words to spoken ones, or the marks on the groove of a gramophone record to the sound waves which it records. Translation of information through various codes can involve considerable changes of form. But the stars emit much light and other radiation phenomena that never enter our eyes at all, being undetectable or having gone off elsewhere, and the same applies to all other events in the universe which are distributed, and we must therefore agree that there is much star data and macrocosmic universe data which our microcosmic senses simply do not receive. So the stars which we 'see' in our brains, while they bear a one-to-one relationship with some of the events in the stars we infer in the external environment, cannot be a complete picture of those stars, but only an inevitably restricted sample of star information, which must leave us at some disadvantage. This must be so with everything we infer about the world of non-mental events.

But the 'private person' within your head is the common end of millions of information channels, the messages of which resonate with the memory chains which have been set up there. Your end of all these

Stages of development of the foetus shown in a biblical context of
the Creation of Man

channels is always the end you know best. True, you infer things about the other ends, as you infer the presence of somebody else on the other end of a telephone line, but you are more certain of your own presence. You can make a guess that if there is any order in the message coming along the line, there must be at least that much order in the existing something which is at the other end. At the same time you may legitimately feel that because you know your end best, your own existence, which you can 'sample' extensively and constantly, is somehow the most 'real' thing of all. It comprises those events in the universe of which you have the most complete information – the most comprehensive copy patterns – and it consists wholly of events occurring in your own brain. So a conscious thought or insight has a personal reality because it is a collection of events more fully and completely 'observed' by your own final techniques than things which you 'see with your own eyes'. It is nearer to the end you call 'you'. Thought exists, 'you' exist, and the stars exist. All are ordered events regularly followed by subsequent events, giving rise to information chains, and so they exist, if events exist. You might prefer the expression 'they take place', which is to say that whatever they do, or are, they take up local space. Reality and unreality, mind and matter, seem only to denote different stages along such causal chains, communication lines and information channels as happen to end up in the associative or conscious part of a human brain.

One scene

Discussion of the structural patterns which underlie the notions of individuality and self in living material has now taken us some distance, when all we set out to elucidate was the nature of the differences between bloods. But no specific biological matter is independent of general biology. The means by which information is coded in antibodies, or in genes, may well turn out to be related in some way to that by which information is 'informed' into our brains. But neither antibody production nor brain function are yet fully elucidated.

A scientist's faith is monotheistic. He believes that in the end the whole scene can be interlinked in one consistent and verifiable explanation, Man and his mind not standing remote from it.

Suppose, for example, that this book was not generally about blood, but about the human hand. It would be written by an anatomist. Apart from a description of the local anatomy, it would require a general consideration of the relationship between structure and function in living matter, and of the nature of movement in protoplasm and particularly of contraction in muscle; then a specific description of the part played in the hand by bones, joints, muscles, tendons, nerves, and skin, in cohesion, support, pliability, movement, covering, and tactile sense.

The embryology of the hand would have to be discussed, and this would link up with a consideration of the evolution of the limbs of four-footed vertebrates. This has a bearing on the nature of human vision, the brain and the faculty of speech. And so human culture itself is not then outside the scope of the discourse, for writing and nearly all the arts and practices of mankind require manual accomplishment.

So it is not surprising that an inquiry into the nature of blood can take us into a wide biological arena — one where, having Animadverted the Brain (as those seventeenth-century philosopher-scientists used to put it) we shall, before long, be Soliciting Some Curiosities of the Womb.

CHAPTER EIGHT

Another Man's Poison

We have seen that biological individuality depends upon an inherited set of unique molecular patterns combined with an ability to 'recognize' and eliminate unfamiliar patterns when these intrude. We have also noted that this ability to recognize is not present from the very beginning in a vertebrate embryo. Consequently there is an early period when material introduced into the embryo may be accepted, unwittingly as it were, because the embryo has not developed its immunological wits or recognition mechanisms. If the material introduced is alive it may establish itself and continue to live as an intruder indefinitely—if it is careful. Some viruses may pass the placenta and establish themselves as persistent parasites in this way, and if they and their host are well adapted to one another—that is, if they don't weaken the host cells too much—they may cause no apparent disease or disability. There is another more remarkable manner, though, in which an embryo may pick up non-self material.

Chimera and cancers

In the ordinary way, a pair of human non-identical twin embryos remain quite separate from one another in the uterus. They are enclosed in separate membranes and attached by separate placentas. Very rarely, however, a scrap of tissue from one may merge into the other at an early stage of development. When this happens, the non-self tissue may be tolerated and so survive. The final effects, then, depend upon what kind of tissue it is. If, for instance, one twin belongs to one blood group and the other twin to another, and if the mixed-in non-self tissue is blood-forming, then it is possible for an infant to grow into an adult who has two different populations of circulating blood cells, each belonging to a different blood group. This has actually been observed, though it is very rare in human twins. The man or woman who has in some parts of the body two non-conflicting genetic identities is something of a scientific curiosity, but may be outwardly normal and at no disadvantage. He or she is called a chimera after the fabulous monster described by Homer as having a goat's body, a lion's head and a dragon's tail.

In cattle twins, however, the placentas do not remain discrete on the uterine wall but regularly merge together and mix their bloods, and therefore double-blood-group situations are common in otherwise non-identical bovine twin offspring.

Another, though still somewhat speculative, aspect of the self-relationships of body cells concerns the growth of a cancer. Some, perhaps all, cancer cells have 'mutated': they derive from a tissue cell which has undergone a chance misprint or other permanent change in its copy-typing. Such a jump is likely to result in a loss of organized properties—probably at the gene level, though it could be at some lesser station—rather than in a gain. (Remember the effect of randomly shaking up an organized system in our consideration of the Second Law of Thermodynamics. The mathematics of the amount of available energy in a closed system and of the amount of information in a coded message both involve the same concepts of order-content.) The effect of this loss of organization can be that the cell, and those deriving from it, fail to respond to controls, and therefore grow faster, or more widely, than is usual in the tissue in which they live. Just how this can happen is not relevant here, but if the cell's molecular patterns differ only by default, and not positively, from the body in which it is growing, then it will have no extra 'foreign' patterns on it and so cannot be regarded as not-self by the defence cells. If they treat it as a friend, it will be immunologically tolerated and will grow unhindered, spreading widely. This may be why the progress of some cancers is often so inexorable and the medical treatment of advanced cases so unsatisfactory, unless the growth is a localized one near a body surface accessible to surgery. But on the other hand cancer cells may all differ positively from those of the normal parts of the body in such a way as to be recognizable as 'foreign' by the immunological defence mechanisms. If this is so, the un-hindered growth of a cancer may be because the defence mechanisms have been overwhelmed, or because they become less efficient with advancing age.

Protective immunity

Knowledge of the biological principles underlying immunity towards parasitic disease is, as we shall see, important for the understanding of blood groups. It is also an important weapon of preventive medicine. Once the microbe causing a disease has been identified, it is often possible to grow it artificially and make a vaccine. In a vaccine the germ itself is dead or weakened, so that it causes no disease, but enough remains of its essential proteins or other molecular parts to stimulate the immune reaction and antibody production in humans or other animals into whose bodies it is injected. Such artificial 'active' (contrast 'passive', below) immunization can be almost as effective in producing long-term resistance to future infection as is a full non-fatal experience of the disease concerned.

Vaccination of people and animals exposed to certain infections has been very successful, at any rate from a short-term point of view. But one must remember that over thousands of years an increasing dependence of technically advanced nations upon such artificially stimulated immunity might in the long run weaken a broadly resistant relationship to the parasite kingdom acquired by natural selection over a very long time; and this might create new situations requiring ever greater dependence on medical technology. But this is true, to a varying extent, of so many current applied technologies besides medicine, as not to need special comment here.

Vaccination is a term which has persisted from earlier days when it was found that a deliberately induced attack of cowpox (*vaccinia*) would give immunity against an attack of smallpox (*variola*). The last is, of course, a dangerous disease, while cowpox is trivial in humans. The cross-immunity is the result of the lucky chance that the viruses which cause both these conditions are very closely related and therefore have some antigenic structures in common.

Temporary protection, or 'passive' immunity, can be conferred by taking serum from animals which have themselves been immunized actively against a chosen microbe and injecting this serum into those at risk. The animal serum contains antibodies which remain active for a few weeks in the recipient and then disappear, but they can give useful transient protection, perhaps while the recipient is waiting for his 'own' antibodies to develop through 'active' immunization.

A considerable amount of antibody passes from mother to offspring in the warm-blooded vertebrates. This is transferred by molecular movement across the placenta in humans; in horses it is contained in the colostrum or first milk (which is absorbed unchanged in the first few days before the newborn foals' digestive processes become too active); while in birds it is concentrated in the egg-yolk. The effect is to give the offspring transient passive immunity towards infectious diseases of which the mother has had experience, and this provides very valuable protection during the first vulnerable few weeks of life. At the same time, this antibody transfer occasionally results in an interesting disadvantage called haemolytic disease of the newborn, which is considered in some detail in the next chapter.

Passive-serum therapy was once thought to hold great promise for the treatment of all bacterial infections. Here, it was thought, was the long-sought *magna therapia sterilisans*, the 'magic bullet', the specific agent which would shoot to the heart of the invading parasite without harming the host. Actually, it is not serum antibodies but antibiotics (such as penicillin and the sulphonamides) which have filled this role, while passive immunization is now mainly used to specifically neutralize dangerous poisons (toxins) released by organisms such as those causing acute diseases like diphtheria, tetanus and gas-gangrene, or the venoms injected by biting snakes and spiders.

However, there is a growing tendency for some of the germs of disease to become resistant to antibiotics, and if this continues it may be necessary in some cases for doctors to return to the methods of specific passive-serum therapy.

Anti-red-cell antibodies

If serum containing antibodies is mixed *in vitro* ('in glass', i.e. in a test tube) with antigens of the type which have originally stimulated the production of the antibodies *in vivo* ('in life', i.e. in the body), a visible reaction usually takes place. If the antigens are on the surfaces of bacteria, blood cells or other particles, there may be agglutination (clumping) or lysis (dissolving) of the cells or other discernible effects. If the antigen is present in solution, there may be precipitation. It is by watching such phenomena and by developing methods of measuring them, even when they are very delicate, that laboratory workers have established ways of identifying antibodies and estimating their strength. Blood groups are determined by observing the actions of antibodies upon red blood cells.

The blood of one individual seldom gets into another. If it does, the latter may treat it as a foreign antigen and make antibodies against it. When rational scientific experimenting began in the seventeenth century, attempts were made to transfuse animal bloods of one species into others, including humans. Structural differences between bloods were not appreciated at the time. The concept that blood bore character traits (some presumed to be desirable, some not) influenced medical thought, and there were, for instance, experiments of transfusing lamb's blood into men. The idea was that such blood was exceptionally pure and harmless, and therefore able to restore them to youthful agile health. We now know that if sheep red cells are introduced into the human body, their structure is so very different from human red cells that there is certain to be an immune response. The human scavenger cells 'recognize' the sheep material as foreign, and appropriate antibody production-lines go into action. In two or three weeks the tailor-made antidotes, anti-sheep-cell antibodies, appear in strength and the transfused sheep cells (which would otherwise have a longer average survival time) dwindle and disappear. The first time this happens the process may be gradual enough to cause no remarkable upset in the recipient. But if a second transfusion of sheep red cells is now given, the antibodies are already present and strong enough to react immediately and violently with the foreign cells, causing their massive disruption and the gross release of irregular substances — in fact an acute haemolytic transfusion reaction, producing serious disturbances in the body, such as shock and kidney damage, which can be fatal. This sort of thing led to the abandonment of transfusion experiments soon after they were first tried three hundred years ago.

Serum taken from an individual immunized in this way contains certain anti-sheep antibodies which will clump sheep cells in a test tube. Agglutination by these antibodies is specific, affecting only sheep red cells; not those of a goat, a horse, a rabbit, a chicken, a lizard, a frog, or a fish, or any animal. This 'immune serum' can, in fact, be prepared for use as an agent for identifying sheep blood specifically. (It may be necessary to remove antibodies that are active against those antigens which the sheep shares with other animals.)

All animal species that have red blood have enough unique molecular patterns upon the surfaces of their red cells to allow such differences to be demonstrated by the use of artificially prepared serums. Some animals, however, including humans, also have a set of so-called 'natural' antibodies in their serums. These develop very early in life (before the end of the first year in human infants) and react with a particular range of the red cells of other human individuals or other species. Their presence seems to be independent of any noticeable original immunological stimulation, which is a bit of a puzzle. Possibly the antigens which provoke the production of these 'natural' antibodies are shared with other species and may be taken in as food or enter the tissues of the body from germs which naturally inhabit the bowel. In which case the immune responses would not be remarkable, although food antigens are mainly broken down to non-antigenic forms by digestion.

Anyway, it is likely that the presence in humans of these 'natural' specific anti-blood antibodies is related to our environment in some important way. They can hardly be biological coincidences – as though someone's bunch of keys or other implements just happened to fit some locks in doors in another country. A similar phenomenon is found in plants: although they don't show 'immune responses' as we do, extracts from certain seeds will specifically agglutinate certain classes of red cells, and are empirically used in blood-group laboratories for this purpose.

Blood groups discovered

At the beginning of this century Landsteiner discovered the first blood groups. Taking humans at random and in general, he found that their serums and red cells when mixed will react as though there were two antigenic substances which can (but need not) be present upon the surfaces of the cells. These two substances, which are specific molecular patterns, came to be called A and B.

According to whether people had one or the other, or both or neither, so were the four groups determined and named A, B, AB and O. Two 'natural' antibodies were found to occur: anti-A and anti-B. Anti-A would agglutinate A cells and AB cells, anti-B would agglutinate B cells and AB cells, while neither would agglutinate O cells. No person ordinarily forms antibodies which will agglutinate cells of his own type, nor has anyone an anti-O, for O is not antigenic. On the other hand, a group O individual who has passed the infant stage *always* has both anti-A and anti-B in his serum, a group A always has anti-B, a group B has anti-A and a group AB has neither.

Although group 'O' was named because it lacked both A and B substances, this does not mean there is 'nothing there'. O and A and B are all single-gene-determined red-cell substances belonging to the 'ABO system'. But the genetic make-up of a person is, as we have seen, derived from each parent equally, so everyone has two ABO blood-group characters. (This applies also to other blood-group systems discovered after the ABO groups.) A person who belongs to group AB has inherited the two detectable ABO blood-group substances, but a person who is group O must have inherited neither of them, so it can be negatively inferred that he must have a double dose of the 'undetectable' O substance. But someone whose red cells react with anti-A only, or with anti-B only, could be either AA or AO, on the one hand, or BB or BO, on the other hand, and ordinary serum testing ('grouping') will not resolve which.

Compatible transfusions

After Landsteiner it became clear that if blood were to be taken from one human and transfused into another, 'incompatible' red cells should not be used. They would immediately absorb large quantities of the 'natural' blood-group antibody already present in the serum of the recipient, and there would be a risk of a haemolytic transfusion reaction with alarming or fatal effects. Some men's bloods were other men's poisons. Bloods of people of the same group could perhaps be safely interchanged, and this became a working rule. And because neither anti-A nor anti-B had any effect on group O red cells, people of this group came to be in great demand as 'universal donors', for it looked as though haemolytic disasters could never occur when their blood was used. On the other hand, it seemed that the AB group, who were unable to form antibodies against the antigens A or B because these were part of their immunological 'selves', could receive blood without risk from their own or any other groups; they were called 'universal recipients'.

A couple of generations passed, and two great wars stimulated the widespread and successful use of blood transfusions for resuscitating broken and bleeding human bodies. Transfusions were given in

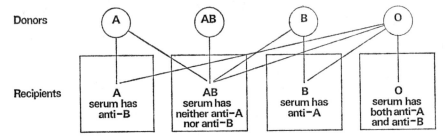

Principles of safe blood transfusion between individuals of different ABO groups. The donor's cells must be compatible (i.e. unreacting) with the recipient's serum antibodies. The lines indicate what are probably safe combinations. In practice, elaborate serum-testing is carried out as a check.

thousands, then in tens of thousands. One-, five-, ten-, then twenty-donor transfusions for a seriously bleeding individual became commonplace. Reactions between supposedly compatible bloods began to be noticed from time to time. The simple system of the four ABO blood groups became subdivided, as sub-groups and other groups were discovered, and the rules for the choosing of bloods for transfusion were modified. The concepts of 'universal donors' and 'universal recipients' were finally abandoned as dangerous, and today, whenever possible, elaborate cross-matching tests are performed between all donors and recipients before every transfusion, no matter how compatible their known blood groups are in theory.

At the same time, the four original ABO blood groups are still the most important in the organization of safe blood transfusions. This is because the A and B blood-cell substances are the only ones against which 'natural' or pre-formed antibodies are developed inevitably and spontaneously in infancy, and thereafter persist throughout life. If 'ABO incompatible' donor cells are transfused, the whole weight of the recipient's antibody from all his circulating plasma becomes concentrated upon their surfaces. The relative dose per cell is large, and they are readily damaged and destroyed, with severe effects.

But although the rule is that the cells of the donor must be compatible with the serum antibodies of the recipient, you may be wondering about the effect of the antibodies of the donor upon the cells of the recipient: what about the anti-A and anti-B in the plasma of the group O donor when they come into contact with the red cells of a group A, or B or AB recipient into whom 'compatible' group O blood is being transfused? Well, there certainly is a reaction, but for several reasons it seldom has any marked effect. In the first place the actual concentration per cell of any such antibody is usually small, because the volume of blood being transfused is usually much less than that which is already in the recipient. The incompatible antibody is therefore spread out over a very large number of receiving cells, including many fixed lining cells which, though not part of the blood, also contain A or B substance in the walls of the vessels. Furthermore, many people inherit the characteristic of having ABO blood-group antigens not only in the red cells, but also freely present in water-soluble form in their plasma and tissue juices, and on their tissue cells. This distributes the sites of antibody-antigen reaction in the recipient even more widely. Nevertheless, if a very heavy transfusion of group O blood is given to a recipient of another group, particularly when an occasional group O donor happens to have antibody of exceptional strength in his plasma, it becomes possible for the recipient's blood cells to absorb destructive doses. This is one of the reasons why the practice of using quantities of so-called 'universal donor' group O blood for indiscriminate transfusion is now avoided wherever possible.

Apart from the ABO differences, it has turned out in practice that the antigenic individuality of human red cells is not sufficient to complicate first transfusions as a matter of course. Immunizations do occur, but often not rapidly or avidly enough to be very serious — with certain exceptions that will shortly be mentioned, but precautions can be taken against these.

As we have already seen, human red cells have restricted life activities and a limited survival time in the circulation, whether in donor or recipient. Therefore a doctor can expect the benefit of a transfusion to be only temporary, and many of the minor differences between red cells of donor and recipient have no opportunity to cause serious trouble. It is a different matter when attempts are made to graft other growing body tissues from one individual on to another on a much longer term basis, when even very minor antigenic differences become important.

Mother–child immunization

When knowledge of the ABO groups and of their 'naturally-occurring' antibodies had been well established, Landsteiner and others began to look for new ways of classifying human bloods according to the agglutinating actions of artificially raised antibodies. Blood was taken from one animal and injected into another. The second animal would form an agglutinating antibody against the red cells of the first. The immune serum was then removed from the animal and tested in the laboratory to see whether it would agglutinate red cells from other animals of the same, and of related, and then of unrelated species. Occasionally it would agglutinate cells from many bloods (especially if the serum had been prepared by very prolonged immunization of an animal), but more often its action would be specifically restricted to one or to a few. Reproducible results were observed, and blood cells became classifiable as 'positive' or 'negative' for the presence of an antigen. Then, if the classification was unique, it was sometimes possible to claim that another blood 'group' had been designated. Biological research of this kind, however, seldom leads to absolutely clear conclusions, because there are commonly more factors in the complexity of living protoplasm than is at first hoped or supposed. For instance, an animal immunized with foreign blood cells seldom responds by making only one antibody. There may be several different antigens on the surfaces of the foreign red cells, and each antigen can stimulate a response, so that subsequent testing of the serum reveals only a multiplicity of interactions which seem meaningless. But sometimes a blood serum can be 'cleaned' or 'specifically absorbed' until it is free of irrelevant antibodies. This is done by exhausting its activity against red cells of one type, removing them, and then retesting the serum against other red cells.

As a result of this kind of work, Landsteiner and his colleagues had described two additional human blood-group systems by the beginning of the Second World War. They had immunized rabbits with human blood and used the resulting anti-serums for agglutination experiments. The new groups they called MN and P. Neither was linked to the ABO groups, being independently inherited and distributed among humans. This greatly increased the number of permutations of group factors according to which human bloods could be classified. The immunizing effects of the MN and P antigens turned out to be weak in humans, and they were found in practice to have almost no complicating effects when transfusions between people of different MN or P groups were undertaken.

Research workers wondered, however, whether from time to time some human transfusions, even those quite compatible on the ABO, MN and P systems, might not be stimulating the production of antibodies which were going unrecognized. They also wondered about the possibility of such immune anti-red-cell antibodies being provoked when two circulations came naturally into close proximity – between a mother and her unborn child.

A study of the inheritance of the known human blood groups had shown that they were all carried as simple characters determined by genes at particular 'slots' on the chromosomes – and as the chromosomes are paired, there is one pair of slots for each blood group. Thus for each of its blood-group systems, a child gets one blood-group character from its mother and one from its father. It is possible, then, for the baby in the womb to differ from its mother in half its blood-group antigens (sometimes called factors, or characters). This might seem unimportant, since all such antigens are parts of red cells, and red cells are too big to pass the normal placental barrier. All the same, during labour, when the uterus is undergoing strenuous contractions, there could be breakage of delicate membranes and some mixing of foetal with maternal blood, particularly at the time of the natural separation of the placenta, just before it is delivered as the 'afterbirth'. This could act as a major initial immunizing stimulus, after which further small doses could increase the degree of antibody formation.

Antibodies, however, *could* get across the placenta from mother to foetus. By the early 1940s it was known that certain maternal immune anti-bacterial antibodies capable of giving a newborn child temporary passive protection against disease were just small enough to be able to pass directly across into the human foetus before birth, so it seemed likely that maternal immune anti-red-cell antibodies, if present, would do the same, and might then act damagingly against the blood cells of the foetus. A blood disease of newborn babies which tended to recur in some families was also already clinically recognized. It was called *erythroblastosis foetalis*, and there were many theories to account for it, including one requiring the sort of immunological mechanism we have just been considering.

In this climate of developing research and opinion, and with blood transfusion being widely organized, studied and practised in several countries under the threat of the Second World War, a group of workers in the U.S.A. investigated the case of a mother who had lost a considerable quantity of blood after a stillbirth. She had been given a transfusion from her husband whose blood, like hers, was group O. The transfusion produced a severe reaction from which she recovered. It was found, using careful laboratory techniques, that samples of her serum would agglutinate the red cells of her husband, and also those of about six out of seven American blood donors chosen at random.

At the same time, in another laboratory in the U.S.A., Landsteiner continued the blood-group research which forty years before he had begun in Vienna. Now he immunized rabbits and guinea pigs with the blood of the little monkey *Macacus rhesus*. He had just discovered that the resulting anti-Rhesus antibodies agglutinated the red cells not only of the rhesus monkey, but those of an average six out of seven of the white people of New York. They apparently had some antigen, which he called 'the Rhesus factor', which they held in common with the Rhesus monkey; they could be called 'Rhesus-positive', and the one in seven who did not react, 'Rhesus-negative' — *Rh*-positive and *Rh*-negative for short. Some of Landsteiner's colleagues went on to show that anti-Rhesus antibodies could also be found in the serums of other people who had had puzzling transfusion reactions, even though the ABO groups of the transfused bloods were compatible with those of the recipients. People who produced such antibodies must, of course, themselves have been Rh-negative, for otherwise their scavenger cells would not have recognized the Rhesus antigen in the transfused blood as 'foreign'.

Then the two lines of work came together. The woman who had had the stillbirth, followed by the transfusion reaction against her husband's blood, was shown to be Rh-negative, and to have anti-Rhesus antibodies. Her husband was Rh-positive. Other women who had had stillbirths were found to be Rh-negative too. Their stillbirths were found to be an extreme form of erythroblastosis foetalis. Then it was realized that this disease was only one of a range of diseases of the newborn, not previously known to be related but shown now to have one cause and appearing in different degrees of severity—from mild through severe to fatal. With the new insight provided by Landsteiner's work and its consequences, the whole set of diseases was renamed *haemolytic disease of the newborn*. Gaps in knowledge were rapidly filled, and the strange twist of physiology by which a woman's antibody-forming defence system sometimes acts against her unborn child became apparent.

CHAPTER NINE

Mother Against Child

About one out of seven Europeans is Rh-negative. As long as Rh-positive blood does not enter the body of such a person, no Rhesus antibody will be formed. In this way the Rhesus blood-group system is altogether different from the ABO groups where the antibodies seem to appear 'naturally' – evidently the Rh antigen is not widely distributed in nature, on foods, germs and so on. If Rh-positive blood does find its way into Rh-negative people, they may – only may, the process is not inevitable – form anti-Rhesus antibody in the following weeks. We have seen that there are two different circumstances where such a transfer of blood may occur, and they are the only two. First, where a transfusion or injection of Rh-positive blood is given to an Rh-negative person. Second, where an Rh-negative female marries an Rh-positive male and bears an Rh-positive child whose blood cells leak across the placental barrier.

'Rhesus babies'

After the entry of the Rhesus antigen, those Rh-negative people who form antibodies behave immunologically like those who have once had an infectious disease, such as typhoid, for they show an intensified immune reaction and make increasing amounts of antibody whenever they get further doses of the antigen thereafter, even after many years.

Now, a transfusion of Rh-positive blood is a very big dose of antigen, and although Rhesus material is weak in initial immunizing power compared with some bacterial antigens, many Rh-negative people will form anti-Rhesus antibody after one transfusion of Rh-positive blood.

On the other hand, immunization by a small leak of blood across the placenta is evidently a poor immunizing stimulus, for although such leaks have been shown to occur quite commonly, in practice only a few Rh-negative mothers with Rh-positive children ever form antibodies as a result of pregnancy. But, once immunized, only a small additional dose is required to stimulate the production of further very high concentrations of antibody at any time in the future. So it becomes a matter of great importance to avoid immunizing any young Rh-negative woman or female child. At a transfusion she should be given only Rh-negative blood because once immunized, if then in the future she should bear an Rh-positive child — and six out of seven husbands of European stock will be Rh-positive — even a minute dose of Rh-positive blood leaking across her placenta will then stimulate her to make high concentrations of anti-Rhesus antibody. So it is the practice always to use Rh-negative blood in transfusing women of childbearing age and under, unless it is known definitely that they are Rh-positive. This is the reason why extra supplies of Rh-negative blood are needed in all blood banks: for the emergency transfusion of women and female children whose Rhesus group is unknown.

Those who will never become pregnant — women past the menopause, and men — are lesser problems from the Rhesus blood-group point of view. The disadvantage to them if they develop anti-Rhesus antibody is small: there would be a risk of a haemolytic reaction but only after a subsequent transfusion of Rh-positive blood at a later date. This is something easily avoided by carefully testing all who have previously had a transfusion, and by giving them Rh-negative blood if they turn out to be Rh-negative or while they remain untested.

The Rhesus factor, and haemolytic disease of the newborn caused by its interaction in mother and baby, received wide publicity. But the precise effects produced, and the risks of any individual incurring them, were not always clearly stated.

First of all, it is a problem confined to western Europeans and the genetic stocks deriving from them. No other nation has so large a proportion as 15 per cent lacking the main Rh-positive antigen. It is true that foetal-maternal immunization, as the process is called, can also take place between sub-groups of the Rhesus groups and within other blood-group systems, but this is rare enough not to be worth any prospective mother's worry. As a matter of fact there are ten or more subordinate Rhesus antigens, and eight other important blood-group systems, but the most antigenic of the lot, and therefore the commonest offender as a cause of haemolytic disease of the newborn, is the original Rhesus factor discovered by Landsteiner.*

If one woman in seven is Rh-negative, six men out of every seven she meets must be Rh-positive, for all the blood groups (except one whose genes are on the X chromosome) are distributed at random among the sexes. Even if she knows she is Rh-negative, it is hardly worth a woman's while, as a general principle, having prospective suitors blood-grouped. If, as she probably will, she marries a Rh-positive man, she still risks at most only one chance in fifteen of becoming immunized by

---

* When haemolytic disease or a transfusion reaction is caused by other blood-group antigens, the principle is the same: someone whose blood lacks the antigen is immunized by a pregnancy or a transfusion of blood containing it.

pregnancy, and serum treatment (see below) can reduce the risk to as little as one chance in a hundred, unless she has previously been immunized by an Rh-positive transfusion.

The most likely time for initial immunization is during an actual birth of an Rh-positive baby. Now, the possibility of preventing such immunization altogether has recently emerged from the curious finding that if a small amount of anti-Rhesus serum (derived from someone else) is administered to non-immune Rh-negative mothers of Rh-positive babies immediately after childbirth, they do not become actively immunized at all. Evidently this passively administered antibody attaches itself to any of the baby's cells which are circulating in the mother, and causes them to be rapidly disposed of by the scavenging system before reaching the lymphocytic 'recognition' centres which control the initiation of antibody formation. This kind of preventive treatment is now becoming general and it requires a very large supply of suitable anti-serum, which can only be obtained through donations from people already naturally immunized, or perhaps from artificially immunized male volunteers or from female ones past their reproductive period.

But if not prevented, the immunizing process, once initiated, increases in intensity with each dose of antigen, though because the main placental leaks occur during actual births, the immunization hardly ever reaches sufficient strength by the end of a first pregnancy to do serious harm to the firstborn (unless the mother has had a previous immunizing transfusion of Rh-positive blood). It is routine practice among obstetricians to arrange for the blood of every pregnant woman to be grouped and tested for anti-Rhesus antibodies. If she is Rh-negative, the test reveals if her serum will agglutinate Rh-positive red cells. This is a delicate technique and various laboratory tricks have to be used to make the effect visible in test tubes. If the antibodies are present, the doctor is forewarned of the possibility of the baby being affected by the disease.

But even if a woman is shown to have these antibodies during a pregnancy, it is still not certain that her child will be affected unless it is quite definite that she has had neither a previous transfusion nor a previous Rh-positive child; the antibodies could have been left over from the past and may not be concerned with her present foetus, for not every baby she has by an Rh-positive husband must necessarily be Rh-positive. This is because there are two kinds of Rh-positive husbands.

Some men will have inherited the Rhesus factor from each of their parents, and will thus be carrying a double dose of it on the Rhesus slots on the appropriate pair of chromosomes. Therefore all their sperm cells which can be formed after the reduction division must each

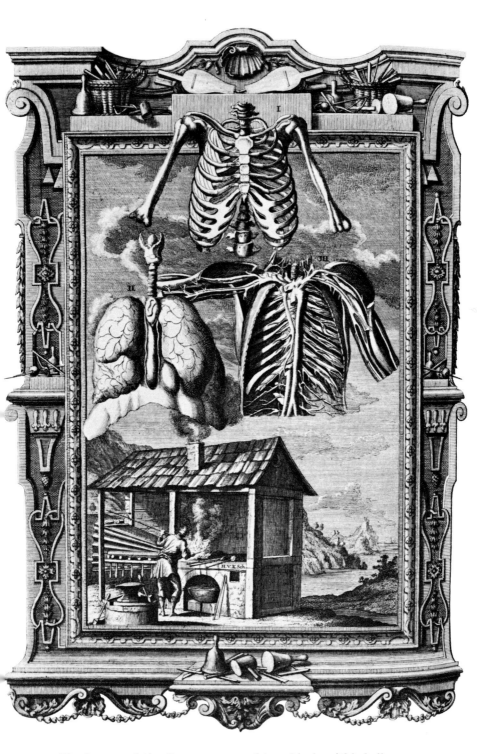

The lungs and the thorax compared to a blacksmith's bellows

receive one of the genes for the Rh-positive antigen, and so all their children must be Rh-positive. But some Rh-positive men inherit the gene from one parent only, so that only half their sperm cells will contain the gene. Then every baby they beget with an Rh-negative woman will have a half-and-half chance of being either Rh-negative or Rh-positive, so half their children will be unaffected by haemolytic disease. It is possible, by careful determination of the Rhesus sub-groups, to say whether a man is a 'double' positive, or whether he is a 'single' positive who at the same time carries a Rh-negative gene. When an obstetrician is advising a woman who has formed anti-Rhesus antibodies, this information about her man is obviously important.

But suppose she is bearing an Rh-positive baby, and suppose she *has* developed antibodies? They will diffuse slowly into the circulation of the growing Rh-positive embryo, where the Rhesus antigen will be present in all the red blood cells. Every particle of anti-Rhesus antibody encountering an Rh-positive cell will lock with it chemically, marking it so that scavenging cells will 'haemolyse' it — break it up and eliminate it from the foetal circulation before its normal wear-out time. However, blood-forming tissue responds to a loss of blood cells by rapid division to make more, and the actual net loss to the baby's circulating blood depends upon the amount of antibody filtering across from the mother and the capacity of the foetal blood-forming tissue to replace cell losses. The strength of the antibody is determined largely by the number of immunizing doses of Rh-positive cells that the mother has had.

Types of the disease

But the foetus in the uterus is a tough little being. Foetal tissues are vigorous, and destruction of red cells by the mother's antibody is usually well compensated by blood-cell replacement. However, if it cannot fully compensate, the newborn baby will become anaemic. This will result in an oxygen shortage, which, in turn, will damage the walls of its capillary blood vessels, so that fluid will ooze excessively into the tissue spaces outside the circulation. This may cause the foetus to become dropsical and die, and is a form of the disease called *hydrops foetalis*. However, the baby is seldom as badly affected as this. Usually it is born looking comparatively normal.

There is a laboratory test which can be done on foetal blood collected at birth from the umbilical cord which will show whether the red cells have anti-Rh antibody attached to their surfaces, and this is a reliable diagnostic procedure. Also a stained film of the foetal blood may show an increase in the number of circulating nucleated immature red cells, a result of the strenuous replacement efforts of the

11

foetal blood-forming tissues which will have released primitive incomplete red blood cells with nuclei. Such nucleated cells were sometimes noticed in the days before the immune mechanism underlying the disease was understood; the cells were then known as erythroblasts, and they gave their name to erythroblastosis foetalis.

Once the infant has been born, it can receive no further damaging antibody through the placenta from its mother. Unfortunately this does not mean it will get better from that moment. The antibody will remain very active for one or two weeks, wearing off finally only over a period of about a month, or sometimes a little longer. And in many ways, even in spite of the Rhesus antibody, life in the uterus is easy and protected compared to life after birth, for inside it many services are laid on by the bloodstream. For example, the foetus has part use of the mother's liver, an effective adult chemical-processing agency which renders harmless a variety of unwanted products which diffuse from foetus to mother across the placenta. Among other things, her liver normally eliminates the yellow pigment which derives from the breakdown of haemoglobin resulting from the ordinary wear and tear of adult or foetal red cells. This yellow pigment is what gives bile its characteristic colour and if it accumulates in the body, it produces the yellow colour of jaundice in the skin. In haemolytic disease of the newborn the amount of pigment is very much increased because of the rapid breakdown of foetal red cells caused by the maternal anti-Rhesus antibody. The mother's mature liver is well able to deal with it all; therefore there is no accumulation of pigment and a baby is not jaundiced at birth even though it has haemolytic disease. But once the baby is born, the haemolytic process continues and now the baby has to rely on its own liver. This organ is not very effective in the newborn; it has to grow for a while before it gains the reserve capacity which it has in the older child and in the adult. At first, therefore, it cannot handle the rapid accumulation of yellow pigment deriving from the continuous destruction of red cells, and so the infant becomes jaundiced within twenty-four hours or so.

Before the Rhesus factor was discovered, such a rapid onset of jaundice was known clinically as a serious sign in a newborn baby, and it was traditionally named *icterus gravis neonatorum* (severe jaundice of the newborn) — one more facet of what is now called haemolytic disease of the newborn. The presence of the yellow pigment is dangerous when massive destruction of red cells results in its reaching very high concentrations, combined with severe anaemia. In the ordinary way this pigment is bound to the plasma proteins in the circulating blood, but when it is present in excessive quantities some remains unbound and then can fix itself to other parts. In a severely affected infant it can within a few days of birth cause particular injury to a small central part of the deep structure of the core of the brain. This is a rare occurrence, but once it happens, no treatment can restore the damage and the child is likely to die. The affected area of brain is stained deep yellow by the pigment, and this is called *kernicterus*: 'yellow staining of the kernel of the brain'. Happily, this gloomy outcome is now rare.

Treatment

Over all, if they were not treated at all, about six out of ten babies with haemolytic disease would die. If they can be transfused with suitable blood, the development of anaemia is forestalled and the death rate then drops to less than one out of ten. You cannot transfuse blood of its own Rhesus group to the baby because not only its own Rh-positive blood but any other Rh-positive blood you might put in (such as the father's) will be attacked by the anti-Rhesus antibody derived from the mother. You must choose Rh-negative blood, which will not be open to anti-Rhesus action. By exchange transfusion (see below) new red cells can be introduced, and some of the baby's own Rh-positive ones can be removed along with the mother's antibody and some of the yellow pigment, the rest of which will at the same time tend to bind to the fresh plasma proteins in the new blood. The mother herself, although Rh-negative, cannot donate blood for the transfusion of her child, because it is the antibodies in her plasma which are causing the trouble anyway, and one does not wish to put in more. (She can help very greatly, though, by giving the laboratory a special donation of her blood, from which serum can be taken and used as a source of anti-Rhesus antibody for preventing Rhesus immunization or for testing the Rhesus blood groups of other people.)

The difference between simple transfusion and exchange transfusion is that in the first, blood is slowly dripped into the circulation through a needle placed in a vein, while in the second, blood is both put in and taken out. For the exchange, a plastic tube is run into the baby's umbilical vein up as far as the large blood spaces of the liver. Although this vein more or less closes itself off at birth, it remains capable of being opened up by this kind of forced cannulation for one or two days afterwards. If an exchange transfusion has to be carried out after the umbilical vein has finally sealed itself, other vessels can be exposed and used.

A syringe is attached to the plastic tube and a syringeful of the infant's blood is withdrawn and discarded. Then a syringeful of Rh-negative blood is put in and allowed to mix with the general flow in the infant's circulation for a few moments. Another syringeful is withdrawn, and another put in, and so on. The syringe cannot be very large, for the entire blood volume of a newborn baby is only about half a pint (a quarter litre), and if more than a few tablespoonfuls of blood are taken out or put in at a time the heart and general balance of the circulation can be seriously disturbed. Obviously the exchange technique* is subject to diminishing returns, for each withdrawal takes out a rising proportion of new cells with the old. When the total amount injected (and withdrawn) adds up to about three-quarters of a pint, it is not worth exchanging any more.

Many mothers of such transfused children wonder about the risk of permanent damage to the blood or to the brain. The answer to this is that those who develop brain damage will almost all die soon after the third day of life. As for permanent damage to the blood, there is none.

By the time the child is two months old the last traces of the mother's antibodies have faded away and its blood is perfectly normal. It is very occasionally left with just one curious and harmless relic of the disease. If some altered blood pigment is deposited in the infant's gums, when the baby cuts its first teeth a year or so later some of them, usually the front ones, are green! The permanent teeth replace them later in life, and are the normal colour.

Can anything be done to absorb or neutralize the antibody once it has appeared in a woman's blood during her pregnancy? Not at present, in spite of attempts to make a preparation of the Rhesus factor which will absorb her antibody without immunizing her further. The only course is to prevent immunization from the start, by careful blood-grouping before transfusion and by passive administration of serum to Rh-negative mothers very soon after childbirth.

There is one procedure, though, which can be helpful where a pregnant woman, through heavy immunization from inadvertent transfusion of Rh-positive blood or a series of Rh-positive pregnancies, has exceptionally strong and active antibodies in her plasma, and would have a very severely affected baby or even a stillbirth. When this is likely the doctors sometimes advise that the mother should be delivered about three weeks prematurely, so that the infant will be spared that much time in contact with the source of antibody. An exchange transfusion after birth may then save its life. Prematurity has its disadvantages too, of course, but in carefully chosen situations it offers the chance of successful treatment.

It has even become possible to transfuse babies while they are still in the uterus, but this is a heroic procedure to be reserved for very severe cases. Such can be assessed from the history of the mother's previous pregnancies and from a spectroscopical examination of the fluid that surrounds the baby in the uterus to see whether it contains an excess of

* Exchange transfusion is sometimes performed on an adult if there is an acute need to remove a deleterious circulating substance, such as carboxyhaemoglobin in coal gas poisoning.

yellow pigments derived from destruction and breakdown of the baby's red cells. A sample of the fluid is obtained by expert puncturing with a needle through the mother's abdominal wall. If there is an excess, and a transfusion is decided upon, this also is done by means of a needle passed through the mother's abdominal wall into her uterus and then through the abdominal wall of the baby, whose position will have been determined by X-rays. It is not possible to pass the end of the needle directly into one of the baby's blood vessels, but red cells injected in the foetal peritoneal space (between the intestines and the abdominal wall) find their way fairly readily into the circulation through lymphatic channels under the diaphragm. These drain into the main lymphatic ducts, which return lymph to the great veins near the heart.

Biological paradox

In general, this immunological attack by a mother against the blood of her unborn child seems paradoxical. From the evolutionary point of view it has meant that (before technological medicine stepped in) populations containing mixed blood groups capable of such interactions have tended to eliminate some of them. It reduces the fertility of outbreeding between variants which have developed different genes in isolation. Among the mammals generally it may have been a factor promoting the development of species differences.

It is thought that the Rh-negative element among Europeans was contributed by an early race, the forebears of the Basque people, and that it is still in process of being eliminated by mixture with Rh-positive tribes who came into Western Europe later. If the future of the human race is to involve, as seems likely, widespread mixing and inter-marriage between races which are at present socially isolated from one another, then we may expect that haemolytic disease of the newborn, though at present almost entirely a European disease, will begin to appear in other continents, based on quite different blood-group systems. It may be that maternal-foetal immunization will be found to produce other diseases of the foetus or the newborn because it is not impossible that antigens on white cells, platelets or plasma proteins will become involved in the same way as the red cells. (In fact, anti-white-cell antibodies have been observed in women who have had babies, and are at present being used in attempts to 'match' organs for grafting.) From the practical point of view it is therefore best, all over the world, and contrary to the sentimental impulse, to avoid transfusing blood to women from their husbands whatever the apparent compatibilities of the blood groups, because of the slight possibility of unexpected immunization.

Haemolytic disease of the newborn also occurs in horse foals (where the antibody passes mainly in the colostrum), in mules (the mother horse making an anti-donkey serum), and it has been artificially induced by deliberate experimental immunization in dogs, rabbits, rats, mice, pigs, cats and even in chickens (where the antibody passes to the offspring in the yolk of the egg).

CHAPTER TEN

Forensic and Such

Blood-group factors, being stable persistent characters in the individual and inherited simply, are useful in arguments over immediate genetical relationships. Today they play an important part in paternity cases and the identification of infants.

Paternity testing

There is occasionally a doubt about the identification of the father of a child. The identification of a mother is less disputed except when the question arises long after birth, or where infants may have been mistakenly interchanged in a maternity hospital. Before the blood groups and their mode of inheritance was discovered, such identifications had to be determined by similarities of skin, hair, eye colour, stature and general physical similarities, all of which are difficult to measure absolutely and are not inherited in a clearcut manner. By contrast the rules of inheritance of the various blood groups are simple, because the different systems are genetically independent of one another (i.e. their gene-slots are on different pairs of chromosomes), and their presence or absence in a sample of blood can be discovered precisely.

Conclusions about paternity based on blood-group findings are negative only. It can be shown that a man is not the father of a particular child, or that an infant cannot belong to certain parents. This is because even the rarer blood-group factors are scattered through the population, and therefore it cannot be said with absolute 'legal' certainty that any combination of blood groups could not possibly be matched by that of someone else—although if all the blood-group antigens currently demonstrable were tested for in mother, child and presumptive father, the statistical degree of probability of identity could be far greater than that which is commonly accepted in courts of law as 'reasonable'.

For an example of the application of blood-grouping in such cases, take the marriage of two group As. Such a mating can produce only group A or group O children, because, as we have seen, the O factor can be present along with the A in the same way that the Rh-negative factor can be present along with Rh-positive. So if after confinement in a maternity hospital the wife is presented with a group B or AB baby, then it is either not hers, or not her husband's. For another example take a group A woman who has a group B baby and claims that a certain man is the father. On testing he is found to be group A or group O. Therefore her claim is false. But if on testing he were found to be group B or group AB, nothing is proved either way—there are millions of group B and AB men in the world—but then one could move on to the other blood-group systems which might exonerate him, and if he is indeed not the biological father, the chances are high that a really wide range of blood-group tests will show this. However, some of the necessary testing serums are rare, and many blood-groupers prefer to keep them for work more directly concerned with life-saving blood transfusion practices.

A list of mating possibilities on the ABO system, and the blood groups of the offspring which *cannot* be produced thereby, is given below.

AB × AB cannot produce O	A × O cannot produce AB, B
AB × A .. .. O	B × B .. .. AB, A
AB × B .. .. O	B × O .. .. AB, A
AB × O .. .. O, AB	O × O .. .. AB, A, B
A × A .. .. AB, B	

Names of blood groups

As in other areas of haematology, the naming of blood groups has not been based upon very consistent principles, except that letters have always been used. Sometimes these reflect the name of a patient in whom the group was originally discovered. Factors which are characterized by a positive serological reaction, like A or B or the Rhesus factor, reacting with anti-A, anti-B or anti-Rh serum respectively, are, unfortunately, not always distinguished from those which have been inferred by lack of a reaction, like O or Rh-negative. Blood-group antigens are sometimes confused with the genes which determine them: although they are closely related, they are not the same thing.

Here is a list of the best-known, most widespread blood-group systems which exist in the human race, the dates when they were first reported by scientists, and their genetic variations:

Blood-group system (main antigens)	Date	Genetic variations
A_1A_2BO	1901	A_3, A_4, A_5, A_m, A_x, H, h
MNSs	1926	M_1, M_2, N_2, M^c, M^a, M^v, M^g, M^k, U, Tm, Hu, He, Mi^a, Vw(Gr), Mur, Hil, Vr, Ri^a, St^a, Mt^a, Cl^a, Ny^a, Sul, Sj, S_2

Blood-group system (main antigens)	Date	Genetic variations
P^k	1926	P_1, P_2, P^k, P_2^k, p
Rhesus CDEcde	1940	D^u, D^w, C^w, C^x, E^w, e^s, G, ce, ce^s, Ce, CE, cE, E^T
Lutheran Lu	1945	Lu^a, Lu^b
Lewis Le	1946	Le^a, Le^b, Le, le, Se, se
Kell Kk	1946	Kp^a, Kp^b, Js^a, Js^b
Duffy Fy	1950	Fy^a, Fy^b, Fy3
Kidd Jk	1951	Jk^a, Jk^b
I	1956	I, i

The above systems cover about a hundred antigens in all, and the number of combinations and permutations which can occur becomes astronomical, especially if one takes 'honorary blood groups' such as genetically determined white cell, platelet and plasma-protein characters into account as well. (This is the technical basis of the remark made about Faust at the start of Chapter Seven.) There are a number of other blood-group antigens: some quite common but others found in so few individuals as to be called 'private' blood groups. Some of these are designated as Y^t, Yt^a, Vel, Ge, Lan, Sm, Cs^a, Gu^a, Gy^a, Diego (Di), Auberger (Au), Xg (the sex-linked group), Dombrock (Do), Levay, Wr^a, Be^a, Sw^a, By, Bu^a, Good, Ho, Bennett-Goodspeed-Sturgeon, and Donna.

Tell-tale stains

The blood of those who have died violently is the subject of many myths. There are rocks and flagstones all over Europe showing brown 'bloodstains' reputedly left from the slaying of long-dead historical personages. The folk belief is that such blood 'cannot be washed away'. The symbolism is clear enough, but the likely physical explanation is that there have been traces of iron oxide in the stone since its geological formation. Also it was once widely supposed that a murdered body would bleed again in the presence of its murderer; there were even official arrangements by which suspects were confronted with the corpse which was closely watched for signs of issuing blood.

Today the blood of dead persons who come under medico-legal investigation can provide useful circumstantial evidence. The blood group can be ascertained easily enough if the blood has not decomposed. Even if it has done so and there are no red cells left to agglutinate it may still be possible to determine blood groups by testing known antibodies for specific neutralization with an extract of the remains of the body or of a bloodstain. In this way the bloods of people dead for quite some time have been grouped, and the method has even been extended to mummified bodies preserved in dry conditions, which prevent final decomposition, for hundreds or even thousands of years in Peru, Egypt and Japan.

Post-mortem blood-grouping may be used by the prosecution or the defence in criminal cases of assault or murder. If an accused person has on himself blood which is the same group as that of the victim and different from his own, then the case against him may be strengthened. More definite, if it turns out to be different from the blood of the victim, his legal defence becomes very strong.

In such circumstances the pathologist must first, before he groups it, show that the blood is human, for a frequent claim is that the blood-stains are those of an animal. If the material for testing is fresh enough, it may not have deteriorated to a point where it is impossible for him to see the form of the red blood cells under a microscope. If the blood is from a bird or lower animal, for instance, these cells will be nucleated. But if the stain is stale, or if it is claimed to be the blood of a non-human mammal, an extract can be tested against a stock battery of animal serums containing precipitating antibodies active against the soluble blood proteins of different species. These antibodies will usually have been raised by injecting a number of rabbits each with the blood of a different common animal, including a human. One rabbit will then have been stimulated to produce anti-goat-blood antibodies, another anti-sheep, another anti-chicken, another anti-rat, and so on. If anti-rabbit is to be included, a horse or a goat or some other animal must be immunized with rabbit blood. The extract of the stain is then allowed to react with the various immune serums. If the stain was made by human blood a precipitate will form only with the serum of the rabbit which was immunized with human blood, and not with the other serums, and so on. (An elaboration of this technique can be used for zoological investigation of the affinities of otherwise obscure animal species.)

It has already been mentioned that many people inherit their A, B or O substances in water-soluble form, so that they appear in their secretions, such as saliva, as well as in their red cells. Using a sufficiently careful neutralization method (as with the mummies) it is then possible, though difficult, to determine an ABO blood group from dried saliva, even on a cigarette butt or an envelope flap, and this too has medico-legal applications.

Such immunological techniques are very delicate but in many cases will not work if the stains have decomposed or have been almost washed away. There are, however, still chemical tests which will identify traces of blood as such. These cannot differentiate species, but some are very sensitive and will reveal whether stains which have been almost completely removed are vertebrate blood or not. They are based either upon the chemical ability of enzymes in blood to release oxygen from hydrogen peroxide, or upon the spectroscopic identification of haemoglobin or of the related substances into which it can turn as it goes stale. Although folk tradition has it (incorrectly) that the blood of a murder victim will never wash off the object on which it falls, traces of blood, very small but capable of being detected by chemical means, commonly remain even after very thorough attempts by the murderer to remove all signs.

Oxygen is released from hydrogen peroxide by extremely small traces of blood. The oxygen is detected by adding to the reaction a colourless substance which has a coloured oxidation product. There is even a dramatic version which uses a substance which is luminous when oxidized. This is useful when traces of blood are being sought on dark carpets or clothing; the test solution is sprayed on in darkness, making the stains glow brightly. Such tests are not quite infallible, for there are a few vegetable substances and some chemicals and metals which will give similar but less strong reactions.

The spectroscope, an instrument which splits up a beam of light into a rainbow band of colours, is used to identify haemoglobin or its derivatives. A characteristic of translucent 'coloured' materials is that they absorb certain colours of light: they appear coloured because they absorb some of the components of white light and leave you with an incomplete light sample which then seems 'coloured'. Various wavelengths of light are absorbed by different materials according to their molecular structures, and many pure substances have characteristic absorption patterns, as unique as fingerprints. The position of the dark gaps, or absorption lines, in the spectrum of white light viewed through a solution or extract of a bloodstain will positively and unequivocally identify haemoglobin.

In criminal investigations, the shape of bloodstains or splashes on a flat hard surface can give some general indication of how they were produced. Blood which has spurted sideways or has fallen from a moving source on to a horizontal surface leaves pear-shaped splashes, the broad parts indicating the part of the drop which hit the surface first and therefore the side from which the blood came. Blood drops falling vertically will usually make round splashes, but the edges become more frilly — more star shaped with radiating spokes — according to the angle of impact, height of fall and velocity. However, above a height of a couple of metres the speed of fall becomes constant, because of air resistance. Further, the size of the drop is a variable which affects the appearance of the splash. Consequently there is a limit to the conclusions which can be drawn from this kind of evidence.

If blood drips into plain water, at first it is an opaque red but quite quickly it becomes translucent as though having 'dissolved'. In those few moments water has been streaming osmotically into the red cells across their semi-permeable surfaces, so that they swell up and burst, releasing their proteins and haemoglobin. This is 'haemolysis' crudely induced. The cells are then no longer opaque solids, so the bloody water becomes a clear red. All blood proteins, including haemoglobin which is part-protein, dissolve more readily in cold water; if you heat a blood-stain you damage its proteins making them insoluble so that they 'set', and the red pigment of haemoglobin then turns brown. This 'setting' is variously called 'denaturation', 'fixation' and 'coagulation'. It is also plain cooking. These effects have a bearing on the removal of blood-stains from clothing or other fabric, which you may wish to do even if you haven't murdered anyone. The only good way is to soak it in several changes of plain cold water; then red cells and plasma will dissolve and disperse. If you put it into hot water, or otherwise heat it or iron it, you will 'fix' the stain, making it very much harder to get rid of. Dabbing with alcohol or spirit will have the same fixing effect. Soap does not make much difference, although it can turn a fresh bloodstain brown because the alkali converts haemoglobin to alkaline haematin (a brown pigment), but it does not fix the stain.

Making the blood boil

It is the effect of cooking which explains the colour and texture of blood sausage, and of drisheens in Cork. Drisheen is a delicate Irish food made from de-fibrinated ovine or bovine blood mixed three parts to one with milk and tenderly cooked in a cleaned length of large intestine. The albumin in the blood serum sets to a jelly at well below the boiling point of water, as does the white of an egg. Drisheens are esteemed in the province of Munster, in the south of Ireland, and are eaten with melted butter, black pepper and tansy (*Tanacetum vulgare*). They look like huge thrombosed veins in the drisheen-sellers' troughs in the market places. The only others who eat blood and milk from their beasts in simple mix are the Masai of Africa, though they drink it uncooked, taking the blood from veins opened in the necks of their cattle, which saves killing.

The longer and hotter one cooks blood or egg-white, the more coagulated the proteins become – and the 'tougher' from the point of view of edibility. The boiling point of water, of course, varies with atmospheric pressure and so differs at different heights above sea level. The lower the pressure, the lower the temperature at which the vapour pressure of water equals the atmospheric pressure, which is when bubbles and steam appear. On the top of a very high mountain, where atmospheric pressure is lowered, water will boil at well under 100°C – at about 65°C on Everest, where it would be difficult to hard-boil an egg or set a drisheen, a fact which probably does not worry the Irish nation over much. Even the highest cities of the world do not approach such a height. The albumin in a boiled egg will gel all right in Johannesburg, for example, where the boiling point of water is about 95°C (the setting temperature of albumin is about 65°C); the egg just takes longer to 'do' than at sea level.

It follows that if you go up high enough without protection, you will sooner or later reach an altitude where conditions will make your own blood boil, literally. Suppose you ascend to 75,000 feet (26,000 metres) in a pressurized jet aircraft. You arrange to be ejected without a space-suit into the very thin, cold, low-pressure atmosphere. The gases in your stomach, intestine and behind your eardrums then expand about twenty times, and the water in your fluids – whether blood, urine, saliva, tears, bile or sweat – boils at the temperature of your body.

Divers' diseases

Less dramatic than being ejected, boiling, from a high-altitude plane or space-ship is a situation which can occur after deep and prolonged underwater swimming or diving where bubbles appear in the blood-stream. In our discussions about oxygen, carbon dioxide and haemo-globin, we have paid little attention to the fact that air is four-fifths nitrogen. Like oxygen, nitrogen dissolves in water or in blood – according to the pressure – and even more easily in fat or oil. As a diver goes down, the pressure at which air is pumped to him must be increased. The deeper he goes, and the longer he stays down, the more nitrogen and oxygen will pass from his air supply through his lungs to dissolve in his blood and tissue fluids, and nitrogen will also dissolve in the fatty sheaths insulating his nerves. Unlike oxygen, nitrogen in ordinary atmospheric form is useless to the body: it is not taken up as a nutrient, or specifically bound by haemoglobin or by any other blood con-stituents; it remains a freely dissolved gas. So if the diver ascends too quickly, there will not be time for nitrogen to diffuse back smoothly to the air in his lungs; instead it forms small bubbles* in his blood and tissues, which get carried as gas emboli to the small capillaries, blocking them and stopping the blood supply to vital parts, such as the brain and the muscle of the heart. Bubbles arising in the fatty nerve sheaths cause severe pains which have mysteriously been called 'the bends'. If divers remain underwater for longer than a prescribed time in a non-rigid suit,

* Robert Boyle, in 1670, reported that while watching a snake which he had put into the glass chamber connected to his *machina Boyleana*, or vacuum pump, he saw a bubble appear in the aqueous humour of its eye.

they must ascend by stages with a long rest at each station on the way up, to allow the nitrogen to be breathed out slowly.

The bends may complicate any undertaking where a person (particularly a fat person) breathing air at a certain pressure is suddenly transferred to a situation where the pressure is much lower, as they are in a rapidly climbing non-pressurized aircraft, or when leaving a compressed air chamber in a building shaft during underwater construction (where the condition is also called 'caisson disease').

Whales and seals, which are mammals like us and dive and ascend rapidly to and from great ocean depths, do not get 'the bends' because they take down with them only one great sniff for a single short trip, not a continuous supply from which quantities of nitrogen will be absorbed over a long period.

The principles of embolism* have been applied with some success in a medico-legal context to the problem of the decomposed human body found floating in water. The police pathologists may have to decide whether the victim drowned or was killed before being thrown in.

Stagnant water in canals and ornamental lakes, and often sea-water, contains diatoms. These are very small unicellular plants, three or four times the size of a red blood cell, and they have a skeleton of silica, which is insoluble in acid. A drowning person takes water into the lungs. The struggles and gasping, and the local effects of water, break some of the small blood vessels in the lungs so that water containing diatoms enters the bloodstream. The heart continues to beat for a few minutes even though the lungs are filling with water. This is long enough for some of the diatoms to be carried to the left side of the heart, then to the aorta, and then in the general circulation, until eventually they stick in the narrow capillaries where they remain after the body dies. The renal arteries opening off the aorta carry a very large volume of blood, and diatoms are therefore particularly likely to lodge in the kidney, but they can find their way anywhere: to the brain or bone marrow, for example. These parts are sufficiently enclosed within the body to be removed from a corpse and freed of external contamination, even when considerable post-mortem decomposition may have occurred in the more exposed parts.

The organs are removed by the pathologist, carefully stripped of their coverings (which must be intact) and steeped in strong acid. The material becomes liquid, and then it is centrifuged to concentrate any solid unaffected particles, and the deposit is examined for diatoms under the microscope. The point is that if diatoms can be detected some distance from the lungs, in deep anatomical areas which could not have been locally contaminated by the water in which the body was found, this is good evidence that the heart was still beating and the circulation

* See p. 274.

still moving when the water entered the lungs. In other words, it can be said, even weeks after death, that the victim was not already dead when he entered the water; he drowned.

A simpler chemical examination is used to determine the fate of a victim whose body has been in water only a short while. If the body is a drowned one, water, as described above, will have entered the lungs and then the bloodstream, travelling in the pulmonary vein to the left ventricle with the last few heart-beats. If the water is fresh, it will dilute the natural salts of the blood in the left ventricle; if it is sea-water, it will increase their concentration (today's seas being saltier than blood). So the pathologist examining the dead body removes samples of blood from the left and right ventricles, and measures the amount of salt (chloride) in them. In the normal way they would be identical; in a case of drowning they should differ accordingly.

CHAPTER ELEVEN

Two Shocks

Fainting is a trivial nuisance that affects many people. It may, for example, affect one person out of fifty attending a blood-donation clinic, with a few more feeling momentarily dizzy without loss of consciousness. Some blood donors may faint before any blood has been withdrawn. On the other hand it is well known that weakness and fainting also results from loss of blood in accidents.

These examples are mentioned because they indicate the medical confusion (which lasted some time) between collapsed states of the body which were caused by blood loss, and those which were not. Extreme cases of either were called 'shock'. The term didn't help. It originally referred to the clash of men in battle, the shock of troops, and transferred to medicine, it suggested that what had collapsed was a spirit suddenly outraged by circumstances beyond bearing. This prevented doctors from considering the question clearly in terms of Harvey's circulatory hydraulics. Eventually they got it right, but the confusion, as usual, persisted in non-medical areas. 'Shock' is now a doctor's jargon word with very specific meanings related to blood pressure. It has nothing to do with value judgments about 'shocking' circumstances or accidental situations in which the condition comes about after a 'clash'.

Strong weaknesses

An ordinary faint (where there is no bleeding) is caused by the temporary activation in the body of a set of nervous and chemical reflexes. The surface capillaries empty; the skin sweats and becomes pale and cold, particularly the tip of the nose. The heart rate slows, and the small arteries relax so that much blood becomes pooled in them. The result is a drop in blood pressure and a reduction in flow through the heart, which may be enough for the brain temporarily to lose consciousness because of lack of oxygen.

The beginning of a faint is the inadequate filling of the heart with blood which should be returning from the great veins. Excessive loss of blood (much more than is given by a blood donor) is an obvious reason for there being insufficient to fill the heart. But also a sudden fright will liberate adrenalin, a chemical substance which causes the heart to give

After death: showing conventional symbols of transcience and
corruption, including a moth and worms

some mighty beats which empty it so vigorously that for a brief period, and without any accompanying blood loss, there will not be enough venous blood returning to allow it to fill properly before the next beat. Nerve impulses which slow the heart may then come into action; this keeps the blood pressure low and maintains the faint. Ordinarily recovery is rapid, but very occasionally a great psychological 'shock' can make the heart rate persistently slow for a long time. If voodoo-type deaths are a reality, this is probably the way they are caused.

A pregnant uterus or a very tight corset are abdominal handicaps which can so compress the large inferior caval vein that insufficient blood will be returned from the lower limbs, and here again the heart tends to empty itself temporarily if it increases its beat. This is why women hampered in these ways have a reputation for swooning.

What's the good of an 'ordinary' faint? An ordinary faint may seem to be a weakness, and therefore a biological disadvantage, but then from some points of view so is sleep. Fainting may indicate simply that someone has a particularly resilient and reactive circulatory system, which in many situations is surely an advantage. However, it is true that some of the strongest and 'toughest' young men or women may faint from fear of something, or even at the sight of blood. This last is popularly supposed to be a special stimulus to fainting. It may not be so, but if it is, this may signify nothing more than the powerful symbolic place of blood in our culture. On the other hand one could say that fainting at the sight of blood is perhaps a suitable inbuilt response to threatened blood loss, because the drop in blood pressure temporarily reduces the flow of blood in superficial vessels and so allows the staunching mechanisms of the clotting system to act more readily. It could also have something in common with the 'freezing' or 'sham dead' reactions of frightened animals. But this is stretching speculation rather far.

As for fainting among the brave, consider the young soldier with resilient blood vessels and efficient, responsive heart standing at attention in thick ceremonial dress on a hot day. He is so still and straight that there is a pooling of blood in his leg veins, which normally require shifting muscular movements to massage the flow back to the heart. Increasing body heat causes general dilatation of his skin vessels, and blood pools in them too. When the dignitary comes to inspect the ranks, apprehensive readiness liberates adrenalin, increasing the output of the soldier's heart, which empties. With so much blood pooled elsewhere, there is not enough blood returning in the veins to refill his heart for the next beat. So the pressure drops. And he faints. It is not want of courage, but the having of it, not faint-heartedness, but strong-heartedness, that makes the young warrior swoon. Lying flat on the parade ground, he quickly recovers. An airman's 'gravity suit' would save him by pressing on the abdomen and lower limbs, thus preventing pooling of the blood, just as it does in aircraft which turn so fast that they may send all the blood into the lower parts of the crews' bodies. The gravity suit could also prevent that dizzy feeling when one stands up suddenly after a warm bath or a heavy lunch, for peripheral vessels dilate in the warmth, and belly vessels under the stimulus of feeding. 'Getting a grip of oneself' by tensing the muscles and moving about purposefully can improve the return of venous blood to the heart, and may be consciously used to forestall the kind of faint that comes on slowly.

The essence of upright crucifixion – the method of execution originally devised in the hot countries of the eastern Mediterranean to bring about death without cutting or mutilating the body – was being tied upright to a tree in warm conditions. (It was not used in cold countries.) It brought about 'orthostatic hypotension' – recurrent and prolonged fainting and unconsciousness in a situation where the victim could not fall down to recover – and was therefore more merciful than is sometimes supposed. Death is due to irreversible changes in the brain brought about by the reduced blood supply. (Something similar happens when a hutch-bred rabbit is held up by the ears for some time.) It must have been difficult for observers to know when a crucified subject had reached irreversible unconsciousness – because circulatory responses vary much from one person to another – and from time to time someone who had apparently given up the ghost might be capable of recovering if laid horizontally in cool surroundings.

There is a schoolboy trick, traditionally called 'the fainting lark', where the boy squats on his haunches and takes twenty deep breaths; then rising quickly, he holds his nose and closes his mouth and tries to blow hard. The result is a deep faint lasting half a minute. Doing this is not advisable, but it is harmless to most youngsters—except they might get injured when they fall down. But it alarms their adult supervisors in a way the boys find very satisfactory.

Another trick, played by men roistering, is to persuade one of the company to stand and breathe very deeply and rapidly for a minute or two, and then suddenly someone standing behind him compresses his chest in an unexpected bear-hug. The victim faints.

These tricks depend on the following facts. Deliberate over-breathing changes the balance of oxygen and carbon dioxide in the blood. In response to this there is automatic dilatation and pooling of blood in certain peripheral blood vessels, but a contraction of the vessels of the brain. When the chest is compressed the pressure inside the rib-cage rises and hampers the return of venous blood by the caval veins, so that the heart pump empties, the blood pressure drops and the already restricted flow of blood in the brain makes fainting more certain. Standing up from a squatting position temporarily pools the blood in the lower limbs, and blowing against closed mouth and nostrils raises the pressure inside the chest with the same effects. Blowing balloons or campfires or wind instruments can produce a faint, because of these mechanisms, which are particularly active in young people with resilient circulations and brisk reflexes. Old people, with their thickened unresponsive blood vessels and commonly less efficient hearts unable to empty in one beat, seldom faint.

A faint where there has been no bleeding is harmless and easily treated, unless the victim has been hurt by falling on to something hard. First-aid policy is to keep blood circulating in the brain and in the vital parts of the trunk, such as the kidneys. It is therefore best to leave the fainted person lying flat, perhaps with the feet slightly raised. In this position the heart-beat and the tone of the blood vessels will soon return to normal, and no other treatment will be required.

A rather different form of faint with lowered blood pressure occurs when people are deprived of drinking-water in desert or shipwrecked situations. They lose water in urine and sweat and the volume of the circulating blood is reduced simply because there is not enough water included in it, and the blood pressure falls. This can happen in a more subtle way when people are deprived of salt. Without a minimum intake of salt, water (even if plentifully supplied) cannot be osmotically held in the tissues and bloodstream. A certain amount of salt is necessarily lost in the sweat, and after several days of heavy sweating one can pass rapidly into this salt-depleted state of weakness, circulatory collapse and shock.

Another kind of collapse with low blood pressure occurs rarely after the injection into the circulation of something to which the individual is allergic. An injection of penicillin can bring it about, and so can a bee sting. The low pressure is caused by a general dilatation of the blood vessels.

The brain is not the only organ which can go short of blood because of the local behaviour of the vascular system. After a good meal the abdominal vessels dilate so that more blood can go to work in the belly, carrying off the products of digestion. Under these conditions a limb muscle may find itself relatively short of blood, and this can occasionally result in cramping pain if the limb is vigorously at work. If the limb is being used in cold air or water, the cramp may come on more readily, and swimmers' cramp is, of course, more dangerous than, say, a runner's, because on land you can lie down and rest, but in water you may drown. This is the physiological basis for the traditional English family advice not to go in bathing for an hour after lunch, dear. There is probably no scientific data on the rate of cramps occurring after meals, but it seems likely that these cramps are indeed more frequent among those who go post-prandially beyond their depth.

So 'you' (that is, the whole sample of millions of you) do perhaps run a slightly greater risk of getting cramp and drowning if 'you' go in straight after lunch; but like so many other risks, for you as an individual it must depend much on your personal constitution and age.

Bleeding

The temporary lowered pressure of a faint without bleeding is very different from the prolonged lowered pressures caused by excessive bleeding, although both produce collapse and unconsciousness in the same way — by depriving the brain of oxygen and reducing the circulatory flow through the capillaries of the body — and so they are superficially similar. This explains the confusion which has surrounded the meaning of the word 'shock'. It refers to both bleeding and non-bleeding conditions. Someone injured in an accident is unconscious and 'shocked'. Someone who has merely observed the accident lies insensibly nearby because of so-called 'shock'. How can you tell the difference? The pulse rate is quite a good guide. After a short time it will usually be faster than normal in the first; slower than normal in the second.

Nearly everyone can lose 10 per cent of their blood in a very short time and scarcely notice it, as in a blood donation. The springiness of the walls of the arteries takes up the slack, the pressure does not fall and all remains well. But after 20 per cent has been lost the pressure usually begins to drop, and eventually the pulse quickens to restore it and the peripheral blood vessels narrow down, conserving the circulation in the more vital parts. After a loss of 30 per cent the situation becomes serious, the supply to the brain fails whenever the body is upright and so there is persistent blacking out and unconsciousness except when one is lying down flat. This is haemorrhagic shock. It requires emergency treatment, preferably by quick replacement of the lost blood, or, if blood cannot be obtained, by the transfusion of some other fluid which will expand the circulating volume again, so that the hydraulic pressure is restored.

The first-aid treatment of someone shocked by gross and obvious bleeding (say from a slashed, torn or avulsed limb) should be to stop the haemorrhage with tourniquets, or by pinching, pressing or tying spurting vessels with anything available. (You could save a life by catching a spouting artery even in a pair of dirty pliers.) The bleeding person should lie in a head down, feet up position, protected from the sun or wind and if possible should not be shifted until blood or a substitute can be transfused into a vein. On-the-spot resuscitation of this kind can save more lives than later attempts in hospital, but of course the technical and organizational facilities that make it possible are often not available.

While waiting for expert help the shocked person will be white and cold. Don't worry unduly about this. The coldness of the skin is caused by the shutdown in surface blood-flow, which is part of a protective reaction reducing the potential volume of the circulatory system and distributing the remaining blood to the more vital internal organs. A hot-water bottle applied to the body in these circumstances can burn more readily, because there is not enough flowing blood to carry heat away from the surface. Also, if the skin is deliberately made too warm by heavily covering with blankets or with hot-water bottles, its capillaries may open up again and greatly increase the shock.

When a patient has been resuscitated, a smooth and gentle journey to hospital is less likely to cause renewed shock (and perhaps death) than a turbulent rush in a rocking and bumping vehicle.

Blood does not necessarily have to be lost externally to produce haemorrhagic shock. Large amounts can flow from broken blood vessels into internally lacerated organs or flesh or smashed bones, as into a huge bruise, so that although the blood remains inside the body it is none the less lost from the circulation, which is what counts in bringing about haemorrhagic shock. This is the cause of wartime 'wound shock', once considered to be a mysterious bodily collapse caused by injury to tissue, but in fact mainly a haemorrhagic condition.* A similar situation occurs when blood plasma abnormally oozes out of the circulation through microscopic spaces in injured capillaries, big enough for water and protein molecules though too small for red cells. These minute holes open up, for example, in a burn, and a blister is evidence of such fluid seepage; but protein from the circulation is lost not only into such blisters but also into the tissues in the whole area of a burn. Similar hidden oozing can occur from the lining of an obstructed part of the intestine where an accumulation of bacterial irritants and toxins can affect the capillaries in the same way, and then plasma is lost into the gut; this is really a kind of subtle 'bleeding' resulting in shock.

If straightforward bleeding causes collapse, it may seem very logical to treat such (and similar) collapses by putting blood back into the body again. All the ancient medical systems recognized blood as an important fluid, and the principle of therapeutically transferring it was implicit in their philosophies. If it bore the 'vital spirit' or some other characteristic life stuff, why not transfuse it from one person to another where necessary? Some of the surgical and manipulating procedures of the Egyptians, Greeks, Romans and Renaissance doctors were much more complex, technically speaking, than that of running a small tube into a vein. What delayed effective transfusion experiments until

* 'Shell shock' was equally mysterious until it became clear that it is quite a straightforward psychiatric state occurring when normal people are subjected to prolonged terrifying experiences.

modern times was simply that until the idea of the circulation had been accepted, a vein was not the most obvious entry to the bloodstream; on Galen's system, the mouth seemed to be the right way in.

Therefore Roman epileptics attended gladiatorial displays in the hope of getting a sip or two of supposedly curative strong man's gore from the unlucky ones among the contestants. Those whose fits were hysterical and not truly epileptic might well have been cured by such a dramatic and public experience, which would have reinforced the legend of this particularly well-known blood cure.

When a doctor said he could rejuvenate the dying Pope Innocent VIII in 1492, he used the blood of three ten-year-old boys and proposed to give it to the old man by mouth. It was standard and rational treatment at that time. To his credit, the sick Pope refused to be rejuvenated by this means; but the three boys died, and that doctor hurriedly left. Such belief in the therapeutic effects of blood was widespread. A medieval lady was criticized for bathing in fresh young blood, not because she was mistaken when she reckoned that this would ward off old age — far from it — but because it was rumoured that two dozen girls had died providing the treatment. Such things may seem impossible in today's humanitarian world, until you recall the locally approved excesses that take place from time to time in our wars and political and social revolutions.

However, it was usually animal, not human, blood which was first used therapeutically, and this extract from a translation of Dioscorides makes recommendations for applying it which were current for well over a thousand years:

The blood of a Goose & of a duck or drake, & of a kidde are profitably mixed with Antidots. And that of an wood Culver, & of a Turtle, & of a pidgeon, & of a Partridge are anointed on new sores of eyes & on such as are bloodshott & are dull of sight. But in particular, that of the Pigeon doth stop the bleedings e Meningibus. But that of the Hee goate, & of the shee goate, & of ye Hart, & of the Hare, being fryed in the panne & soe taken, doe stop Dysenteries and the fluxes of the Coeliacall, & being dranck with wine it is good against poyson. And the Hares bloud being anointed on warme, doth cure sun-burnings & ye Lentigines. And doggs bloud being dranck, is good for such as are bitten of a mad dogge, & for such as haue drancke poyson. But ye bloud of an earth Tortoise being dranck, is sayd to be good for the Epilepticall, & that blood of a Sea Tortoise, being dranck with wine & ye Rennet of an Hare and Cummin, is good for the bitings of venemous beasts, & for ye drinking of a toade. But the blood of a Bull being applyed with Polenta, doth discusse & mollify hardness. And the blood of Stalion Horses, is mixt with medicines that are septicall. But ye blood of the Camaeleon is believed to make the eye-lids bare of haire, & that of green froggs likewise is thought to be of the like efficacie.*

Wren and Boyle

Thanks to the random tumbling of genes, which determine mental potentialities as well as other bodily characters, every generation has its percentage of outstandingly brainy people. But now and again, social conditions and needs, and the status of learning, are such that an unusually large number of such geniuses combine in an integrated exploration of ideas. It happened in the Athens of Pericles. It happened again in the seventeenth century when Wren the architect, Boyle the chemist, Newton the mathematician, and some others, founded the English tradition of experimental science. The same period saw the development of experimental medicine (not yet regarded as a separate subject) by physicians like Willis and Sydenham upon the foundations laid by Harvey. It was part of the extraordinary flowering of discovery which affected all civilized Europe. Mostly this took place outside the universities: men of genius freed themselves from the bondages of Church and traditional thinking, sometimes combining to form what they liked to call 'invisible colleges' or 'secret academies' of their own.

When the facts of blood circulation had been established by William Harvey, one of the first to see the possibility of giving medicine through a vein was Christopher Wren. Robert Boyle, the 'Father of Chemistry and Brother to the Earl of Cork', saw him perform an experiment using a quill and bladder to give intravenous injections to Boyle's dog. Boyle tried it out himself and then suggested that 'tryal might be made upon some humane Bodies, especially those of Malefactors'. Then, 'some Moneths after, a foreign Ambassador, a curious Person ... inform'd me, That he had caus'd tryal to be made with infusion of Crocus Metallorum, upon an inferior Domestick of his that deserv'd to have been hang'd; but that the fellow as soon as ever the Injection began to be made did (either really or craftily) fall into a Swoon; whereby, being unwilling to prosecute so hazardous an Experiment, they'd desisted ... '†

Round about this time, Samuel Butler (author of *Hudibras*) wrote a parody about Boyle and his friends and their dogs. He pointed out how careful one must be to use a dog rather than a cat: 'For a Cat, you know, is said to have nine Lives, that is eight in Reversion and one in Pos-

---

* *The Greek Herbal of Dioscorides*, trans. John Goodyer (1655), ed. R. T. Gunther (O.U.P., 1934).
† *Some Considerations Touching the Usefulnesse of Experimental Naturall Philosophy* (Oxford, 1664).

session; and it is a matter of no mean difficulty exactly to trace and observe, how many of these the lethal Force of this destructive Medicament will reach ... ' and 'it is wonderful to behold this exquisite and solert Dr. whose Province lies in the Cabinet of fair Ladies, and whose daily Employments are to sollicit the tender Arteries of their Ivory Wrists; that he, I say, should nevertheless condescend to animadvert the languishing Diastole of an expiring Mungrel.'*

Boyle looked on blood as a chemical substance and he was out to discover its properties. He pointed out that the anatomists

> mind the solid parts of the Body, and overlook Enquiries into the Fluids, and especially the Blood ... [This] were little less important in a Physician, than it would be in a Vintner to be very solicitous about the Structure of his Cask, and neglect the consideration of the Wine contain'd in it ...
>
> I remember I once kept Humane Blood for a year together, in a Glass very carefully, and if I mistake not, Hermetically clos'd ... But when the Blood came to be expos'd to the contact of the Air, the stink was so great and offensive especially to some Ladies that liv'd in the house, that we were fain to have it hastily thrown away. Another time, having caus'd some Sheeps Blood to be digested in a pretty large Vial Hermetically sealed, after it had continued a good while in the Digestive Furnace, upon a sudden, tho no Body touched it, it broke with a surprising noise, and blew off the long neck of the Vial. Two or three almost like mischances I had with attempts made on Humane Blood ... For tho to me the bad smells of all these Liquors seem to be much alike, yet divers Ladies, and those of very differing Ages, affirm they find a manifest difference between the smells, and do abhor the odour of Spirit of Blood as a stink, though they will with pleasure hold their noses a great while over ... Salarmoniac (which is in effect a Sp. of Mans Urine) and affirm themselves to be much refresh'd by it.†

In 1667, an experiment was performed before the Royal Society in London in which some sheep's blood was successfully transfused into a man (who received twenty shillings for his trouble), and it gave rise to much speculation as to whether personal traits or characteristics could be transferred from the donor ('the emittent' as Boyle called him) to the recipient. Samuel Pepys, the diarist, himself to become President of the Society in 1684, mentions that it gave 'occasion to many pretty wishes, as of the blood of a Quaker to be let into an Archbishop, and such like'. And, indeed, the usefulness of transfusion was widely conceived in this way. Blood was still a spirit, a vital essence, and it was

---

* R. Thyer, *The Genuine Remains in Verse and Prose of Mr Samuel Butler* (1759).
† *Memoirs for the Natural History of Humane Blood* (London, 1684).

decided to try transfusion for insanity, or for bowel disease, or as a means of correcting temperament by transfusing a melancholic with the blood of a sanguine person, and so on, even to the suggestion that married discord should be settled by reciprocal transfusion of husband and wife.

Boyle's attitude was at first no different from that of his contemporaries; for instance, he asked whether a dog would still recognize his master after receiving strange blood. But when, much later, he published a book summing up his experiences with blood, he wrote that transfusion 'seems not like ... graffing, where the cyon turns the sap of the stock, graffed upon, into its nature', but that 'The most probable use of this experiment may be conjectured to be, that one animal may live with the blood of another and consequently those animals that want blood, or have corrupt blood, may be supplied from others with a sufficient quantity, and of such as is good, provided the transfusion be often repeated, by reason of the quick expence that is made of the blood.'* These two suppositions, that transfused blood retains its anatomical identity in the recipient and that it is eliminated after a while, must have been intuitive; yet according to our modern observations, they are absolutely correct.

Transfusion experiments were so popular and repeated so often in Western Europe that disasters quickly followed. Unknown to the experimenters, immune reactions were following upon the transfusions of animal bloods into humans. There were the infections caused by the introduction of germs into the circulation by unsterilized instruments, and there were the complications caused by bloods clotting and so clogging the tubes and junctions made by even the most cunning inventors. A pity those transfusionists did not know that, carefully observed, the mixing of a few drops of the bloods of different humans on a white porcelain tile would have shown blood groups and founded the science of immunology two hundred years early. A pity they didn't find out that ritual boiling of instruments would have prevented infectious disease by killing the germs. And the blood-clotting, could they have controlled that? Well, they were adept at making mixtures of any ingredients they could lay their hands upon, so they might have found that citric fruit juice or the crust from wine vats could stop blood from clotting. They might have found that the bloods of people who had died a violent death were unclotted and suitable for transfusion; but they didn't. The history of medicine might have had a different sequence if anyone had stumbled on these things. But perhaps discoveries have to be made in a right order; perhaps they need an optimum number of supporting ideas before they can 'dawn'. It will be the same looking back three hundred years from now.

* Ibid.

Boyle himself, looking forward, three hundred years ago, in his book on blood, says that those who come after him will

> arrive at such attainments that the discoveries upon which the present age most values itself, will appear so easy to them, that they will wonder that things so obvious should lie so long concealed to us, whom they will perhaps look upon with some kind of disdainful pity, unless they have the equity to consider the difficulties this age surmounted in breaking the ice, and thereby contributing to those advantages that have enabled them so much to surpass us.*

(The quotation is shortened. As a genius, the Father of Chemistry and Brother to the Earl of Cork was longwinded. Not everyone knows that the full title of his famous book *The Sceptical Chymist* was *The Sceptical Chymist: or Chymico-physical Doubts & Paradoxes, touching the spagyrist's principles commonly called hypostatical, as they are wont to be propos'd and defended by the generality of alchymists. Whereunto is præmis'd part of another discourse relating to the same subject.* But he was a genius.)

* Ibid.

CHAPTER TWELVE

Shared Blood

After Boyle, the entire practice of blood transfusion fell into disrepute because of the observed danger to life which it involved in its crude form, and so it remained for two hundred years. But in the nineteenth century Pasteur discovered ways of avoiding bacterial contamination, and in the early 1900s came knowledge of the blood groups and their importance, and of how to forestall clotting. This last was first achieved by coating the inner surface of all tubes and containers with unwettable wax or grease, since such a surface prevents a triggering of the clotting process. Then in 1915 several workers in different parts of the world, all at the same time, found that sodium citrate could be safely mixed with blood, and that this would prevent it from clotting. Citrate or citric acid is a physiological substance which the body can 'use' in its internal chemistry as harmlessly as lemonade. Added to blood, it traps the free calcium of the plasma, and blood will not clot without available calcium.

The blood bank

Transfusion was then immediately liberated, by the intermediation of the glass bottle, from being an arm-to-arm business. Citrated blood could be collected, bottled, stored in a refrigerator and used as required. The blood bank was born. Improvements have since been made: by adding sugar to give the blood cells something to live on while they wait, and by altering the acidity of the citrate mixture, so that now the shelf life of a bottle or plastic bag of refrigerated whole blood is between three and four weeks. It may well be possible in the future to further lengthen the storage period, perhaps by giving the cells some additional foods more subtle than sugar on which to sustain themselves while in store. As a matter of fact it is already possible to preserve them for years in extremely low temperatures (far below freezing point), but this technique (mentioned below) requires special conditions and is at present too elaborate for general use.

   In the ordinary way, red blood in a routine hospital blood bank is not frozen solid but is kept at a temperature just above freezing point. This has two objects: to restrain the growth of any contaminating germs which may have entered the bottle (say from the skin where the needle punctured it at the time of the donation), and to lower the living rate of the red cells so that they won't use up all their resources and die. Even so, kept at this temperature they die in three to four weeks.

But if the blood is to be frozen solid special precautions must be taken, because the formation of ice crystals unevenly removes water and alters the saltiness inside and around the red cells, which damages them. This can be avoided by adding glycerol before suddenly cooling to extremely low temperatures. Then the blood instantaneously snap-freezes without any slow formation of crystals. A steep drop in temperature like this brings the life of the cells to a virtual standstill. After many years, even long after the death of the donor, it is possible to thaw them again, wash off the glycerol, and have perfectly good live cells which can be safely transfused; but this is a very expensive way of handling blood, even if it does avoid some waste. For banking purposes it is unlikely to be widely used, except in military medicine, until there is some cheaper way of carrying it out.

Other kinds of cells can also be preserved alive by this method, semen for example. For years animal sperm has been successfully deep-frozen, then thawed and used for artificial insemination of females — even generations later. Bone marrow can be stored in the same way, and in theory it is possible to have a sample of one's marrow frozen and stored, then to sustain a fatal dose of radiation (as explained on page 228) and have one's damaged blood-forming tissue successfully re-populated by an injection of the stored material.

Tissue grafts

The storage of other more solid tissues, by freezing or drying or a combination of both, is also practicable, but it is still not widely used because at present the grafting of living parts or organs, whether fresh or stored, from one human individual to another is not permanently successful, except between identical twins and in a few other situations. It is not possible to neutralize completely the complex immune response which such a graft provokes, and which usually leads to its being rejected. In the bone marrow situation just mentioned, it is generally only one's own marrow that can be reinjected with any real hope of a successful 'take', and of course this principle applies to any transfer of tissue by autograft within one body, provided the operation is surgically practicable. If someone else's marrow is used, there is a strong possibility of an immune host-against-graft response, or — since here the graft contains some cells belonging to the scavenging-antibody-manufacturing series — even the reverse. There are, however, the naturally occurring examples of the chimera and the placenta, where immune reactions between genetically different tissues apparently do not occur. If they understood the mechanisms involved here, surgeons might be able to make artificial grafts with more hope of success. But at present only certain specialized parts without blood vessels can be freely interchanged between immunologically mature people without consideration of immune responses; such areas are the cornea of the eye and the cartilaginous parts of the skeleton.

The immune mechanisms of graft rejection are mediated through lymphocytes, antibodies and blood capillaries. These mechanisms cannot yet be made specifically tolerant of grafted tissue, though there are signs that this may be possible in the future. The most that can be done now to suppress the reaction against, say, a kidney graft is to give a drug (or antiserum) which damps down the rate of lymphocyte production in the recipient. Cell-discouraging drugs of this kind were originally developed for different purposes (the treatment of leukaemia and cancers). A difficulty is that when given continuously to 'cover' a graft, they reduce the body's general defence against infection at the same time. The chief hope for successful long-term grafting is that reliable natural systems of 'tissue groups' will be worked out, analogous to blood groups, by which 'graft-compatible' donors and recipients can then be selected by tissue-typing, using anti-white-cell antibodies to classify them, since it has been established already that the white blood cells share many relevant antigens with the solid tissues.

One can reasonably regard liquid blood in a container in the blood bank as 'alive'. Its red cells are living, and they 'eat' the dissolved sugar they are given as 'food', although having no nuclei they cannot divide. Cells need not 'die' just because they have left the body, nor do they all die immediately the body 'dies'. This is because cells vary in their sensitivity to lack of oxygen. As a matter of fact, cells of many body tissues, if removed up to a day after the death of the individual, can be shown to be as alive as ever and will divide and grow in artificial culture. Whole body death is therefore different from cell death; parts of an organization can cease to function at different times. There are even artificially nourished cultures of body cells alive today that were obtained from people or animals generations ago. None of the original cells of those cultures is still in existence, but their descendants belong to the same genetic line, and have been dividing, just as many body cells do. Death then is a complex idea. So is life, when what is meant is 'life as organization', and both notions become further confused if some sort of 'spirit' or 'vital force' is postulated as 'inhabiting' living matter. The eventual 'death' of a vase of flowers is a reasonable comparison with the eventual 'death' of cells in a container of outdated bank blood.

The blood bank—the sharing out of individual body substances in emergencies—is a remarkable invention of man. As a biological phenomenon it is comparable to cannibalism or to the emergency practice, found among some insects, of eating their own eggs or grubs. But man, by creating blood transfusion, now shows a versatile capacity for biological deployment along a novel line which may be greatly extended if grafting of whole organs, such as kidneys, hearts, livers and secreting glands becomes generally possible, as already it is in certain cases.

Blood transfusion symbolizes biological altruism and charity, the unity of species and the independent vigour of the cells, which are at the same time subordinate to the requirements of the larger organism to which they belong.

Blood shared

Many religions have used blood as a mystical emblem of the truths and realities of human life gained, shared or lost. The pelican feeding her young with blood from her own breast was a symbol of family piety among the ancient Egyptians, for which reason pelicans were spared as food birds. The fable was carried from North Africa by the early Christian Fathers as a symbol of Christ-like charity, since when it has constantly recurred in bestiaries, in poetry and in ecclesiastical imagery and ornament. Today a pelican 'in her piety' is often used as a badge by blood-donor organizations. Actually, the mother pelican feeds her young with regurgitated food by pushing their beaks into her pouch. Some pelican species have a red-tipped bill, and the mother, pressing her beak against her breast as she brings up food, may have given rise to the tale that she feeds her brood with her own blood. The notion of important biological substance being shared is valid, even if the precise zoological observation is not.

Two generations ago, volunteers who gave blood and took no money for it were heroes and heroines. Today they are no more than millions of properly civilized people who, in an unobtrusive way but one which is dramatized by the symbolism it generates, put themselves to some inconvenience and mild discomfort for the sake of others.

The average healthy man or woman of ordinary weight and stature has a circulating blood volume of about ten pints (five litres). Removing 10 per cent of this (one pint or half a litre) has no serious effect. It is as though a spare tank containing a pint or two was being tapped for an emergency — only there is no tank. When the half-litre is lost, the springiness of the fluid-filled tubes of the circulatory system takes up the slack. Then over the next hour or two, water moves in from the tissues until the volume of the blood has returned to pre-donation level. It is then difficult to perceive that any has been lost. Even so, $2,500,000,000,000$ ($2 \cdot 5 \times 10^{12}$) red cells have been given away, and must be replaced over and above the $250,000,000,000$ per day, which is the normal number produced to cover natural loss by wear and tear.

It takes three or four weeks for the bone marrow to make the extra red cells to replace those donated, and iron is needed for this. Most people in a community with a social standard sufficiently high to maintain a blood bank will be taking in enough iron in their normal food to have a small store in the body, provided they don't give blood too frequently. It is nevertheless good practice for regular blood donors to take extra iron as tablets from time to time. With this, most healthy people in well-fed countries can reasonably give a pint of blood every third month. But individuals differ. Women are likely to have low iron stores and when pregnant or with small infants they should not give blood donations.

There are scarcely any risks in giving away your blood under medical supervision. Mechanical accidents of the one-in-millions type have occurred in blood-donation clinics as in other areas of medical work. If serious, it is usually because some irregular substance, such as air or a small piece of metal, is inadvertently introduced through the bleeding needle into a donor's vein. But all good blood banks are well aware of these 'needling' hazards and take elaborate precautions to avoid them.

Transfer risks

Perhaps it is as well to state categorically that character traits are not transferable by transfusion. Transient allergies and certain infectious diseases can be passed across in blood from donor to recipient, but that is all. If, for example, a blood donor is allergic to fish and his allergy operates (as is possible) through the presence of an anti-fish antibody in his plasma, then it may happen that the recipient will experience a transient allergy to fish that lasts as long as the transfused antibody survives in him (not more than a few weeks and maybe much less). This is the same thing as the passive transfer of certain other immunities.

The most important dieases which *might* be transferred by transfusion are malaria, syphilis and virus jaundice (virus hepatitis). The malarial parasite can survive for weeks in chilled blood and the blood bank can therefore inadvertently act as its stand-in mosquito. This is a transfusion risk only in malarious countries (which are becoming fewer every year) and the disease is easily controlled by a dose of an anti-malarial drug.

Syphilis is a more subtle hazard. Every blood donor is tested to see whether he has formed antibodies against the germ of syphilis. If he has, there is a possibility that he has the disease. But the characteristic antibodies are not formed until a few weeks after the original infection, and it is at this early stage that the syphilis germs may be widespread in the blood. However, they are readily destroyed by cold or by penicillin. This was a greater hazard in the early days of transfusion, before blood was commonly kept chilled in refrigerators, and before there were antibiotics.

Virus hepatitis or virus jaundice has given the blood banker real trouble. Quite a number of apparently healthy people carry the virus, and when transferred in a blood donation it can have serious effects. These effects are often not ascribed to the transfusion because the jaundice (caused by viral damage to the liver cells) comes on after a long incubation period of two to five months. Unlike the germs of syphilis or malaria, the jaundice virus is not necessarily destroyed, even when the cells are removed from a blood donation and the plasma is fractionated, by chemical or physical methods, into special or long-storage components. However, there is now quite a good test for its presence and soon it may be possible to eliminate bloods containing it from the bank, so that this form of infectious jaundice will no longer have to be accepted as a necessary hazard of transfusion. There is the further likelihood of a vaccine being developed by which one can be immunized against the disease.

Those communities which base their blood banks on voluntary un-paid donor panels have an advantage over those which offer money for blood. A paid panel of donors must always include more people who have an interest in concealing from the blood bank some previous sick-ness or some habit of life (such as drug addiction) which either makes their blood potentially infectious or increases the risk to themselves of giving blood.

White cell, platelet transfusions

The white cells and the platelets in banked blood die long before the red cells, which ordinarily have a storage life of three or four weeks. But transfusion of white cells has little value even when fresh blood is used. They have sets of antigens which are independent of the red-cell blood groups, and which provoke antibodies in the recipient but do not in general complicate transfusions. (As mentioned before, these anti-bodies are now being used to 'match' organs for grafting, with partial success.) Transfused white cells disappear from a recipient's circulation in a few hours. It may be, of course, that they have moved into the tissue spaces where white cells normally lurk. But wherever they may be, their natural lives are short, and the fact remains that people who lack white cells do not benefit clinically by attempts to transfuse them.

Platelets, like red cells and unlike white cells, are found only in the bloodstream. Lack of platelets is a serious matter and is often accom-panied by bleeding. The transfusion either of a large amount of fresh blood containing platelets or of a concentrated suspension of platelets can provide temporary relief, and can restore a patient sufficiently to allow surgical removal of the spleen, an organ that can sometimes

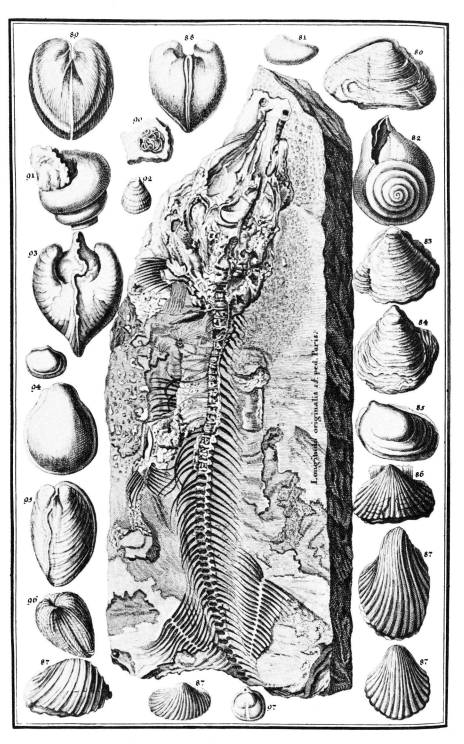

Marine fossils. Evidences of evolution

abnormally reduce the numbers of platelets and other blood cells in the circulation.

Plasma fractionation and storage

If all cells and platelets are removed from a donation of blood, the remaining plasma can be stored for a long time. It can be frozen, dried or split up ('fractionated') into its constituent proteins.

Apart from water, salts and various soluble body materials in transit, plasma is made up of albumins, globulins and fibrinogen, which are soluble proteins differing in molecular size and shape and in the electric charges on their molecular surfaces. They can be sorted out by precipitation in different strengths of salt solutions or alcohols, or by being passed through columns of clay or other finely divided materials that delay the different molecules according to their sizes, shapes or charges; or, similarly, by electric currents flowing in wet strips or columns, or by high speed centrifuging.

Albumin is the smallest plasma-protein molecule — small enough to exert an osmotic pressure — and so it is the protein mainly responsible for holding water in the plasma in the capillaries. Apart from its osmotic function, albumin has important binding actions in the circulation. Because it is small, it is also the protein which is lost into the urine through molecule-size spaces in damaged filter tufts of the kidney in the disease called glomerulo-nephritis. If urine containing albumin is boiled, the protein coagulates like egg-white, and this is a simple test for kidney disease. Human albumin solution preparations can be made from plasma, and albumin is as effective as whole plasma as a transfusible blood-volume expander in an emergency. It has the great advantage, too, that it withstands slight heating (nothing near the boiling-point of water but enough to kill the virus of infectious jaundice; whereas plain plasma or blood is damaged by being pasteurized in this way).

Fibrinogen too can be extracted in pure form from plasma. There is a rare condition where fibrinogen temporarily disappears from the circulation after surgical operations or childbirth: the blood cannot clot and there is a risk of bleeding to death. Purified and concentrated fibrinogen is useful for treating this emergency.

Certain other clotting factors, such as anti-haemophilic globulin, can also be concentrated. The main globulin fraction contains the circulating antibodies and these are useful for conferring temporary passive protection against infectious diseases in certain circumstances.

It can be seen, then, that special concentrations and fractions of blood are useful, and a truly rational blood bank would fractionate and process all its supplies so that each patient could have just that part of the blood which is clinically required. It is true that from time to time this one needs anti-haemophilic globulin, that one needs platelets, and so on, but in actual fact just plain blood is what is wanted by the majority of the bank's 'customers', and that is what is most often given, for one of these two reasons: first, people may be very anaemic and in urgent need of red cells; second, they may have lost blood to the point where depletion of the fluid volume in the circulation produces shock, which is relieved by transfusion of blood.

Anaemia and shock

In the ordinary way, anaemia can be effectively treated with medicines —iron, Vitamin B_{12}, etc.—which will produce steady recovery. But sometimes a deficiency of red cells must be restored really quickly, perhaps near the end of a pregnancy, or before a surgical operation. Or, again, the cause of an anaemia may be some form of red-cell destruction which will not respond to medicines at all. Then the red cells which the body needs can be transfused in ordinary straight stored blood from the blood bank. Alternatively, they can be given somewhat more conveniently in a double concentration, which is easily prepared because of the sedimenting property of the cells. When a donation of blood is left standing in a container in a refrigerator, its red cells settle to the bottom half of the container within a day or two (the process can be hastened in a centrifuge). Then the plasma on the top can be siphoned off, and since human blood is half plasma, half cells, the red cells from two containers may thus be packed into one.

This double-strength red-cell suspension is somewhat viscous, but it is a useful preparation in transfusion for serious chronic anaemia, particularly where the anaemic blood has for some time been carrying insufficient oxygen to nourish the heart muscle properly, seriously reducing the action and reserve capacity of the heart as a pump. No mechanical strain should be placed on such a heart, and a sudden abnormal increase in the volume of blood returning to it in the venous circulation could be a severe embarrassment. In such a case of chronic anaemia, the total blood volume is quite normal (a situation fundamentally different from shock caused by bleeding); therefore, to avoid overloading the heart, any transfusion for anaemia must be given slowly and in as small a volume as possible, and this can conveniently be done using these concentrated red-cell suspensions.

There is one general rule, however, which doctors observe before treating a case of severe anaemia by transfusion: they investigate its cause. A precise examination of the blood and bone marrow may become embarassingly difficult, even impossible, after the circulation has been swamped with normal transfused red cells. Careful diagnosis is essential if effective treatment is to follow on after a transfusion which, even though restorative, cannot be permanently effective.

If transfusion for chronic anaemia has to be slow, deliberate and sometimes small, transfusion for shock has to be rapid, forceful and large, because what is lacking in shock is volume — something to fill the sagging bag of a bleeding circulation. In an emergency, real blood is not essential for such transfusion; a bland, watery solution of any material of approximately the same molecular size as plasma albumin is, in theory, a suitable substitute, because it provides sufficient osmotic pressure to prevent water from passing through the walls of capillaries and so depleting the volume of the circulation. Plasma albumin itself can be obtained by fractional separation of plasma proteins, and is an excellent emergency resuscitation fluid and keeps well. There have also been many attempts to make artificial solutions which will be adequate surrogates in an emergency where blood cannot be obtained. No one has succeeded in producing an oxygen-carrier like the red cell, nor are they likely to: haemoglobin is an extremely complex substance with almost unique properties and the way it is concentrated inside a cell is not understood. But, as we have seen, carriage of oxygen is not the first blood function in jeopardy when someone is bleeding to death; the few remaining red cells will carry out this task well enough if only they can circulate. Simple expansion of the blood volume is the priority, even if the remaining blood is diluted by the expander.

Plasma substitutes

Non-oxygen-carrying plasma substitutes have been made from animal, plant, bacterial and chemical substances. Such substances, besides being composed of molecules of the right size, must not be poisonous or biologically antigenic, and ideally they should finally be broken down and re-used or excreted by the ordinary life-processes of the body — in fact they should be intravenous 'foods' as well as blood-volume expanders. Very few meet these requirements, and many which at one stage were received enthusiastically have since then been rejected.

Plasma substitutes of non-human animal origin are bovine albumin (made from abattoir blood) and gelatin. It is difficult to make an acceptable bovine albumin which is not antigenic in the human body. but it may yet be practicable to do so cheaply and on a large scale. Gelatin is made by boiling the fibrous connective tissue of animal carcases. It can be made non-antigenic and of the right molecular size, and it is fully utilized by the body afterwards. Unfortunately a gelatin solution of suitable strength does not remain fluid at ordinary storage temperatures and would have to be warmed and melted before being administered; a serious disadvantage in emergencies, but one which could be accepted if necessary.

Plant derivatives include gum acacia and fruit pectin solutions. These are not used or broken down or excreted but are permanently stored in the body tissues. This makes one hesitate to use them if something more suitable is available, because no one can foretell the long-term effects of their continuous presence in the body. The same disadvantage attaches to the use of polyvinyl pyrrolidone, a soluble plastic, which is a by-product of the petroleum industry and therefore the nearest man has yet been to getting blood out of a stone – unless you include the treatment of anaemia with mineral iron as having the same proverbial sense.

The disadvantages of these plasma substitutes might be accepted for the sake of saving life in emergencies, were it not that there is another substitute more suitable than any of them. This is dextran, made by a bacterium, *Leuconostoc mesenteroides*, which knits sugar molecules together into larger units. The pharmaceutical industry takes advantage of this and prepares dextran with a molecular size appropriate for a plasma substitute. In the body these sugar lumps, molecularly speaking, are broken back to normal size and used up as sugar. Dextran is not antigenic, and it is very widely accepted as an artificial plasma substitute – so much so that it has largely ousted its competitors.

Amounts transfused

However useful a plasma substitute may be, it is not as good as human blood or plasma or albumin solution in the treatment of shock from wounds, burns or other situations where the blood volume is reduced. On a wounded person, one can make a first-aid estimate of the amount of blood probably lost into the wound itself by comparing the area or volume of the wounded part to an open hand or a closed fist: each represents a pint or half-litre of blood, so that three fists indicates a need for a transfusion of at least three donations. Added to this are any losses by external bleeding from broken arteries or veins. Losses of plasma in burns can be estimated in much the same way: by a rough calculation from the surface area involved.

When blood is lost externally during surgical operations, or in childbirth, one can measure the actual liquid. It is more difficult to estimate the amount of bleeding into inner natural cavities, such as into the stomach or intestine from an eroded blood vessel in the floor of an ulcer, and losses into any internal space such as may complicate disorders of the blood-clotting system. One can often only guess. But whenever there is bleeding, it is rapid transfusion that saves life, and the patient's response is often a good guide to how much more is required. Whole blood is transfused if possible. Plasma or human albumin or a substitute is used if whole blood is not available or while its arrival is awaited. But if plasma rather than whole blood is lost, as in a burn, then plasma or albumin is the logical first transfusion fluid, though here red cells in the burned area are likely to have been damaged by heat and will probably be eliminated within a few days, so that some whole blood may be needed too.

Blood-pressure measurements are a guide in the case of a person suffering from haemorrhagic shock, since blood pressure will usually be below its ordinary level. Resuscitation by transfusion will raise it again, and in this situation rapid transfusions of five or ten donations are commonplace. Where there is continuous bleeding, even larger amounts are given: there are cases occurring now and again in every large hospital where thirty to fifty donations are used before the condition comes under control.

Usually, more blood has to be given than is at first thought to be required, but even though the blood pressure is carefully monitored, there is still the danger (as with slow deliberate transfusion for anaemia though not so great by comparison) of giving too much and overloading the heart. If this happens, the excess volume embarrasses the right side of the heart so that the right auricle becomes dilated, and back pressure fills up the local veins. Doctors get warning of right-sided overloading or failure by carefully examining the side of a patient's neck for signs of engorgement of the external jugular vein, a natural venous pressure gauge visible through the skin.

Taking and giving blood

The actual technique of bleeding donors, and of transfusing blood, is quite simple. A sterilized glass bottle or pliable plastic container holding suitable anti-coagulant solution inside, is used, and two tubes lead out from it. One is attached to a hollow needle, the other opens to the air through a small filter which prevents the entry of bacteria. A band is placed around the upper part of a blood donor's arm, sufficiently tight to restrict the low-pressure return of venous blood towards the heart, but not so tight as to stop the flow of high-pressure arterial blood coming down into the forearm and hand. This passes through the capillaries and into the veins which then swell and become engorged below the obstructing band.

There are two veins which run over the elbow joint when the arm is held palm uppermost. They are on the inner and outer side of the forearm, and an oblique crossing vein connects them in the elbow crook called the cubital fossa. (*Cubitus* is the elbow or forearm, and *cubo*, 'I lie down', refers to the Roman habit of reclining propped on an elbow. A cubit was the distance from the bent elbow along the forearm to the fingertips, and this distance was also called the ell—'Give him an inch and he'll take an ... '—a reference to the L-shape of the bent joint, and the same L as in *el*bow.)

These veins have always been used for blood-letting because of their convenient position, and if the hollow needle is put into one of them there will be enough pressure in the swollen vein to cause blood to flow out of the arm and downwards by gravity into the container below which fills in a few minutes. The tubes are disconnected or clamped before the blood is sent to be stored in the bank, and some samples from each donation are checked and grouped.

When the time comes for the blood to be transfused, the patient's serum is carefully matched with the donor's cells, and if no conflicting antigen-antibody activity has been demonstrated, another pair of tubes is inserted into the bottle: an air tube similar to that used before, and a long tube (ending in a needle) with a chamber in which the rate of flow of the blood can be measured by counting the number of drops per minute. The container is hung up over the patient and the long tube is allowed to fill with blood to exclude air bubbles. The needle is inserted into any available vein – usually in the arm – and the blood will flow in quite rapidly by gravity if there is no obstruction to the venous return to the heart. If it is necessary to give the blood faster, pressure can be applied to the container and this is usually done when actively treating haemorrhagic shock. But one must be very careful to remove any such pressure before a rigid container empties, to avoid air embolism (page 275).

Unresponsive shock

There are some kinds of circulatory collapse which will not respond to transfusion. When the heart muscle is damaged by a local failure of its own blood supply, as in coronary infarction, it cannot contract properly, and the beat will be weak. Low-pressure strokes from a weakened pump mean low pressure in the circulation, which is shock. But transfusion under such circumstances only embarrasses the heart further.

If severe haemorrhagic shock persists, the small blood vessels may become paralysed through lack of oxygen so that they lose all contractile 'tone' and become dilated. Then the circulating blood, in filling them, drops its pressure disastrously, and transfusion is like trying to fill a bottomless container. Sometimes a bacterial infection will have a similar effect, because poisonous material released from the germs makes the peripheral vessels sag in the same way, and 'irreversible shock' sets in.

Cardiac massage

When the heart stops in cases of shock, or in cases where there is general deprivation of oxygen as in smothering, drowning or gassing, the final arrest may be caused by the coronary arteries carrying insufficient oxygenated blood to the heart muscle itself. The result is a vicious circle: without oxygen the muscle cannot contract, and without proper contractions there is insufficient blood pressure to fill the coronary arteries.

Sometimes in such cases a transfusion given into an artery rather than into a vein may be life-saving. It is not easy to do because arteries are thick-walled and deeply placed. But the procedure rapidly raises the arterial pressure by back-flow (there are no valves in arteries), and then a collapsed aorta quickly becomes turgid again and the coronary arteries, which open directly from it, refill. The flow of blood to the all-important heart muscle enables it to beat strongly once more. Then the rest of the transfusion can be completed intravenously.

But emergency resuscitation of people who have been rescued from drowning, smothering or sudden collapse may require a more drastic attempt to start the heart again if it has stopped. It used to be done some years ago by cutting open the abdomen on the left side just below the ribs, putting in one's hand and squeezing the heart hard and rhythmically through the diaphragm up against the underside of the breastbone. This often started the circulation again, and if the breathing passages were clear and some form of artificial respiration was also given (such as mouth-to-mouth inflation of the lungs) there was a good chance of recovery—so long as the heart was undamaged and had ceased beating for only a few minutes.

But it has been found that cutting the abdominal wall is not necessary. Sufficient forceful rhythmic pressure can be applied to the outside of the chest wall over the heart. The patient is laid on his back, and the heel of the palm of one's hand is placed upon the left side of the lower end of his breastbone. Then, with the other hand on top, nearly all the weight of one's body is applied in heavy jerks through stiffened arms at one-second intervals. This is effective in squeezing the heart and carries less complications than the cut-down method, but it has to be carried out with enough force to risk breaking the ribs if it is to be successful.

Artificial kidney

There is a special need for blood donations when a sick person needs to be connected temporarily to a subsidiary circulatory device outside the body, such as an artificial kidney, or a heart-lung apparatus. Both machines need a quantity of donor's blood to prime them.

The artificial kidney can be used to tide patients over periods of temporary kidney failure, or to maintain life when kidney failure is permanent. If kidneys stop functioning there is a serious and eventually fatal accumulation of water (dropsy) and waste products (uraemia). The artificial kidney is a filtration machine which can reduce the concentration of the waste substances in the blood and greatly improve the patient's condition, and the treatment can be repeated every few days if necessary.

When the artificial kidney is to be used, the machine is primed with donor blood and the intake is connected to a needle inserted into one of the patient's large veins or small arteries. A suitable anti-coagulant prevents clotting. The important part of the device is a long tube made of semi-permeable viscose material, like cellophane. This is immersed in a large tank, and blood issuing from the patient moves through it and then is returned into a needle in another vein. The flow is aided by a small pump. Substances of small molecular size such as salts and urea can diffuse through the wall of the viscose tube and pass into the large volume of fluid in the tank. This fluid is changed from time to time and contains the concentrations of salts ordinarily present in normal blood so that diffusion from the patient, who starts off with a higher level of these substances, will proceed only until equilibrium is reached. The semi-permeable tube may be wound on a rolling drum which washes the tank fluid over its outer surface. This speeds up the diffusion rate, or dialysis. Another method is to use a tube within a tube, with the blood moving in one direction in the inner tube, and the washing solution flowing in the opposite direction between the outer and inner tube. Consecutive chemical measurements of the constituents of the blood or of the washing fluid indicate how the dialysing procedure is going.

Heart-lung machine

We have seen that the heart is a pump; and the lung is a bellows. Perhaps, then, it is not surprising that an engineering equivalent has been devised which temporarily acts for both. The heart-lung machine is a device consisting of a pump and a gas exchanger. It can short-circuit the heart and lungs while a surgical operation is being performed on the heart. The pump (or 'heart') rhythmically milks the blood along a resilient tube. The gas exchanger (or 'lung') can be a chamber of blood with oxygen bubbling through it; or a large surface over which the blood runs as a wet film in an atmosphere of flowing oxygen; or a thin membranous tube through which the blood flows, with a stream of oxygen passing over the outside, so that an exchange of gases takes place across the membrane. The purpose of the machine is to oxygenate the blood, and if this can be done effectively, carbon dioxide, which is relatively more diffusible than oxygen, will satisfactorily move in the opposite direction.

These heart-lung machines hold a large volume of blood and have to be primed with anything up to ten donations. As with the artificial kidney, a general anti-coagulant is used to keep the whole circulation fluid.

CHAPTER THIRTEEN

Blood and Iron

It was chilly weather. A young woman who wore short clothes had cold, bluish-purple patches on the backs of her legs, and goose pimples. She went to a doctor, who told her she had *erthrocyanosis frigida crurum puellarum* and *cutis anserina*, and to keep warm. Alarmed, she spent the days crouched in front of a fire. A reddish-brown network appeared on the fronts of her legs. She went again to the doctor, who told her she had *erythema ab igne reticulatum*, and that he had meant her to keep warm by wearing woollen stockings and taking exercise. More distressed still, she went on brisk walks, but her shoes were too small for the unaccustomed thick stockings and she got a sore big toe. The doctor told her she had *unguis incarnatus*, and that he had not meant her to ... Has such jargon any value nowadays?

Scientific method imposes intellectual order upon observations which have accumulated higgledy-piggledy. This requires that things be labelled. Each label is shorthand for a strict definition. Animals, plants, weather, ideas, religions, minerals, and so on, can be named and classified, and this is usually helpful; but you can allot many names or symbols and forget that this is but a preliminary to real thinking. All definitions are finally circular: every dictionary has its residue of words defined in terms of one another. Even the relations between numbers can go round and round endlessly if you let them. For example, $1/7 = 0.142857142857142857 \ldots$ *ad infinitum*. So why label diseases?

Simply because this is a way of relating the problems of a sick person to the accumulated records and experience of the doctors. The importance of 'diagnosis' is not that diseases are named, but that this helps in choosing appropriate treatment, or indeed in finding out whether any is available. The importance of 'prognosis' is that it forecasts the probable future course of an illness and is therefore very useful indeed for the people concerned, whether patients or their dependants.

Naming each disease implies that they all have distinguishable signs and symptoms. But in practice, the names signify abstractions, derived from compounding many different individual observations. Besides, diseases are processes, not static structures. So there are individual stages and varieties which render naming imprecise, just as there are many days in the year when it is difficult to tell from the weather if it is summer, autumn or winter. But if a diagnosis is made, an agreed name can be used, and this saves much time when doctors communicate with one another. The forecast for the future of the illness obviously depends upon the accuracy of the diagnostic label and the precision of doctors' notions and records about the disease in question. The need to name diseases and their signs and symptoms is unhappily accompanied by a tendency to produce a jargon. It is both this jargon and the rigid structure of the official medical profession which tend to ward off amateur interest in medicine.

Amateur medicine

There are few worthwhile amateur physicians, and it is generally agreed that any number of them would do harm. But the development of widespread literacy in the past half-century, together with modern communications, means that the closed knowledge of an expert professional few of some years ago becomes the commonplace conversation of everyman today. Some say that our technical civilization is directed by a dangerously small handful of experts, but this is not true of the life sciences. Medical knowledge is being popularized, and so are other professional human technologies, such as law, economics and military strategy. The adept who sets no store by obscurity shares what he knows, making his subject simple without distortion for those who cannot give as much time to it as he. Also, of course, an informed patient has an advantage for a doctor over a patient duped into a state of compliance. In an active relationship of mutual trust, the doctor may be able to reveal to the layman the simple fact that man survives every illness but his last; that medical treatment, while it may control a disease, frequently has no effect on it and indeed may make it worse.

The accepted natural history of the human body in health and disease is not intrinsically difficult to grasp. There is not much barrier to a sound dilettante interest in the subject: plenty of books are available, and one can readily observe sickness when it occurs in oneself and others. Some may question whether an entry into medicine is possible without some knowledge of the fundamental sciences on which it is supposedly based. Actually, sustained interest and a biological sympathy for the sick human body will take you much of the way, as it has many a nurse, especially if you are intuitive enough to sift the almost endless medical literature: separating that large part which is tentative and vague from that comparatively small fraction which deals with established human biological fact.

And indeed, if you do make abnormal human biology one of your interests, you have a great advantage over those who collect moths or study cabbages: you have the privilege of insight, living inside a human body yourself. There is one difficulty, however: that of taking an impersonal view of matters of human life and death, which can cause emotional disturbance and upset the judgment of those not conditioned by a medical training.

Taking responsibility for the actual treatment of patients is another matter. Quackery is in general a bad thing. A sick person delivers his body, which is biologically and genetically unique, into the doctor's hands. The agreed generalities of disease may not apply exactly in his case and long medical experience is necessary for handling this variability. Further, the apparatus of an organized profession is necessary to provide a social guarantee that the sick person's trust will be honoured, and that the safest treatment will be given. One cannot say categorically that an unqualified practitioner will not provide both these safeguards, or that every qualified practitioner will do so. There is simply less guarantee in the former case, because the quack, being unsupervised by colleagues, stoops more easily to dishonest practices. Few such practices have to do with blood, but one of them has, and is notorious.

Have you heard of the Charadrius of the medieval Bestiaries, an interesting bird which was supposed, on being brought into the sickroom, to look fixedly at a patient who was destined to recover, but turned its head away from one whose disease would be fatal? The bird is actually the stone curlew, or thick-kneed bustard, formerly *Charadrius oedicnemus*, now *Burhinus oedicnemus oedicnemus* and common in southern Europe. Is it necessary to say that it does not actually have these powers of divination and that it has never been used diagnostically in orthodox medicine? Nevertheless today there is a device, much easier to get hold of but pretty well equivalent to the Charadrius, often used by quacks; and because it makes use of a drop of blood we should deal with it here. It is Abram's Box, usually just called 'The Box', and it has roughly the same relation to official medicine as water-divining to geology. As with the Charadrius and water-divining, for those who want to believe in this sort of thing, this is the sort of thing in which they will want to believe, as the man said.

A spot of blood from the sick person is applied to The Box. The blood need not be fresh and the patient need not be present—in fact he can be thousands of miles away. The Box has a series of numbered and graduated knobs which turn variable rheostats that are not connected to any conventional power source. Also unconnected is a thin sheet of rubber covering a metal plate let into the instrument. The operator concentrates his mind on the blood spot and turns the knobs while he strokes the rubber diaphragm with his fingertips. Various numbers and readings indicated by the turning of the knobs are related on an arbitrary list to particular diseases and to organs of the body. When the disease from which the patient is suffering 'tunes in', the operator is supposed to feel a stickiness or resistance to the stroking of his fingers on the rubber. The principle is hopefully called radiesthesia or radionics, and presumes radiation interacting between the personalities or bodies of patient and operator. It is claimed that the frequencies of this radiation are altered in disease and that they can be detected as a 'resonance' with the aid of The Box. Such criticisms as that the design of The Box is electrical nonsense, or that no personal radiations have been noticed by physicists, or that The Box has on occasions ignored the fact that a patient is dead, or that a particular blood spot came in fact from a mouse, or that the diagnosis implied an opposite sex to the patient's, are met by statements that wireless waves and most other radiations now commonplace were also unknown and unthinkable a century ago, and that orthodox practitioners occasionally make mistakes in diagnosis so why should practitioners of radionics not be allowed to do the same?

The worst kind of mythologies are those which are not justified by any consistent or widespread faith, and therefore do nothing to support any public or social philosophy, existing merely for the exploitation of the lone individual by the unscrupulous.

Blood disorders

'Disease' is hard to define, because the concept becomes non-scientific where it is related to cultural concepts of what is 'normal' or 'healthy' for a given society. For instance, is nicotine- or alcohol-addiction a disease? or sunburn? or a constant fear of losing one's job? Some medical sociologists seem to equate disease with any disorder of 'ease', so that it means any 'absence of well-being'. A more scientific definition is 'human biology at extremes of adaption'—a neat concept which sees disease as evidence of the continual operation of the evolutionary process in and on the human species.

If any important part of the body is diseased, there are likely to be changes from the normal condition of the blood. This is because blood is the general transport system, and the goods carried by it are a kind of market index of the state of the body. Raw materials can pile up. End-products may run short and not be available for delivery. Chemical messages may not be acknowledged. Disturbing 'things' which are normally kept behind closed doors may get out on the streets.

Such changes are not really 'primary diseases' of the blood system. They are best called 'secondary disorders', since they reflect disease in other systems served by the circulation. This distinction between a primary disease of the blood, and a secondary disorder occurring in it, was often not made in the early days of scientific medicine.

A sample of blood can easily be obtained from a sick person—nearly as easily as a specimen of urine, and far more easily than a fragment of flesh or other tissue. Blood is readily spread on a piece of glass and its cells can be stained and examined under a microscope. Its constituents can be measured accurately in a hundred different ways. Doctors have been examining the bloods of countless sick people for three generations, so it is not surprising that many variations from the normal have been described in scientific papers. It is a mixed blessing that writing about a minor 'discovery' has prestige value as well as general usefulness. Many bloody variations, both common and rare, but all with unknown causes, were raised by their discoverers to the status of 'diseases of the blood'. Others were given high-sounding names: leucopenia (white cells reduced in numbers), leucocytosis (white cells increased in numbers), anisocytosis (red cells not uniform in size), poikilocytosis (red cells misshapen), and many more.

At one time it looked as though the science of haematology was becoming unmanageable, but the orgies of measuring and describing and naming turned out to be the reports of surveyors covering very small bits of territory. Now their work is pieced together and the map of the whole country is clearer. The splitters have had their haematological day; now it is the turn of the lumpers. More grandly, we are leaving a phase of analysis and entering a period of synthesis. All sciences march in this manner. At first there are vast accumulations of data, through which only an expert can find his way. He can fully discuss his views only with other experts, who will frequently see things differently, so confused is the picture, and this leads to argument. At the lumping stage the tracks of the main pathways become generally agreed, and at last the new knowledge is explainable in simpler terms.

Perhaps every science has some final form in which nothing remains a mystery within its boundaries, and then it becomes static, concerned only with the conservation and passing-on of its corpus of knowledge. The science of gross human anatomy, for instance, has more or less reached this stage, partly because it got off to an early start in the Renaissance, and partly because its discipline is mainly descriptive and deals with one species only. Haematology is not yet in this happy situation. There is much still being learned about the behaviour of the blood in health and disease.

The official terminology of blood disorders is not very consistent because of the piecemeal way in which it has grown; here it differs little from most of the other branches of medical science. Most of the words have a Greek or Latin flavour. They sound all right to most of us, though scholars sometimes wince — yet word manufacture in English has never paid undue attention to scholarship.

Haima is the Greek for blood. Hence *haemo*rrhage (discharge of blood), *haema*temesis (vomiting blood), *haemo*ptysis (coughing up blood) and *haema*turia (passing blood in the urine). If one of the constituents of blood is altered, we use such terms as ur*aemia* (increased urea and associated substances in the blood, as in kidney failure), hyperglyc*aemia* (increased sugar in the blood, as in diabetes) or hypoprotein*aemia* (reduced protein in the plasma, as in starvation).

These are blood disorders, perhaps transient ones, perhaps lasting, but not really 'blood diseases', in spite of their names. We use *anaemia* (Greek, 'no blood') to mean 'deficiency of red blood'. This may be caused by a disease of the blood cells themselves, but more often it is a disorder secondary to some other change in the body .

These Greekeries (and, elsewhere, Latinities) usefully convey shorthand ideas but have to be watched, for they can become absurd. There is a sound tendency among physicians today to refer to 'a high blood urea', 'a low blood-sugar level', and so on, thus avoiding jargon when describing the state of single components of the blood. ('Jargon', wrote the schoolboy, 'is a rare gas.' He was mistaken — but he had the right idea of what it should be.)

Iron and blood

'Not by speeches … ' roared Bismarck in 1862, in the course of a very effective speech. 'Not by speeches … but by Eisen und Blut!' Bismarck was standing on the threshold of a major career as the Iron Chancellor of Prussian politics. In an eventful life, he had many brushes with his doctors. A strong-willed patient who consistently overeats is a difficult one to treat, but at one stage a wily physician managed to place him on a very restricted diet for six long weeks. It consisted largely of salt-and-vinegar-pickled herring fillets, which even a man of iron can eat in limited quantities only. Whereupon the people of Germany and France, variously fascinated, admiring and apprehensive of Bismarck's daily doings, named it the 'Bismarck herring'. Now, paradoxically, it is surely his best-known folk-memorial and, mercifully, the catch-cry of his strong-arm politics has faded from public memory — but there is no harm in using it for an introduction to some paragraphs on anaemia.

Mars, the red planet, symbolized both fire and iron for the alchemists. Iron, the strongest metal, was forged into the weapons of fiery martial men. It would not have been surprising if a physician in, say, the sixteenth or seventeenth century prescribed iron on the presumption that it would 'strengthen' the body. Thomas Sydenham, an English contemporary of Robert Boyle, was one such physician, and he became the founder of modern British clinical medicine. Perhaps it was alchemical influence (or the symbolic redness of the planet, or of rust or of fire) which he had in mind when he first said, 'We give Mars in the pale colours.' But experience must have shown him it worked, for iron certainly did cure some pale people, and Dr Sydenham's reasons thereafter rested on the better foundation of experimental results. He wrote:

> ... I comfort the blood and the spirits belonging to it by giving [iron] thirty days running. This is sure to do good. To the worn-out and languid blood it gives a spur or fillip, whereby the animal spirits, which before lay prostrate and sunken under their own weight, are raised and excited. Clear proof of this is found in the effects of [iron] upon chlorosis. The pulse gains strength and frequency, the surface warmth, the face (no longer pale and death-like) a fresh ruddy colour.*

He goes on to say he has heard that crude iron ore is a more effective iron-bearing ingredient of a medicine than filings of steel that has been refined in the fire. He was right. You *can* get blood from stones, though indirectly, by eating iron ore. (A very direct connection between iron and blood might seem to have left its trace in the English countryside, where 'Bloody Mars' was once well known as a variety of wheat. Disappointingly, this turns out to have been an English mishearing of the French *blé de Mars*, or 'March grain'.)

Iron, so plentiful in the earth's crust, is a precious metal in the body: there is only enough in each of us to make one small iron nail. About 70 per cent of the iron in a healthy man is in his blood; there is a little in muscle, and the rest is stored in the bone marrow, spleen and liver in a form in which it is readily available for manufacture into haemoglobin if required.

Iron can be scarce in our civilized food. When a red cell has completed its hundred and twenty or so days in the circulation, the iron released from its haemoglobin is carefully conserved in the body and used again; very little is excreted. We are iron misers. A goldsmith is not more careful with his dust.

Blood lost outside the body is iron lost. In a healthy man there is enough spare iron in store to replace only about a quarter of the blood at full strength. Therefore, say he should lose, by bleeding, three pints of the ten to twelve that is in him, then he has lost the maximum he can readily replace in a reasonable time without taking iron medicines. The phrase 'a healthy man' is used deliberately because man is meant, not woman, who is often at a special disadvantage in this matter.

Some foods are quite rich in iron according to plain chemical analysis, but this is a fallible guide. The iron is not always 'available', because in animal or plant foods, as in our own bodies, it tends to be firmly bound to other things. Swallowing iron-rich food is not enough; one must then split the compound by digestion to free the iron, and complete the process before the food passes through the gut. Even then

* Epistolary Dissertation to Dr Cole, 1681–2, in R. G. Latham, ed., *The Works of Thomas Sydenham M.D.* (London Sydenham Society, 1850), para. 96.

there are snags, for there may be other items in the meal such as phosphate, which can refix newly freed iron as an insoluble compound and once again hinder its absorption. For this reason eggs can interfere with iron absorption because the yolk is very rich in phosphates. There are substances in the stomach juices and in the intestinal cells which combine with iron and prevent it from being absorbed excessively. The amount of these substances is reduced when more iron is needed by the body.

Red meat has much iron because it is muscle and blood, yet you will get the benefit of only some of the iron in that fillet steak – though more than from vegetables (except for soya beans, from which the iron absorption is excellent). But in general a luxury intake of meat and vegetables will provide you with adequate iron, while a poor or faddy town-diet seldom will. Fruit sugar can bind iron, but as it happens the iron-sugar complex is more readily absorbed than plain iron – so much so, that those who drink much sweet wine with food can absorb excess iron, even though wine itself contains little or none. For instance, ordinary dry red burgundies, popularly supposed to be good for the blood because of their iron content, seldom contain iron and do not contain fruit sugar. But both these substances may be added to 'medicinal' wines, swallowing which is only another way of having a drink (quite a good sedative in some circumstances). However, if you sit like the king of Dunfermline toon, drinking the blude red wine, your tipple has at least its colour to recommend it, if you follow the ancient arguments which rely on sympathy or similarity: red wine = red blood.*

By the same token, blood oranges, beetroot, raspberry juice, tomato sauce and red herrings have a little iron too, but no more than most foods. Apart from meats, those foods (indeed often coloured ones) which have most iron and probably yield it fairly readily in absorbable form in the human digestive system are sardines, chocolate, peas and beans, molasses, oysters and other bivalves, oatmeal bran and strong-tasting greens like parsley, watercress and dandelion. Some menu! Quite enough to bring a shudder to anyone feeling queasy or to a girl retching with the morning sickness of early pregnancy. Then, of course, there's the famous spinach which has a wide reputation as an iron-containing food. There are three parts of iron in every hundred thousand parts of spinach, about one-eighth of which you will absorb. If you rely on it entirely for your iron, you will get by if you eat your own weight in *épinards à l'anglaise* every year, or twice your weight if a fertile woman. That is a lot of spinach, and unless it is very young and tender, probably includes enough oxalic acid (the cause of the astringent taste) to put you in danger of getting kidney stones.

* The great repulse of the Turks by the Hungarians in 1552 was credited to the super-human strength the Magyars got from their red wine, Egri Bikavér or Bull's Blood.

Adam and Eve

The best sources of medicinal iron are minerals or chemicals which contain the metal in the form of one of its soluble salts. Today these are made into sugar-coated pills, though they used to be made up as simple draughts, which had the disadvantage of blackening the teeth so that sometimes they were taken through a straw. The iron saucepans and great round iron pots of bygone days allowed traces of the metal to combine with the salts of the food cooked in them. So the introduction of aluminium cooking vessels in this century removed a valuable source of dietary iron from many kitchens.

We should ask why on earth our intestinal capacity to extract and absorb iron from our food should be so tentative. The answer may be that there are as great dangers in absorbing too much as too little of this biologically active metal, and it is better to be on the safe side. Our Stone Age and simian ancestors lived on foods which, cruder than ours, may have contained more iron, and they probably absorbed the iron they needed. Refined and processed foods have altered the balance that our forebears struck, and the human gene pool may now be casting around for some increase in our capacity to absorb iron. Iron molecules, whether in physiological use or in store, are always 'bound' to other body molecules (to globulin in plasma, for instance), and the relative avidity of such substances for iron is under genetic control. It is, then, perhaps not surprising that we occasionally observe some people who inherit a capacity for absorbing great excesses of iron, which, deposited around the body in large amounts, disturb the function and appearance of certain tissues and organs and provoke a diffuse fibrous or scarring reaction. This disease takes different forms and is known as *haemochromatosis*. The great excesses of stored iron can be removed, in the form of haemoglobin, by bleeding the patient at weekly intervals. This stimulates red-cell production in the bone marrow, which takes up body iron to make more haemoglobin. Such bleeding would make a normal person anaemic, but not people suffering from haemochromatosis, who may have ten or more times the normal stocks of iron. In most 'normal' people the incapacity to absorb all iron that happens to be in the food must surely have developed originally to protect us from the effects of over-absorption. It is a matter of finding the right balance with the environment, and that is what genes do for a population but not necessarily for an individual.

To say that a patient is *anaemic* means that the blood is defective in circulating haemoglobin. There may not be enough red cells, or there may not be enough haemoglobin to equip each red cell properly; in both instances the amount actually circulating is below normal.

Anaemia has various causes. Perhaps haemoglobin is lost by bleeding; or the body might be unable to manufacture it in the absence of essential raw materials such as iron, protein, or some important

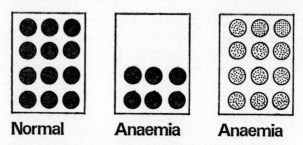

Normal   **Anaemia**   **Anaemia**

The amount of circulating haemoglobin may be reduced
either because there are not enough red cells or because
there is not enough haemoglobin in each one.

vitamin or other trace-substance. Occasionally a poison hampers the
normal function of the red bone marrow or destroys the red cells soon
after they are made. Poison may come from a microbe, or from the
food or the surroundings, or it may be traced to some drug which,
usually harmless, has a poisoning effect on a rare individual with a
genetically determined constitution that makes him susceptible. Sometimes anaemia is caused by the invasion of the bone marrow by a
cancer.

The symptoms of anaemia are diffuse because poor oxygen carriage
affects the whole body. Anaemic people, especially anaemic women, are
occasionally and incorrectly labelled 'neurotic' by their friends. Severe
anaemia can produce pallor, weakness, headache, fever, nightmares,
palpitation or breathlessness.

But not all pale people are anaemic. Some are merely thick-skinned;
others frightened like the cream-faced loon whom Macbeth wanted
damned to blackness by the Devil. An opinion about anaemia based on
appearances, without a blood-count, can be mistaken. Usually the pale-
ness of severe anaemia will extend to the underside of the eyelids, to the
lining of the mouth, to the skin seen through the nails and to the creases
of the palms of the hands; this is not so with constitutional pallor. In
severe anaemia there may be swollen ankles, fissures at the corners of
the mouth, a sore tongue, difficulty in swallowing, indigestion, and
flattening and cracking of the fingernails. Such signs and symptoms are
not evident in a mild case, where there is perhaps only petulance,
persistent tiredness and complaints of being 'run down'; then a
laboratory examination may reveal an unsuspected lack of good red
blood.

Nutritional deficiencies or chronic infections caused by microbes or
parasites are found in peoples with low living-standards because of their
poor food-intake and lack of education in matters of hygiene. These
conditions regularly lead to anaemia (which can be rapidly diagnosed by
a simple blood measurement); consequently the prevalence of anaemia

in a population is perhaps the best simple objective index of its general state of health.

Women and iron

A woman needs more iron than a man during the fertile period of her life. Every month she loses blood and therefore iron. This doubles her need for it and commonly prevents her from accumulating the same reserve stock as a man, particularly if she menstruates heavily; by her regular blood-losses an otherwise healthy woman may be brought precariously near to iron deficiency. Young women who work in cities and live on bread snacks instead of varied meals, or who decide to eat practically nothing at all in order to slim, are very likely to be short of iron in their diet. Normal menstruation will do the rest.

The menstrual flow has always been accorded great symbolic significance because it is associated with fertility, and because its periodic rhythm apparently matches the cycles of the moon. This last might seem strong evidence for parallelism between the microcosm and the macrocosm.

According to Pliny the Elder a menstruating woman can disperse hailstorms, whirlwinds, and tempestuous weather at sea; and she can drive all vermin and insects from cornfields, but must be careful, in doing so, not to harm young vines or to empty hives of their bees. The menstrual fluid itself, says Pliny, will blacken linen, blunt razors, turn copper to verdigris, soften pitch, tarnish mirrors, spoil purple cloth and neutralize magic spells; it will cure gout, boils, epilepsy, malaria, and the bite of a mad dog. Its effects, he also says, are most powerful when it is obtained from women whose virginity has been lost solely through the lapse of time (*per se annis virginitate resoluta*), whatever that means.

The menstrual fluid is three-quarters blood, the remainder consisting of waste cells from the lining of the uterus and some mucus, which tends to make it stringy. Owing to the decomposing effects of bacteria which ordinarily inhabit the vagina, it may have a characteristic odour, and its colour can change from red to brown. It is often said that mysteriously it doesn't clot, but there is no mystery, because it has already clotted inside the uterus. The beginning of the flow consists of serum (which of course won't clot) mixed with cells, and the clot remaining in the uterus then undergoes liquefaction through the activity of a fibrinolytic enzyme released by the uterine lining, so that nothing but fluid material is actually discharged.

Do you remember Viola in Shakespeare's *Twelfth Night* who sat 'with a green and yellow melancholy'? Later, in 17th–19th-century Europe, it was very common for upper-class girls in their late teens or early twenties to sigh and pine and turn pale, and their pallor was indeed very odd, being tinged with green. The colour has been vouched for by physicians of experience, otherwise we might doubt it, for green is an unexpected colour in medical practice and the disease is never seen today. It was called chlorosis (Greek *chloros*, green) and though essentially a state of iron-deficiency anaemia, it seems to have been brought about by the physical stress and demands of puberty combined with a manner of living which was restricted both psychologically and physically. Undoubtedly the conventions of female life at the time had something to do with it: voluminous, tight-laced clothes; staying indoors in poorly ventilated rooms; a poor diet (not because of poverty but because of affectations of delicacy); maybe exacerbated by a romantic capacity for falling hopelessly and unmentionably in love with some heedless male. It all responded to treatment with iron. We may smile, but the disease was real and frequent enough. Today in Europe, with different habits of life, a mixed diet and outdoor activities for teenage girls, it has completely disappeared. Certainly there is still iron-deficiency anaemia in young women, but not for such curious reasons. Girls today are never green.

As for men, well, there's only Robespierre, whom Carlyle called 'sea-green Incorruptible': a reference to his sallow complexion. The phrase is one of those that sticks disturbingly in the mind, probably because it has a paradoxical flavour: the corruption of a body often results in greenish discoloration if bacterial action releases the green component contained in the pigment of bile or blood.

A pregnant woman gives her iron to the baby growing inside. It would be just as correct to say that the foetus takes it — even that it steals it, for the child in the womb is a pitiless parasite, remorselessly satisfying its needs at its mother's expense. It absorbs her iron, though she may already be anaemic through lack of it; it will take her calcium, though her bones may be soft and collapsing; it will use her protein, even when she is wasted by starvation. The hungry foetus absorbs all its needs even though the mother may nearly die as a result. Most mothers are quite happy about the relationship, and a moment's reflection will convince you that it is an appropriate one in terms of primitive biology. But there is a civilized corollary: that no woman should have to sustain a foetus she cannot bear or does not want. So demanding a guest should be an invited one, not a gate-crasher, and the current almost world-wide acceptance of contraception and therapeutic abortion is a welcome realization of this principle.

The foetus absorbs the iron it needs for its red blood, and stores enough extra to last for the first six months of its life after birth, until it can eat a mixed diet, because breast milk is poor in iron, and so is cow's milk. But the mother has to go without even more of her iron than this, for she will lose some blood at her delivery, both in the vessels attached to the placenta and from the broken uterine vessels from which it separates, and of course this blood, too, is iron lost. Every completed pregnancy takes, in ten lunar months, at least a sixth to a quarter of all the iron usually in a woman's body, which is greater than she would ordinarily lose in the same time by menstruation. If bleeding at childbirth is extra heavy, then she must part with still more.

Iron-deficiency anaemia in pregnancy is common. A distaste for food induced by 'morning sickness' makes it more so. About one-third of all the pregnant women in Western countries would suffer from anaemia in the last three months of their pregnancies, some of them seriously, if they did not take iron tablets throughout the pregnant period, as nowadays most of them do. Fortunately, as well as iron pills and potions taken by mouth (the most reasonable way of putting medicines into the body), injections of iron can be given to urgent cases or to the occasional one that simply cannot absorb it from the intestine. Blood transfusion is a final stand-by, and so today there is always some reliable and effective medical treatment for iron-deficiency anaemia even when it occurs as an acute emergency.

CHAPTER FOURTEEN

Bad Humour

There are varieties of anaemia which can come on very rapidly, and which can go through recurrent stages of recovery and relapse, with the patient being sick and well by turns. This can occur with persistent concealed internal haemorrhage and with types of *haemolytic anaemia*, with which we shall deal presently.

Vampires

The occurrence of weakness with pallor, as if all the blood had been drained away, was the sort of thing which in the past gave support to tales of vampires. Belief in these blood-sucking ghosts originated chiefly among the Slavonic peoples. Individuals who gained a sinister reputation, perhaps as wizards, or those who had committed suicide, were the kind who were thought to become vampires after death; but the transformation could take place quite by chance, if a cat leaped or a bird flew directly over the corpse. The soul of the vampire was supposed to quit the body at night to suck the blood of living persons. The forms in which it travelled were various, but commonly it was something wispy like a ball of fluff or straw, though not a bird or bat. Hungary went through a vampire neurosis on a grand scale in the mid-eighteenth century, and for a short time all Europe was filled with reports of the supernatural goings-on in that country, which explains why Anglo-Saxons still think of vampires as middle-European.

When the Spaniards explored tropical America they encountered bats like small wispy balls of fluff with peculiar teeth which could pierce the skin of sleeping animals or humans and lap their blood, sometimes without awakening the victim. This is the only real variety of blood-eating vampire, but combined with a bat's ancient reputation as a Thing of the Night, it managed to give the vampire legend of Europe a new twist and eventually produced the Dracula theme.

Pernicious anaemia

Although it is mainly women who are affected by iron-deficiency states, either sex may get another kind of anaemia which has an upsetting name – *pernicious anaemia*. Tens of thousands of men and women who have suffered from it in late middle-age have been alarmed by the threat in that word 'pernicious'. But since the early 1920s, when the cure was discovered, it has been 'pernicious' no more. Today many doctors call it by the offhand abbreviation 'p.a.'.

A man or woman with pernicious anaemia has no trouble in making haemoglobin, but finds it difficult to make the red cells to contain it. This is because of the lack of an essential vitamin – Vitamin B_{12} – which is present in many ordinary foods. Without this vitamin, red cells develop in an abnormal way in the bone marrow, and wrongly grown forms accumulate. It is as though an assembly line had run short of an essential component, distorting production so that crazily assembled pieces of work are occasionally delivered to an exasperated market.

These abnormal red cells reach the circulation in small numbers. They contain normal concentrations of haemoglobin but are much larger than they should be. This is because lack of B_{12} affects the development of the cell nucleus (which is not extruded until mature), but not of the haemoglobinized cytoplasm, so that there is a great delay in production but an excessive amount of cytoplasm in such units as are produced.

Vitamin B_{12}

It is a paradoxical fact that people with 'p.a.' may be eating large quantities of Vitamin B_{12}, without being able to use it. It is a matter of absorption. The normal stomach exudes something over the swallowed food which attaches to the vitamin, so that it can be absorbed by the intestine lower down. Without this stomach substance, one cannot absorb the vitamin even though one's gut may be full of it. Pernicious anaemia is caused by a falling-off in certain older people of the stomach's ability to secrete the important additive. It follows that the disease cannot be cured by giving the vitamin by mouth, because what is required is this stomach substance, which might perhaps be manufactured artificially, but this has not as yet been done satisfactorily. Alternatively an absorbable type of Vitamin B_{12} could perhaps be made, if it were known just how to alter the ordinary form. At present, the barrier in the gastro-intestinal tract can be overcome only by giving injections of Vitamin B_{12} into a muscle. From there it is carried around the body by the circulation until it arrives at the developing cells which are short of it, and then these restore themselves to normal in a matter of hours. Regular injections of the vitamin must be given for the remainder of the 'p.a.' patient's life, for the stomach defect, once established, is permanent; but the treatment controls the anaemia lastingly.

Our sources of Vitamin B_{12} are ordinary bacteria and fungi in natural food: they can make the vitamin, we cannot. Our state of dependence has probably developed simply because they make so much of it, and we can readily eat them. (We cannot make our own Vitamin C either, therefore its absence from our diet causes scurvy. In this we are like the guinea pig but unlike most other mammals which make Vitamin C for themselves.)

Perhaps it is as well to point out here that only a very small number of the various species of microbes cause disease. Most live in perfect balance with nature, and many are 'useful' to their large relatives, the vertebrates. There are large numbers which live innocently in the ground, and for this reason the upper layers of the soil often contain appreciable amounts of B_{12}. Cobalt is essential for the formation of the vitamin, and cobalt-deficient land will not contain it; so domestic animals in the region may develop B_{12} deficiency. There are other similar innocent germs whose normal habitat is the intestines of animals. They form the natural 'intestinal flora'. Animals which own them (and this does not include humans) therefore have built-in sources of B_{12} in their own guts. For this reason certain excrements are very rich in B_{12}, and poultry manure is especially notable for it.

Unlike many other vitamins (such as Vitamin C), Vitamin B_{12} is absent from ordinary green plants; indeed very strict vegetarians are in danger of becoming anaemic for lack of it, particularly if they eat very clean vegetables and fruits. (A bit of dirt readily provides some B_{12}!) Most animals store heavy reserve supplies of Vitamin B_{12} in their livers, as do healthy humans. It was the discovery that regular injections of refined liver could cure pernicious anaemia which first showed that the disease need no longer be a progressive and fatal condition. Years of further research finally led to the isolation of the active substance from liver, and its identification as the new vitamin. Vitamin B_{12} is now prepared commercially on a large scale by growing suitable bacteria in a vat of nutrient liquid which is then purified and concentrated — in much the same way as alcohol is made by using yeast.

Pernicious anaemia is a true disease of the blood, because growing red cells are more affected by lack of the vitamin than other tissues. But other body cells rely on Vitamin B_{12}, too. For example, the tongue and the intestine can be affected, and classically the disease may be accompanied by degenerative changes in the cells of the nervous system, and this causes numbness and weakness of the limbs.

Gutty thieves

We noted above that the foetus steals iron (and other things) from its mother, and that its 'right' to do this may differ according to whether it is guest or gate-crasher. But there is a real gate-crashing thief of Vitamin B_{12} at large in Finland — if you can say that an internal parasite which never sees daylight is 'at large'. It is a broad fish-tapeworm. This animal, like all tapeworms, has a chancy life-cycle. Its eggs, passing into fresh water, hatch to form minute larvae which find and enter water-fleas. If an infested flea is eaten by a small fresh-water fish, the larva burrows from the flea into the fish flesh, where it settles as a small cyst. If the small fish is eaten by a bigger fish, then once more the larva wakes up, transfers its resting place again, and becomes a waiting cyst in the larger animal. This may happen several times, until eventually a fish is captured and eaten by a dog, cat or other carnivorous animal, such as a Finnish man or woman fond of lightly smoked salmon or un-cooked river- or lake-fish in any form. Then the little larva leaves the fish flesh and turns into a tapeworm the colour of old ivory. This attaches itself to the wall of the small intestine of its new host and lives there, growing to a length of up to thirty feet. It lays millions of eggs which one day may pass into fresh water, to infect water-fleas, to be eaten by little fish, to be eaten by bigger, and bigger, fish, and finally to be caught, when inside a big fish, and eaten by a warm-blooded animal again. And so the worm's life-cycle is perpetuated, and it is biologically 'successful', which is to say it survives in adequate numbers and holds its own as a species.

Many people are revolted at the very idea of being parasitized like this. Maybe they should reflect that the worm's odyssey is an admirable rich gamble of nicely judged risks with a variety of hosts. If the chances it takes are to come off, the number of eggs it lays in the host's intestine has to be very great. It happens that the worm's eggs require Vitamin B_{12} to develop properly. Not surprisingly the worm therefore steals all the vitamin it can get from its host's food, in the darkness of his own intestines. If it has attached itself sufficiently high up in the intestinal tract, it may take all the Vitamin B_{12} before he can absorb any. Then he will sink into a disease indistinguishable from pernicious anaemia, except that it can be cured simply by expulsion of the worm. In practice, however, the worm is a 'good' parasite and usually takes up such a position in the gut as to leave a share of Vitamin B_{12} for the host. Although it is estimated that at least ten million people in various parts of the world harbour these intestinal gate-crashers, the incidence of anaemia among them from this cause is confined to Finland. The reason for this is not clear. Perhaps the Finnish species is slightly different.

Similar anaemias can be provoked by invasions of the intestinal tract by irregular bacteria which steal or destroy Vitamin B_{12}, and by other diseases and surgical operations which interfere with the absorptive capacity of the intestine.

Blood suckers

There is another intestinal worm, much smaller than the fish tape-worm, which infests many people in tropical countries. This is the hookworm, which is not only a thief, but a waster as well. As a small larva it burrows through human skin, usually of the foot, and eventually finds its way to the intestine. It goes by way of the venous bloodstream to the lungs, then travels up the air-passages and down the gullet. In the intestine it grows to its adult size, which is about as long as one's little fingernail. By a small simple horny mouth, it holds on to the soft membrane which lines the human gut, and gets nourishment from the underlying rich network of blood vessels. If the infestation is heavy, there may be thousands of such worms in one person, and so it is not surprising that they are the cause of marked iron-deficiency anaemia and debility in millions of people in tropical countries. Somehow it would seem less reprehensible to us of the puritan tradition if the worms made good use of the blood they steal, but they digest only part of what they take, letting the rest run to waste, as though they had a biological interest in weakening their host as much as they dare — which is probably true, for it seems that they can establish themselves more readily in a debilitated than in a healthy person.

Leeches are worms which suck blood from the surface of the body. Some leeches live in water, and some on land in the tropical rain forests. They do not direct their activities especially towards humans. Their blood-sucking is aimed, more or less, at anything suitable which passes by, whether it be a frog, fish, turtle, snail, ox, horse or other beast. From the time of early Hippocratic medicine until the middle of the nineteenth century, leeches were frequently applied by physicians as a means of blood-letting for various ailments, even to the extent that the doctors themselves became known as 'leeches'.

The leech's mouth has three small jaws covered with hard rough material, and when it has sucked its fill and dropped off there remains a characteristic three-pointed, star-shaped wound. A trickle of blood may continue from the point of attachment, because the saliva of the leech contains an anticoagulant substance which locally prevents the blood from clotting. The leech can store a full meal of blood in its distended crop for many months, digesting only a little at a time.

The leeches of damp tropical forests hang from leaves, tree-trunks, stones, grasses, or from any places where there is the chance of fastening on to an unsuspecting passing animal. They can insinuate themselves between folds of leather or clothing, or even between the meshes of coarsely woven cloth. Their puncture is painless and the harassed traveller may first know of their activity by the trickle of his blood after they have dropped off, satisfied. Leeches medicinally applied remove up to ten cubic centimetres (under half an ounce; one large teaspoonful) each, and about as much again may run from the wound after they fall off. More will be lost if their tails are snipped after they are applied, for then the blood simply siphons out through them. This was Galen's method, but it kills the leech.

So popular was this treatment in the eighteenth and nineteenth centuries that by 1800* wild leeches were hard to find. Leech farms were set up to satisfy the demand, and these flourished in England and America: it is said that at one time the London hospitals alone were using seven million leeches a year. Even a hundred years ago a boy could make a few pence pocket-money by catching leeches in a stream and selling them to the local pharmacy; there a bowl of water was always ready on the counter with the lithe black worms swimming in it. But calls upon leeches dwindled with the rise of modern medicine, and today they are never used. It has taken us two thousand years to find out that they seldom do us much good.

How, you may wonder, did the many different and unrelated species of blood-sucking parasites get the idea in the first place? After all, most of them belong to orders of animal life that were widespread on the earth millions of years before the appearance of large victims with soft skins and complex blood circulations; so how could the adaptation take place? Probably, once you have developed sucking, boring or biting parts for living upon plant or fruit juices, for burrowing in wood or soil or other firm material, or for chopping up leaves, you are then equipped so that if one evolutionary day you should make a mistake and inadvertently enter through the covering of some large unfamiliar animal, you may find yourself with a mouth full of a headier and more subtle drink than fruit juice or vegetable sap. There might be an intermediate stage of feeding on skin-sores, eye secretions or sweat, but it is blood that contains valuable sugar and essential proteins in such soluble, rich, manageable forms. After a blood repast many a worm or insect might be better able to lay eggs, travel a long distance or overcome an enemy. It only required the habit of drinking blood to become inborn (and feeding habits are readily altered by natural selection) for this to be adopted as a permanent, though more dependent, way of life.

For instance, fleas have evolved from insects which originally lived on vegetable waste. Then they turned their attentions to shreds of animal matter dropped from the bodies of vertebrates on the floors of their lairs or nests. Next came blood-sucking, and an adult life spent clinging to relatively huge, warm, hairy or feathered bodies.

The eggs of the flea hatch into maggots that still live the ancient unattached life on the floor of a vertebrate's lair, chomping the old vegetable foods of scavenging flea ancestors. In spite of this the parent fleas have evolved a method of passing down to each maggoty youngster some of the affluent bloody life that they live on the beast above. When a flea feeds, it does not digest and assimilate all of the blood it takes, but

* In that year the poet Wordsworth met an old leech-gatherer in the Lake District, who told him that demand and scarcity had pushed up the price of leeches from half a crown to thirty shillings a hundred. It was after this that Wordsworth wrote 'The Leech Gatherer' (later called 'Resolution and Independence').

it passes some out in its tarry excrement, which dries and falls down as small black granules when the great host scratches. The maggots find and eat these pennies from heaven (or from the heavenly host, as you might say). This explains the black marks left by fleas on your sheets after they have bitten you in bed, and the dark flakes you can comb out of the fur of your cat or dog.

The phrase 'I was drunk last night' is quite appropriately used by somebody who has slept in a room infested by bedbugs. These animals, like the rat, mouse, cockroach, flea, louse, housefly and many viruses and parasites, have adapted themselves to densely living mankind. The bedbug was once a parasite of bats, and the peculiar odour it produces is thought to be one which protects it, because it is distasteful to bats, which are mostly insect-eaters, though some suck blood themselves. Bats generally live in caves, and primitive man also became a cave-dweller, though much more recently than the bats. The bugs took a few drinks of the newcomers and developed a special strain that has stayed to take dinner off humans ever since.

These bugs are very flattened in shape and live in cracks and crevices, crawling out at night to take a quick drink. The bite itself is painless, but the bitten place becomes itchy. After a meal of blood the bug hides away for a few days to digest it, then grows, molts, and then needs another feed before it can grow to the next stage. It takes six molts, and therefore six good feeds, to reach adult life, and the females need further feeds to support egg-laying.

Bedbugs have largely been eliminated from affluent societies. They are very much present in so-called underdeveloped communities. Like many other such animals, they are widely becoming resistant to chemical insecticides. It would not require a very great relaxation of standards of hygiene for this nuisance to return universally to our ever more densely-living human population of the world. But there is one thing to be said for the bedbug. It is not known to transmit any disease to humans by its bites.

No biting insect takes enough blood or feeds in large enough numbers to cause human anaemia directly, but mosquitoes can nevertheless, by their bites, cause serious disease in man. Only the female mosquito is a blood-sucker. She boozes on a drop of gore now and again (usually from a sleeping bird) to help her with the eggs, poor dear, while the male lives more wistfully on dew and nectar.

In probing through skin for blood, the lady mosquito may squirt into a man a parasite much smaller than herself, but one which is a great nuisance to him; the microbe of malaria. This germ was originally an insect parasite, but it has taken the evolutionary opportunity of getting itself injected into a richer host through a conveniently bitten hole.

Many varieties of malarial parasite have adapted themselves to birds, and wherever there are mosquitoes quite a proportion of the bird population is likely to have malaria. (Some of the drugs which are so effective against human malaria were developed by testing in birds.) Reptiles may also be infected. The parasites live mainly in the bloodstream and use the mouth-parts of the mosquito as a hypodermic syringe. In much the same way, other biting arthropods spread the germs of sleeping-sickness, yellow fever, typhus, kala-azar and plague.

The parasites which cause human malaria, though larger than bacteria, are small enough to be able to live inside the red cells of the blood, which they destroy after a short while and thereby produce a *haemolytic anaemia*. 'Haemolysis' means 'a dissolving of blood', and some explanation of the term is necessary.

Haemolysis

If a few drops of blood are allowed to mix in a tumbler with physiological salt solution (i.e. salt and water of the same strength as is found in the tissue fluids generally), the resulting redness will be hazy because the millions of small red cells are scattering light and clouding the mixture. But if blood is mixed with plain water, the salts inside each red cell will osmotically draw in water through the cell membrane, and the cells will swell until they burst, releasing their haemoglobin into solution in the water. The redness then becomes clear and translucent, no longer hazy, because the cells have been 'haemolysed'. The same term is used for the premature destruction of red blood cells in the circulation.

The most characteristic clinical feature of malaria is the rhythmic recurrence of ague (fever and shivering) at intervals of two or three days. This happens because all the malarial parasites injected by the mosquito develop at the same rate, and enter red cells simultaneously. Then, still all in phase, they go through a cycle of growth, multiplication and ripening. This leads to destruction ('haemolysis') of the red cells. At the time of simultaneous destruction of large numbers of red cells, a flood of waste excretion products and dark pigment granules deriving from the organisms which were living in the cells is set free. These substances are poisonous and travel in the bloodstream to the temperature-control centres of the brain, irritating them and producing the attack of ague. The parasites enter a fresh lot of red cells and the cycle is renewed, taking two or three days.

Different species of malarial parasite go through cycles of different length. The periodicity of recurrent bouts of fever has been noted since ancient times in marshy malarious places (*mal* bad, *aria* air). 'Tertian' malaria recurs every second day, and 'quartan' every third. This nomenclature is easier to understand when you remember that, in counting the numbers of days which have gone by since, for example, yesterday, the Romans numbered the starting day as 'one'. Then with yesterday 'one' and today 'two', that makes it two days since yesterday. So that our 'second day since' was their 'third', and our 'third' their 'fourth', and so on.

Apart from malaria there are other agents which can cause rapid destruction of red cells within the circulation, thereby releasing haemoglobin and producing 'haemolytic' anaemia. Haemolysis is just about the nearest one can get in human haematology to 'blood turning to water' (in icythyohaematology there are the fishes with colourless blood). But *pace* those who like to see traditional beliefs confirmed scientifically: there is no case on record of haemolytic anaemia having been caused by fright. The pallor and sinking feeling that go with terror are the results of nervous and chemical messages sent to the musculature of the blood vessels and of the intestine, and though the experience may feel like the blood turning to water, it is nothing of the kind.

Haemolytic anaemia can be caused by poisons such as lead salts, snake venoms, bacterial products, many uncommon chemicals and, in some curious rare cases, by the inheritance of unusually structured red cells, which become sensitive (sometimes only at night, or during exercise or in the cold) to natural agents or conditions in the blood plasma, which results in their massive destruction.

Rarely, the immunological tolerance of 'self' which develops in the embryo can break down in later life and then *auto*-antibodies may be made against the 'self's' red cells. Antibody molecules fix to the surfaces of the red cells, which are then trapped and eliminated by the scavenging system of the spleen as though they were 'not-self' items. This shortens the circulating life of the red cells bringing about an *auto*-immune haemolytic anaemia. Comparable 'auto-immune' diseases of other blood cells and of fixed tissues can occur when auto-antibodies appear against the platelets, the thyroid gland, the liver, the central nervous system and so on. Such antibodies may be carried to the fixed tissues by lymphocytes.

Another blood disorder in the same class occurs when 'cold auto-antibodies' active against the 'self' red cells appear in the blood in strength, sometimes after virus infections. These antibodies are very much more active in the cold than at the normal body temperature. When an extremity of the body such as the fingers or nose gets chilled, the cold auto-antibodies come into action in the blood of the part. These antibodies usually have an agglutinating effect, which clumps the red cells, causing blocks in local capillary flow, with pallor of the part and perhaps minor damage. Warming reverses the effect, and usually there is only a mild haemolytic anaemia because the cells passing through the spleen have been rewarmed and have more or less shed the auto-antibodies which they picked up in the cold spots.

The above are examples of 'acquired' haemolytic and allied conditions. There are others which are inherited and may be present from birth. But haemolytic diseases of any kind are rare. They may be diagnosed by finding chemical evidence of the rapid breakdown and excretion of haemoglobin pigments and derivatives; by an increase in the number of reticulocytes, which indicates that the bone marrow is hard at work, trying to make up for the haemolysis; by changes in the osmotic fragility of the red cells; and by finding antibody attached to the red-cell surfaces.

There are enzymes in the normal red cell which facilitate certain chemical reactions that protect it from deterioration or alteration during its usual life-span in the circulation; and inherited lack or absence of any of these enzymes may produce haemolytic tendencies. For example, in a few people of the south of Italy and the eastern Mediterranean, haemolytic anaemia can be brought on by eating broad beans. The broad bean is *Vicia fava* and the disease is called *fabismus* or *favism*. It is not clear what substance in the beans provokes the disease, which is in part the result of an inherited individual lack of a particular enzyme of the red-cell surface and, because of a sex-linked mode of inheritance, is commoner in males.

Many doctors interested in medical history, and knowing of the ancient Pythagorean objection to eating beans, have pointed out that Pythagoras had his colony of initiates in a part of southern Italy where favism occurs. If his reason was based on clinical observation, we have a nice traditional piece of preventive medicine. Several other explanations have been given: that the tradition is not to be taken literally but is an example of secret Pythagorean language meaning that the brotherhood should keep out of politics (voting was by casting a bean into a helmet); that it means Pythagoreans should abstain from sexuality (the bean symbolized the male testicle); that the bean was a mystical symbol of reincarnation, in which the Pythagoreans believed, and as the souls of the dead were thought to be reborn by entering into beans in the expectation that these would be eaten by women, then men who ate them would be impiously interfering with transcendental natural processes.

On the other hand Lucian, a late Latin writer, says the reason for the prohibition was that beans turned into blood when cooked and placed overnight in moonlight. We know now that this could be another example of the growth of *Chromobacterium prodigiosum*, which causes the 'bleeding Host', and other classic instances of food 'turning to blood'.

Evolution and disease

Certain other people, again mainly from the countries around the

Mediterranean, may, rarely, be found with another type of haemolytic anaemia. This is caused by an inherited anomaly in the structure of their haemoglobin, which instead of developing into the adult form, retains the rather different qualities it ordinarily has in the foetus. This results in the red cells being flattened and thin, and shortens their life in the circulation. Because of its racial incidence the affliction is called *thalassaemia*, literally meaning 'sea-bloodedness' (Greek *thalassa*, sea. 'Thalatta! Thalatta!' was the famous cry of Xenophon's Ten Thousand, when with relief they saw the sea at Trebizond on their long march home.) It is a poor name for the disease, because those who suffer from it neither have more sea-watery blood than the rest of us, nor, as it turns out, do they invariably come from near the Mediterranean or any other sea.

In various parts of the world, but mainly in the hot countries, other rare inherited abnormalities of human haemoglobin produce different degrees of disability. Among Africans there is 'sickle-cell' anaemia, in which the red cells can form curved shapes like sickles; and a couple of dozen other haemoglobin or red-cell anomalies have been described which do not result in sickling but are changes from the ordinary molecular configuration of either human haemoglobin or the red-cell envelope. Such alterations begin in a community as chance mutations, and afterwards are inherited.

It is as though the genes for human haemoglobin have been casting about in an evolutionary way for more appropriate varieties. Most of the try-outs are a distinct disadvantage to their owners, producing ineffective red cells and anaemia of varying severity, so it is hard to see why these defects were not weeded out long ago by natural selection in those parts of the world where they are common.

Perhaps the explanation lies in the fact that African peoples with a high proportion of sicklers seem to suffer less from malaria, and sickling of human bloods is generally most evident in areas which have been malarious. The human malaria parasite has adapted itself to normal human red cells, and is perhaps less at home in sickling cells. If the hypothesis is correct the peoples who carry the sickling 'defect', or perhaps any of the other abnormal haemoglobins, should be at a relative advantage when there is malaria about, in spite of the anaemia from which they suffer, and so they would survive differentially or be 'naturally selected'. Thus evolution proceeds. And when (as is happening now all over the tropics) a countryside is cleared of malaria, the 'advantage' should disappear and then the sickle-cell defect should fade out after some hundreds of years.

Disease has been described as existence at the limits of adaptation. The mutating genes move blindly to new, occasionally more appropriate, designs of human being, but more often this random process

IUDÆORUM NUGÆ.

The frog, an animal much studied by muscle physiologists, beginning with Galvani. Its developmental stages are pictured around
the frame, and the background illustrates one of the biblical plagues.

generates inherited abnormality or 'disease'. It is not surprising then that we should have some people among us with short-lived red cells, some with unusual haemoglobins, some who absorb more than a normal amount of iron from their food, some with pernicious anaemia, some with diabetes, and so on. From their personal points of view these people are perhaps unfortunate. From the broad human point of view we are fortunate that they exist, for they are a mark of the continuous operation of the variability that makes for evolution, a process that has just brought us to self-consciousness, and which must take us much further yet before self-consciousness will be able to take over from the blind genes the full directing of our biological destiny.

'Blood poisoning'

Among the blood diseases, we have first considered the abnormalities of the red cells because of their prime importance in blood as oxygen carriers. But there are also the abnormalities of the white blood cells and the platelets which are manufactured in the bone marrow alongside the red cells. All perform functions which the human body cannot long do without. Nevertheless without its red cells it would die in a couple of minutes, while with luck it could manage with very few of the others, if not without all of them, for some days, perhaps even for a week or two. Substances exist which can poison the bone marrow, destroying immature red cells, white cells, platelets, the lot. When the marrow, poisoned in this way, ceases to produce blood cells, the effect is known as *aplastic* anaemia (*aplasia*, 'no growing tissue'). However the effect is felt soonest among white cells and platelets which have a circulating life of only about a week or less, whereas the red cells, which have a normal time in the circulation of about a hundred and twenty days, can still show a muster rate of 50 per cent after seven weeks of no production.

Rather than complete aplasia, there is more often a lack of one or more of the different types of white cells of the blood. If the disappearance of the scavenging white cells is the main feature, the condition is called *agranulocytosis* ('no cells with granules') or *granulocytopenia* ('few cells with granules'). The scavenging phagocytes ('eating cells') are front-line defenders of such parts as the nose, throat, mouth and gums, where bacterial contamination is constant. Without these defences the body risks uncontrolled spread of infection, and therefore sore throat or sore gums may be an early symptom of agranulocytosis. If it is the blood platelets which are affected, we get *thrombocytopenia* ('few clotting cells') which commonly leads to bruising and to small bleeding spots just under the skin, the symptom known as purpura.

The substances which can poison the bone marrow may come from microbes or foods, but mainly they are manufactured chemicals. Some are valuable drugs; others are materials used in industry. In the strengths in which they are ordinarily encountered they seldom do any harm, but a very few people are unlucky and seem to have a personal sensitivity even to small doses. Probably they have inherited an exceptional biochemical constitution which, highly sensitive to certain substances, is unable to tolerate them. Examples of drugs which have been known to damage the bone marrow are the sulphona-mides, chloromycetin, gold and other heavy metals, headache powders or tablets containing amidopyrine, and thiouracil. Benzene is the offender to which industrial workers are exposed most frequently. There are many other substances useful in technical processes and in medicine which can occasionally affect the marrow and blood cells deleteriously.

The acute risks which immediately follow marrow poisoning are therefore not so much anaemia as haemorrhage due to lack of platelets and infection due to lack of white cells. A bacterial invasion of the body, if heavy enough, may defeat even a full normal white-cell defence, and will certainly overcome one weakened by agranulocytosis. After gaining an entry through an abrasion or a raw surface, spreading bacteria tend to grow through the soft tissues and along the lymph channels, not along the blood vessels. A wound permits the entry of infection because the unbroken skin is the main defensive barrier. Surgeons speak of *sepsis*, but an older and still common layman's term is 'blood-poison-ing', though this is no longer in medical use, because the blood does not specifically become 'poisoned' in uncomplicated sepsis. The spread-ing redness and swelling with heat and pain is caused by the irritants released by the bacteria. This 'inflammation' may appear on arm or leg as red tracks which lead to enlarged regional lymph nodes in the armpit or groin, but these follow lymph channels, not blood vessels, and the name 'blood-poisoning' goes back to the days before the nature of the circulation and the part played by bacteria in producing sepsis was known. (Incidentally, dye in a sock today will not 'poison' a skin cut, and a cut from anything made of tin or brass or rusty iron is not more likely to become infected than one caused by a knife of, say, stainless steel.)

Occasionally bacteria can enter the bloodstream itself and multiply in it, though this is far less common than local tissue sepsis. Sometimes they can get into the circulation if some local focus of bacterial disease unluckily erodes into a blood vessel, or they may be introduced by a lacerating injury or by the manipulation of dirty needles or other instruments in veins (commonly by drug addicts), or even during the inexpert extraction of an infected tooth. Then they can multiply in the circulating blood and produce the serious and widespread condition termed *septicaemia*. Now this could much more appropriately be called 'blood-poisoning'. Bacteria in the bloodstream can settle on the valves of the heart and, growing there, can damage these vital silky flaps beyond repair: this is *bacterial endocarditis*, a very dangerous condition.

But perhaps the truest specific 'poisoning' of the blood is that caused by carbon monoxide, which alters haemoglobin to a point where it can no longer carry oxygen. Carbon monoxide is a constituent of coal gas (now widely being replaced as a household fuel by 'natural gas' which is not poisonous), but it may be formed whenever combustion is incomplete, and it is present in motor-car exhausts. It combines with haemoglobin, forming carboxyhaemoglobin, a cherry-pink pigment which is more stable than scarlet oxyhaemoglobin, and in which any attachment of oxygen is now blocked by the presence of carbon monoxide. In fact carbon monoxide has almost three hundred times the affinity for haemoglobin that oxygen has. The combination, however, is reversible, and a victim rescued from an atmosphere containing carbon dioxide can recover if enough haemoglobin has remained unaffected to carry oxygen to the brain and other vital centres. Those who have reached the borderline may be resuscitated by breathing pure oxygen or by being placed temporarily in an atmosphere containing oxygen under pressure, which both increases the oxygen supply to the brain and accelerates the reconversion of carboxyhaemoglobin to oxyhaemoglobin. Exchange transfusion is another emergency measure which can be used.

Radiation sickness

'Death rays', once the darlings of space-fiction writers, are now a reality, though their range, so far, is short. They take different forms. They can be waves of electro-magnetic energy or they can be fast-moving particles. One can encounter them as X-rays, as the emanation of radium or some other radioactive substance, or as the product of an atomic or hydrogen bomb explosion. The blood-forming tissue is very sensitive to all these rays, and easily injured by them. They can irreversibly alter the configuration of molecules of living matter if they strike them, perhaps in cells deep inside the body. They can penetrate deeply because their relative amplitude is much less than the widely spaced atoms and molecules of a living structure, and they fly through them, just as bullets might go quite a distance through a forest before hitting branches or leaves. If the dose of rays is large, then vital parts of many cells can sustain hits. A stone tossed into a machine is more likely to cause spreading damage when the mechanism is moving rapidly, and, similarly, cells which are growing and multiplying fast are the most vulnerable to the molecular hits. The bone marrow and the lining of the gastro-intestinal tract are particularly likely to be affected, for in both these areas there is a constant high output of new cells to meet normal replacement needs.

Heavy doses of radiation cause very severe anaemia, which may be fatal, depending upon how many cells in the bone marrow are killed, since the tissue will have to regenerate slowly from the surviving cells. Milder doses produce less intense anaemic states, from which recovery is usual. As a general rule, small damaging doses of radiation over a long period will ultimately have the same effect as large ones over a short period—what matters is the total dose. The effect is the same as with more conventional marrow poisons: the white cells are the first to disappear from the circulation, then the platelets, then the red cells.

There are also the sinister slight changes which are caused by occasional rays, which hit in such a way that they significantly alter the intimate genetic copying mechanism of the nucleus of a cell without killing it. This change may do no harm, but it can be passed on to two new cells if the damaged cell divides, and again when the daughter cells divide, and so on. It is a 'somatic mutation' (confined to the body in which it occurs) and is to be distinguished from a mutation of the same nature occurring in a sex cell, which thereafter can be inherited by sexually reproduced offspring of the next and later generations. Very rarely, the change in mutated somatic cells may be such as to render them incapable of responding to the normal controls of the rest of the body. Then they can become rogues, growing wildly. If they are in the bone marrow they will damage neighbouring red-cell and platelet tissues, so that there is increasing anaemia and an upset in the blood-clotting mechanism. They occupy more and more space, colonizing tissue outside their home base, in areas where they have no business. White blood cells which have so mutated can multiply and appear in the blood stream in five, ten, twenty times their normal numbers. This is the nature of the comparatively rare disease called *leukaemia* ('white blood', but not making the blood white; it was originally 'leukocytaemia', meaning 'white-celled blood').

Leukaemia

Leukaemia is a cancer of the white blood cells. There is usually no local primary tumour, because the cells forming it are not from a fixed site but are distributed throughout the body. Radiation is certainly not its sole cause; virus and chemical damage to the white-cell tissue are other possible ones. The full disease may not appear until many years after an exposure to radiation: after the bombs, the surviving inhabitants of Nagasaki and Hiroshima were a little more subject to leukaemia than people living in other Japanese cities.

Doctors who spent many years working with X-rays in the earlier, less protected days of radiology have perhaps been slightly more prone to leukaemia than other doctors.

Leukaemia is becoming somewhat more common, and although not all the reasons for this are known, the disease is to a small extent related to the steadily increasing use of X-rays and radiation in civilized communities. Of course, to say that a disease like this is 'becoming more common' is usually to refer only to the experience of European and American doctors over the past three or four generations, since the condition was first recognized. For all we know, the incidence of many diseases, apart from the infectious ones which are influenced directly by control of the microbes which cause them, may vary from one century to the next for genetic, environmental or other reasons which we cannot yet clearly see. A good biological evaluation of human disease would require organized medical experience all over the world to be passed on and critically examined by scientists for something like a thousand years or more.

Whatever its cause, leukaemia is at present generally irreversible and progressive, though its progress can be restrained. If I got it, I would know that I would have it until I died, and if I happened not to die *of* it, then I would surely die *with* it. There is not at present any certain cure. There are forms of treatment which can palliate it in the early stages, especially in children, and sometimes the suppression of the disease lasts for many years; but in the end the patient nearly always succumbs to the accompanying anaemia and to increased susceptibility to infection. Cures *do* occur, *but they are extremely rare.*

Haematologists recognize different forms of leukaemia, but these are merely variations on the one morbid theme. Some run a quick course, some march more slowly. People of all ages get it. To some degree the younger they are, the more rapidly fatal it is. Young people commonly die in a few months, but sometimes they do so in as little as a few weeks after the onset of symptoms. Older patients may survive for some years, and mild forms occur which need not noticeably shorten the average expected life-span of an old person.

In some strange way leukaemia may be related to a high standard of living, for the better-off countries and classes appear to be more subject to it. But remember that such people can often more readily get expert medical attention, with consequent greater accuracy in laboratory diagnosis, so that more cases of leukaemia are recognized among them.

One should bear in mind, of course, that although leukaemia is a much publicized and dreaded disease of childhood, and although its incidence may be slightly increasing, it remains a very rare hazard, like many medical bogys which have news value and therefore seem to pose a greater general threat than they really do. You or your children have a very small statistical chance of contracting leukaemia. The risk is far less than that of dying in a motor-car accident, which seems to be tacitly accepted by the community as 'worth it'. At the most, only about one person in every two or three thousand gets leukaemia, and that includes infants and children. Not many. After all, it is not so long ago in our history that dying in early youth from smallpox, cholera or diphtheria was commonplace. Today, however, families tend to be smaller, the standard of living is generally higher (in the Western world anyway), and there is consequently more time and love available per individual child than there was in times past. And the human fact is that the sudden death of a child is emotionally easier for parents to bear or contemplate than a sickness which is drawn-out and then fatal, or one which is permanently crippling. Again, in many prolonged diseases there is the ever-present hope of a cure, even if only because the diagnosis remains in doubt till the end. But leukaemia is different: it can be diagnosed with great accuracy, and the outcome is almost invariably fatal.

The parents of a child who gets the disease need to be wise people advised by a wise doctor, for they have acute roles to play in a human tragedy forced on them. They are told that their child will die, but at first he or she may not seem very sick. They may doubt the diagnosis, but examination of bone marrow and blood cells is now so commonly and so expertly done that very rarely will a mistake be made, and no physician would come to a conclusion of this kind without several checks and counter-checks.

When the child deteriorates, treatment is designed to relieve discomfort, and to sustain intelligent hope. Blood transfusions, X-rays, hormones, drugs which act against the white blood cells: all these may temporarily restore the child, or improve its blood-count. Often the parents hope at this stage that a real cure has been brought about, that the diagnosis was wrong. But almost always there is a relapse, and in the end the palliative measures cease to work. By this stage the family may seem almost to have lived out the death of a much-loved son or daughter two or three times, instead of once, so prolonged is the situation. If they have not had the medical information clearly and frankly put to them, all the family savings may have been spent on ineffective or quack treatment. The correct course is not for children to be cherished any less, but for the doctors and others concerned to enter into whatever frank and honest understanding with the parents can best bring some dignity and happiness to the dying child, in spite of family heartbreak. Treatment can be realistic without being stupidly heroic. Nobody should be abandoned, but nobody should be hounded into prolonged and useless endurance. When death comes it represents a kind of failure for the doctor, but he has still the task of helping the family to pick up ordinary life again, with sadness but with some comfort that all helped to make death bearable.

One of the palliative treatments for the more slowly progressive forms of leukaemia is exposure to X-rays. This seems paradoxical: how can a process which causes leukaemia also alleviate it? Yet there is no anomaly. As we have noted, X-rays in small doses can intimately injure white blood cells without killing them, and in this way the rays are an occasional cause of leukaemia. But in larger doses they will kill rapidly-dividing cells, and the leukaemic tissue is dividing very rapidly indeed. Yet such doses of radiation, and also the anti-cell drugs which act similarly, are broadly poisonous, and they are not selective. In doses which the normal parts of the body will tolerate they seldom kill all the abnormal cells. In the end leukaemia becomes resistant to radiation treatment.

There is a rare disease of red cells which to some extent can be regarded as the counterpart of white-cell leukaemia, but it does not affect children and the outlook for those who have it is not so serious. Called *polycythaemia rubra vera,* it causes the circulating red cells to increase greatly in numbers until the blood becomes thick and viscous. Although persistent, its effects can be successfully modified for long periods by medical treatment.

CHAPTER FIFTEEN

The Bleeders

If the word 'leukaemia' has come to have alarming connotations, then 'haemophilia' has acquired an aura of romantic intrigue, because of its occurrence in the royal houses of Europe in the nineteenth century, and because it had a bearing on the machinations of Rasputin, the influential monk at the Court of the Czar. The disease has been known for a long time, but only recently, in the early nineteenth century, it received its present name (a bad one, literally meaning 'blood-fondness': in this sense, leeches, fleas, vampires, lice and lady mosquitoes are the real 'haemophiliacs'). It is a hereditary defect in the blood-clotting mechanism, and is inherited in such a way that it can appear only in males.

Sex-linked disease

Genetically, as we have seen, the maleness of men is determined by their inheriting two different sex chromosomes, X and Y, while the femaleness of women is the result of a double dose of the X-chromosome. The egg-cells formed in a woman's ovaries each carry one X-chromosome. About half her eggs will have one of her Xs, and half will have the other. In the male, half the sperms carry an X, and half carry a Y. When a sperm unites with an egg, the sex of the baby which will grow from the fusion depends upon whether an X-sperm gives it a female combination (XX) or a Y-sperm gives it a male one (XY).

The inherited defect in haemophilia is 'sex-linked', being carried on one of the X-chromosomes. That is to say that although the disorder is in the blood-clotting mechanism, the actual genetic 'instruction' which determines it is located on one of the pair of chromosomes which also determines sex. The defect appears by chance—a gene mutating during the formation of an egg or an X-sperm—but once present it can be inherited for generations. In geneticist's language, it is a 'recessive' character. This means that if it is matched by a normal (non-mutated) gene on an accompanying X-chromosome, it will not produce its effects in the person who owns it, who in such a case will always be a female (XX). But a Y-chromosome is a different shape, and its units of inheritance do not match or counter those on

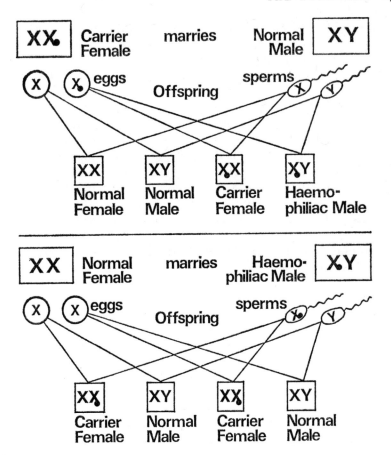

The inheritance of haemophilia

the X-chromosome at the gene-slot where the haemophilia mutation is situated. Therefore a male will have the disease if he inherits the one X-chromosome gene determining it. Because the disease is severe enough to prevent many male sufferers from reaching reproductive age (at least until recently), a female child is likely to inherit only one affected X-chromosome (from her mother), and so although she can carry the trait she will not have the disease, because the effects of the gene will be countered by her normal X-chromosome. But half the egg-cells which will form in her ovaries will bear the mutated gene, and so if she ever has a male child, there is a fifty-fifty chance that he will develop from one of the defective egg-cells. Then he will be a haemophiliac, as will (on average) half his brothers also. On average half his sisters will carry the trait, as his mother did, and half will not. If he lives to marry—which is a possibility—then all his daughters, and those of his affected brothers, will also carry it, because these girls must derive one of their Xs from their fathers, who have only an affected one to give them. On the other hand his sons, who derive their Y from him and their X from his wife (who we shall presume is normal), will be entirely free of it.

The boy bleeders

In haemophilia the blood clots very slowly, taking perhaps fifteen or thirty minutes instead of the usual three to six. Therefore automatic staunching of haemorrhage is defective, and a haemophiliac can bleed to death from a small cut. This is responsible for the folk belief that a 'bleeder' lacks two of the 'seven skins' supposed to cover a normal individual, or alternatively that 'his skin is too small for him.'

Haemophiliacs lack one of the plasma substances which are involved in the very first — prothrombinase — stages of the formation of a blood-clot. These stages can be short-circuited by other substances, which can be released from injured tissue cells. An abrasive or lacerating type of injury will release these tissue substances, and in this case a haemophiliac may not suffer abnormal bleeding. On the other hand, a cut from a sharp blade severs blood vessels while causing a minimum of damage to tissue cells, and such a wound may prove dangerous, though bleeding can be prevented where firm pressure or bandaging can be applied, because this pinches the blood-vessel walls together. The greatest constant hazard a haemophiliac has to reckon with is internal bleeding, which often results from quite minor knocks and blows. A frequent disabling event is haemorrhage into a joint. This occurs because the lining membrane of a joint has a folded fringe-like structure, rich in small blood vessels that can get nipped and broken between the bone surfaces in some unexpected fall or strain. This means that blood will flood into the joint cavity, ballooning it and causing inflammation and perhaps permanent damage. Therefore haemophiliacs frequently have stiff joints. Unfortunate though this is, there are other internal parts of the body where the swelling caused by a local haemorrhage can bring about death. This may happen anywhere inside the skull, or in the soft tissues of the neck where the air passages can be compressed by it, causing smothering.

Haemophilia was known to the ancient civilizations, and must have excited much notice in races which practised the rite of male circumcision: Jewish tradition, for example, waived the operation in families known to be 'bleeders'. If a trivial injury causes a young boy's joints to swell, or produces an unexpectedly severe spreading bruise, then haemophilia may be present. If it is, such procedures as tooth extractions and surgical operations become dangerous, and life has to be one of studied care. The disease may be inherited with different degrees of severity, and in some cases the haemorrhagic tendency waxes and wanes from time to time. This has given many a charlatan cause to claim success for some 'treatment', and it was because of a situation of this kind that the Czarina believed in the monk Rasputin's power to influence her son's disease.

A transfusion of fresh normal blood can temporarily restore the clotting defect in a haemophiliac by replacing the missing plasma substance, and it is also possible to make a concentrated extract from normal plasma that is more effective still. But the benefit lasts only for a short time, and eventually there may be a falling off in the effects of the treatment if it is repeated too often. This means that such treatments must be kept for times of special risk and cannot be constantly used.

The life of a haemophiliac is bound to be difficult, but less so than in the past. A real 'cure' of an hereditary disease like this, where the disorder is inborn in the body structure, is unlikely, unless manipulation of gene material in the individual becomes possible; but increasing knowledge of the chemical mechanisms of blood coagulation may lead in the end to precise chemical identification of the substance lacking in haemophilia, and then to the artificial manufacture of an active substitute which will have a prolonged and reproducible effect.

This raises an important contemporary problem. Those who suffer from certain directly inherited diseases (such as haemophilia or the hereditary haemolytic anaemias, and numerous other conditions not primarily involving the blood) may now live in the shelter of modern medicine sufficiently long and effectively to marry and have children. In times past they were usually not vigorous enough to survive or to raise a family, unless they were sustained in a rich or aristocratic household. But today, with palliative treatment, such diseases are in some cases being passed on by their bearers to an increasing proportion of children in each generation. There may also be inherited physical dispositions towards other sicknesses which respond to elaborate treatment but whose genetic component we are not yet directly aware of. From the medical point of view there is no doubt that at present we should 'treat' all disease in individuals so far as we can, for this relieves much suffering and is the only way practicable in a humanitarian culture in our present incomplete state of knowledge. There is also the probability that a few genes which are disadvantageous or disease-producing in one environment may be of positive advantage in another. But it is becoming increasingly clear to those communities with very high standards of medical knowledge and development that in the long run certain medical policies may be an economic or social disadvantage. This is a problem best assessed by each community in the context of its local situation; wide generalizations cannot and should not be made. From a slightly different point of view it is also obvious that, because many of our medical techniques involve highly developed, expensive scientific team-work, a population which might normally carry a high proportion of hereditary physical dependants would become very vulnerable in times of national stress if elaborate medical teams became disorganized. However, these problems may not present themselves widely for some generations yet, and meantime more information will have been gained.

A haemophiliac who is enabled to marry is in a special genetic and moral situation. His children will all be outwardly normal and his sons will have no defect at all. But all his daughters will be carriers. Therefore some of his grandsons born to his daughters are likely to have the disease, though these will be a minority of all his grandchildren. Would you say that he should abstain from having children because of this possibility? Perhaps he would feel unwilling to create an individual, no matter how indirectly, who would have to go through the same trials as himself. Artificial insemination of his wife by semen from a non-haemophiliac donor is one possible solution. Another which is still in the future, but maybe not too far off, is a technique for choosing the sex of one's children. But apart from these possibilities, what is essential at present is to make sure that all haemophiliacs, and their wives and daughters, fully understand the chances of the disease reappearing in their descendants. Women whose fathers are not haemophiliacs, and who have had two or more affected sons, must assume that they are carriers in whom the haemophilia mutation is expressing itself for the first time in that line.

Christmas disease

Some few years ago classical haemophilia was shown to have two forms, inherited in the same way, but distinguished by different blood-clotting factors in their plasmas. The British doctors who first observed this decided that one form should continue to be called 'haemophilia', but they felt that to give the variant a scientific name before the real nature and chemistry of the missing clotting substances was known would be pretentious. They therefore called it after the person in whom they had first observed the new disorder. His surname was unusual and easy to remember, and 'Christmas disease' was added to the haematologists' list.

Because haemophilia is a chronic disease with definite and dramatic symptoms, we are perhaps more 'aware' of its presence in the community than we are of other rare inherited conditions. There is not in fact much of it around, but, as biologists, we should ask why it has not died out long ago. It seems that just about as often as a haemophiliac line disappears, another appears somewhere else as a result of a fresh, rare, but regularly recurring mutation.

The royal haemophiliacs

Such a mutation probably affected Queen Victoria. Her husband, Prince Albert, and her father, the Duke of Kent, were not haemophiliacs, nor were her ancestors on the maternal side. She was an only child and therefore had no brothers or sisters in whom either frank haemophilia or the carrier trait might have been observed if her mother had grown from a cell with a mutated X-chromosome. The mutation must have occurred either in one of her mother's, or her maternal grandmother's egg-cells; or in one of her father's, or her maternal grandfather's X-sperms. Several of the children of Queen Victoria inherited the haemophiliac gene from her. She had four sons, one of whom, Leopold, was a haemophiliac who married. At least two of her daughters, Alice and Beatrice, turned out to be carriers. Alice passed the gene to a son who died young, and to two daughters, Alix and Irene. Irene had three sons, two of whom were haemophiliacs but had no children. Alix married a Romanov and became Czarina of Russia, and her son, Alexis the Czarevitch, was a haemophiliac. All members of this Russian family were reported to have been executed in 1918, but from time to time we hear a rumour that they survived in hiding. For instance, there is a woman claiming to be the Grand Duchess Anastasia, one of the Czarina's daughters, and if she could show she is a carrier of haemophilia it would somewhat strengthen her case. There is even a candidate for the Czarevitch; he, of course, should have frank haemophilia.

Victoria's daughter Beatrice married Prince Henry of Battenberg, a cousin of her sister Alice's husband. Beatrice's daughter, Victoria Eugénie, became Queen of Spain, and two of her sons were haemophiliacs and died without having children. The Battenberg (now Mountbatten) line that continues in England is free of haemophilia because it is descended from one of Alice's unaffected daughters who married another Battenberg, and had a daughter who became Queen of Greece and the mother of Philip, the husband of the present Queen of England.

There are still some great-great-granddaughters of Queen Victoria, descended from her haemophiliac son Leopold, who had a son and a daughter, or from the Queen of Spain. They may be carrying the gene, but it has died out in the rest of the family.

Cousin marriages

It is widely believed that cousin marriages are likely to result in offspring with hereditary diseases. This is true in some circumstances, but although European royalty has been closely intermarried, this is not the reason for the preponderance of haemophilia, because a sex-linked disease of this kind appears whenever males inherit the gene, whether their parents are cousins or not. There are nevertheless many other genes which can be inherited on any of the non-sex human chromosomes. All the non-sex chromosomes are present in matching pairs, unlike the non-matching pair of X and Y chromosomes which determine male sex. Recessive genes on non-sex chromosomes will not express their effects in the body unless both members of the chromosome pair have the gene.

Many recessive genes which determine abnormal features amounting to 'disease' are rare, and it is statistically unlikely that two people bearing the same recessive gene will meet and marry. But if they do, then one in four of their children will be born with a double dose of the recessive gene and are likely to have whatever 'defects' are characteristic of the gene action. And in cousin marriages there is already an increased chance that both partners will be carrying the same recessive genes inherited from a common grandparent, and so in that case they are more likely than random partners to have children suffering from hereditary defects. Whatever form the 'defects' take (and of course these vary with the genes involved), their most general biological effect, in spite of medical palliation, would seem at first sight to be a reduction in the children's fertility: that is, fewer survive to maturity, and so on average fewer have children.

But there are inbred human lines, such as those of minority religious groups, or of island or isolated valley peoples, or of royal houses, where cousin marriages are frequent, and these are not always seen to suffer excessively from inherited defects. It seems that in such established inbred societies these defects are revealed quickly in the generations following immediately after their origin by mutation, and are then quickly eliminated from the stock by the lower viability and lower fertility of the individuals bearing them. In fact it is in the outbred communities, where cousin marriages are the exception, that rare genes inherited from a common grandparent continue to come together occasionally in double dose in the offspring of such marriages.

Evidently human stock, like animal stock, adapts itself after a few generations to consistent inbreeding or consistent outbreeding. Really close or incestuous inbreeding has usually been prohibited in human society, but it is not, genetically speaking, an absolutely bad policy. It can establish and maintain seemingly desirable inherited features. Its disadvantage is that it tends to restrict the gene pool, leaving fewer potential variations, which might be of great use to us humans if some remarkable change occurred in our environment necessitating an adaptive evolutionary response in subsequent generations.

Devil's pinches

There are other bleeding diseases, some transient, some prolonged in their effects. One due to lack of blood platelets, usually temporary, is *thrombocytopenic purpura*. Another, caused by lack of prothrombin, is the result of malnutrition or of liver disease. Many others are caused by changes in the small blood vessels. The prime indication of a bleeding disease is easy bruising, but some normal people are quite easily bruised, even though their blood-clotting mechanisms are active so that they do not bleed unnaturally after injury. Easy bruising is commoner in women than men, because their skins are more delicate. Inexplicable bruises on the bodies of young women were taken, in medieval times, to be evidence of an incubus having visited them while they slept, and you will still hear such marks called 'devil's pinches'.

CHAPTER SIXTEEN

Blood of our Fathers

Considering blood and its diseases has involved us several times with the mode of inheritance of blood groups and similar factors. At this point we can take a break from examining disease, always a depressing theme, and consider the broad national patterns of inherited blood groups.

A million years back, and the first batch of Eves and Adams was walking the earth of Africa. They had dropped down out of the trees because there was a drought on and the trees of the forests had thinned out to savannah, and even the best Tarzans can't swing between trees that are fifty metres apart. They were a hairless, simian, long-limbed lot compared to the other mammals, and a very small company.

But they could stare and grab and be clever. Bigheads. They must have lived by energetic hunting. Eating a high-protein diet of meat gave them some relief from endless chewing of fruit and seeds. In their spare time they were able to think about the weather, because then it suddenly began to change from dry to wet to icy and back to dry desert again. They thought to some purpose; they thought of tools and weapons and fire and clothes, and passed the knowledge from one to another. They evolved neat little sets of teeth. And so they thought themselves into a state of independence of the weather, independence of the ice ages and the droughts which came and went and altered the face of the earth. So they travelled and wandered and migrated, choosing where they wanted to go and moving out of Africa, regardless now of the world's unexpected climates and menus; they interbred without biological restriction, and set up civilizations.

Over all the planet now, we humans vary little, outwardly, one from another. All cousins to a degree, nearly all capable of fertile intermarriage, we all derive from that handful of forebears that lived only a few seasons ago, geologically speaking.

Badges of race

Admittedly, skin and hair and eye colours differ among our 'races', and so do the shapes of noses and lips, the hairiness of cheeks, the foldedness of eyelids, the fuzziness of heads. But not much. Certainly there is not as much difference between us as there is between many

240

Ice crystals and frost

breeds of dog, which are, of course, 'artificially' selected by Man: but then, so is Man!

Whether any race of us humans is 'superior' to another in a Darwinian sense is unknown. The evidence is not available. All peoples have much the same range of mental and physical capacities. But in our behaviour we make a great fuss about some of the small external visible physical differences. Why?

A social or a territorial mammal has ways of recognizing an acquaintance in the herd, or in the home territory, by smell or sound or taste or touch or sight. Man, poor at smelling, hard of hearing, passing by in too much of a monkey-hurry for accurate tasting or touching, is good at looking. He looks at faces. As an infant he looks up at his mother, and he compares her face with others that float in and out of his baby view. He develops in his brain a brisk way of coding the trigonometrical dispositions of the eyes, noses, mouths and hair margins of the faces of friends and strangers, until finally at a glance he can recognize an acquaintance half a lifetime and half a million faces later.

Territoriality is a common kind of biological behaviour. It may refer to land with boundaries, or to the personal space around an individual which is respected by others and moves with him. In a man's own territory he lives with his trusted neighbours. But over the way, in the adjacent territories, there are ... his enemies. Those against whom the aggression of a hunting beast can pleasurably (and, on past evolutionary occasions when some steady ratio of numbers to areas was important for long-term survival, perhaps usefully) indulge the fantasy of non-love, of hate. And how recognize enemies or loved ones? Usually by their faces. A European beard, a Semitic nose, a Negro's lips, and of course by much lesser differences too. We may dislike an oriental cheekbone or slant eye, and fall in love with the chin or eyebrow of the girl next door. Locally there is the variable hairstyle, cut of coat, shape of hat, colours of shoulder flash, or national flag. Human-to-human recognitions, at the irrational levels at which territorial race-hate and group-love operate, are triggered by all these various visual symbols. Yet it seems to be the genetically determined external bodily features which are the most psychologically penetrating and most consistent in exciting reaction, perhaps because they change only over long periods. Culturally determined clothes or flags or the like are much more open to rapid modification and fashionable change, and so don't prick so deep. Where socio-cultural characteristics have a non-visual impact, as in speech or cooking or music, the same fierce lasting responses are seldom encountered.

Whenever geographical boundary, race boundary and cultural boundary coincide, all is well. But technology now transcends the old barriers of rivers, seas and mountains. And cultural boundaries are being widened by communication systems which cut across the ancient divisions. As a result, deeply held irrational race hatreds based on physical appearances are becoming politically undesirable because they threaten social stability.

Biochemical constitutions

Underlying the inherited external anatomical badges of race are specific internal molecular biochemical constitutions, controlled by the codes in the genes. Some day soon we will be biochemists enough to understand fully the chemical differences between individuals and races. In the meantime we can already, if we wish, regard these from a molecular viewpoint, and this might have advantages. For example, hating English, Americans, Chinese or Irish is easy enough if we are accustomed to it. But who can say seriously, 'I hate people whose red blood cells have less glucose-6-phosphate-dehydrogenase than mine'? Yet 'I hate people whose skins are black' is a remark based only on a few biochemical differences of this kind.

So, the categorizations of scientific biology, if they became general in our culture, could do something to redress deep-seated, irrational race prejudices. Fundamental studies of the structure and behaviour of human living matter go deep, and the methods are internationally agreed; whereas historical studies of the power structure and fate of the few recent human societies that have a well-documented history are susceptible to prejudice. The arguments are strong for teaching human biology (particularly genetics and ecology) to very young children before telling them anything of our past racial history.

While the biochemistry of individuality is awaiting full molecular delineation, there are some spy-holes through which a kind of preview of biochemical knowledge-to-come can be obtained. For instance, you may know from experience that you excrete the red pigment of beet-root, or the aromatic flavour of asparagus, in your urine, but that there are other people who do not. Perhaps you have realized you are unusual in not being able to taste certain bitters in grapefruit or cabbage. Such capacities are inherited, and must have a precise biochemical basis. There are many others.

We have seen that inherited biochemical differences in red blood cells can give them abnormal shapes. Blood-clotting factors, hormones, enzymes and vitamins are all specifically-acting gene-specified agents which can be isolated in experiments and which must each have a specific molecular structure; but their existence as chemical entities usually is, or has been, scientifically apparent long before they are or can be purified and their individual biochemical properties fully analysed.

Antigen-antibody phenomena are of this kind too. They are relatively simple to observe experimentally, and they are capable of discriminating among what must be very slight molecular differences between antigens, which in most cases cannot yet be distinguished chemically, in the same way as simple keys discriminate clearly between locks whose internal structures are hidden. And the human blood groups are based on antigen-antibody interactions which can minutely categorize different human inherited molecular structures on the surfaces of red blood cells.

Blood relationships

The red cells in a drop of blood normally remain separate from one another so that the liquid seems uniformly red to the naked eye. On adding a serum antibody which has a specific affinity for those particular red cells, they stick together. This is because the antibody molecule has more than one specific combining point and it can link adjacent cells together. Aggregating in clumps, the cells become clearly visible red-pepper-like grains against the clear background of serum. Had the Almighty created human blood entirely for the convenience of human blood-groupers, He could hardly have made it more suitable (which is one possible answer to the question, Why blood groups?).

The surfaces of red cells represent a small sample of the various human inherited chemical body-structures. These all originally arose in our stock by mutation and now differ in thousands of permutations from one human to another, except in the case of identical twins. If all body cells could be obtained as easily as blood and could be separated into stable fluid-borne suspensions like red blood cells, then it is likely that the convenience of the technique of antigen-antibody grouping would already have provided us not only with blood groups, but with liver groups, kidney groups, skin groups, muscle groups, and so on. There are even many non-cell items dissolved in blood plasma which are detectable by immunological or electrical methods and which, like the haemoglobins, can be regarded as 'honorary blood groups'. The current interest in transplanting human organs is leading to a great extension of knowledge of tissue and organ groups of all kinds, but such knowledge will be harder to come by than knowledge about blood groups, because of the difficulties of obtaining and handling tissue-cell samples.

Each blood-group 'system' is a collection of separate characters, molecular in size, and inherited through separate genes at one chromosome gene-slot. Some are present also in body tissues other than blood, but a few are, as far as is known, confined to the red cells. Blood-grouping tests generally indicate in plain yes-or-no fashion that a certain inherited molecule is either there on the cell or not. Its presence or absence can be related directly to the presence or absence of the particular inherited gene that determines it. The molecule or antigen cannot be the gene itself, because red cells have no nuclei, and also because it is known that the chemical structures of blood-group substances are not the same as those of the gene material on the chromosomes.

Blood-group characters are ideal human gene indicators; simple tests can establish them unequivocally. In sizing up the inheritance of an individual, say in the context of deciding whether two people are closely related (as in paternity testing) the blood groups are much cleaner and more satisfactory markers than the grosser measurements of body build, or of skull shape, of hairiness, pigmentation, or the rest, which though all inherited and controlled by genes are neither un-equivocally measurable nor single-gene-dependent characters. In fact blood groups make some sense of the popular old belief in 'blood relationships'. The hidalgos of Castile may not have had blue blood, but taken all together their community may well have had blood-group proportions locally characteristic of their noble caste, par-ticularly if, as is said, they kept their stock free from marriage with peasants, Moors and Jews, and had a distinctive racial origin.

Where the idea of 'blood relationships' misleads is in its suggestion of a blending of fluids rather than one of mixing of fine but discrete genetic particles. Parents' bloods were once thought to blend in their offspring. But breeding situations and experiments show clearly that after back crosses, an inherited character which may otherwise seem to have been lost in a series of blendings can reappear in original form in later generations. This can be explained only by the Mendelian inheritance of particulate units (genes), which obey simple statistical laws, an idea for which the scientific world was unready when Mendel first put it forward in the mid-nineteenth century, but which was universally accepted later.

It is not often that a human race or tribe is utterly separate from others in the same neighbourhood. Sooner or later intermarriage occurs at the overlapping edges of the geographical and social boundaries. Therefore there are no human equivalents of our highly selected and discrete 'breeds' of domestic birds, dogs, horses or plants, but there are, over sufficient distances, obvious race distinctions. An Englishman doesn't look like an African. But some English look like Dutch; some Dutch look like Belgians; some Belgians look like French; some French look like Spaniards; some Spaniards look like Arabs; and some Arabs look like Africans. Blood groups vary in the same way, often endorsing the traditional distinctions or connections between separated or contiguous races, and commonly seeming to reveal traces of older relationships set up by the migrations and movements of antiquity.

One can, then, speak in a more or less meaningful way of Gaelic, Norman, oriental, negro or 'noble' blood, although of large communities rather than of individuals since the statement is one of statistical probability. The blurring at the edges caused by human mixture, either contemporaneously or in the recent or distant past, makes it unlikely that any caste or race or community will have any individual blood groups uniquely characteristic of itself. The differences distinguished at present are in terms of the frequencies and combinations in various populations of the approximately eighty different antigens known to occur commonly on fifteen or so genetically independent systems of red-cell blood groups. Some antigens are more frequent or rarer in some nations than in others. Given a large random sample of people in a community, such as the donors belonging to a blood transfusion service, one can express numerically the frequency of the local occurrences of all the groups.

For instance, the character O on the ABO system reaches an average inherited frequency of 68 per cent in the United Kingdom, where on the same system and in the same areas B is 6 per cent and A is 26 per cent. Such measurements can be made for all the other genetically independent groups. A combination of some commonly occurring antigens in British individuals is written as O, Ms/Ns, P_1, CDe/cde, Lu(a−b+), K−k+, Le(a−b+), Fy(a+b+), Jk(a+b+), Yt(a+b−), Au(a+), Do(a+), Xg(a+).

Before we consider the world patterns of a few of the blood groups most widely tested for, we should ask another question: How persistent or unchanging are the groups?

First of all, the technique of blood-grouping has been established long enough for us to know that the blood group of an individual does not change throughout his life. Secondly, the overall frequencies may not change much in large communities over periods of some hundreds of years. This is indicated by a general uniformity of blood-group distributions in human stocks known to have had a common historical origin but who have been separated and more or less isolated for a few hundred years. Jews, gypsies, Negro slaves and overseas colonies provide many examples of this. It might of course also be interpreted as indicating that changes going on in a people are occurring at the same rate and direction whether they stay at home or travel the earth. Yet if this were so, it would still leave us with handy race markers.

But why might blood groups change? This, you will notice, is an aspect of the earlier question—Why blood groups?—to which a frivolous answer was given a few pages back. The question would have been more penetrating had it been asked in the form, Why so many different human blood groups?

If blood groups are only particular examples of the general fact that many chemical characters, which happen to be antigenic, on the surfaces of all cells are under genetic influence and differ between individuals, then such characters must be the subjects of intensive natural selection. For example, if they are molecules such as enzymes, actively engaged in chemical synthesis, a particular 'group' could confer on the individual who owned it a capacity for some chemical activity that rendered him more effective in the environment in which he lived. Suppose such a molecule had to do with the effective processing of sugar in the cell wall, and suppose only a few members of a primitive meat-hunting tribe possessed it, and suppose that that tribe wandered into a strange new valley in which almost the only food was sugar syrup which dripped lavishly from tree-trunks: it is then conceivable that in the following generations a selection would take place in favour of those of the tribal descendants who inherited the appropriate sugar-processing gene and that their kind would multiply. Those who did not have the lucky gene would even seem to be 'diseased' in the sugary environment, suffering from a sort of 'diabetes'.

Molecules that confer blood-group properties on cells might also be concerned with, say, cell-wall resistance towards entry by particular viruses; or cell-wall capacity to absorb or transport oxygen, water, trace elements or suchlike, inwards or outwards; or cell-wall capacity to receive chemical 'signals' from other organs in the body. Therefore many genes which determine particular blood groups are quite likely to be under selection pressures which could lead to either their survival or their extinction in populations. One might even expect that numerous 'unsuitable' groups would long since have disappeared in the apparently uniform modern human environment, leaving only a few to be represented in the great majority of humans. But observation shows that so many different blood-group genes survive in the human species that our world environment, so far as blood groups are concerned, cannot be biologically uniform, it being a greater advantage to be of one blood group here, another there.

ABO groups and disease

On the ABO system, there is scarcely a large population on earth which does not have some O, some A and some B. As we have seen, blood-group genes are not recessive and they are carried in pairs which determine two characters per person. In a situation where (as is possible) there is an interplay of factors in the surroundings so that there is some advantage in being O, and some advantage in being A and some in being B, the advantages can be additive, so that those people who inherit two different antigens (such as O and A, or A and B or B and O) may be at an evolutionary advantage over any who inherit a double dose of only one antigen (such as O and O, A and A or B and B). When this is so, specific mixtures of these blood groups appear; all groups tend to survive, because of the extra viability of the unlike combinations, but the proportions in the local human gene pool vary according to the strengths of the local advantages associated with each of the genes.

In many parts of the world the records of people who have entered hospital and been blood-grouped have been checked in order to see whether their diseases show any correlation with their blood groups. It turns out that there is, statistically speaking, a somewhat greater tendency for people who are group A to get stomach cancer and for those who are group O to get duodenal ulcers. These are diseases which would seem to be weak 'natural selectors' of humans, because they mainly affect people who are past the reproductive period. Therefore, it is curious that there is this clear correlation with the ABO genes.

Theoretically it would seem more likely that a 'naturally selecting' relationship would exist between the blood groups and human infectious diseases, most of which affect all age groups, and especially the young. Our capacity to make protective antibodies against 'foreign' microbial antigens depends upon our lacking these antigens ourselves. Therefore if a microbe happened to have a chemical part which was the same structure as a 'blood-group' antigen in some of us (as is possible), it might be that those of us who belonged to that blood group would be more likely to become infected by that microbe; however, this need not necessarily be so, since there would probably also be other antigens by which our cells could recognize it and set up resistance. Up to the present time there have been many attempts to find a relationship between the possession of particular A or B or O antigen and susceptibility to epidemic diseases such as plague or smallpox, which in the past must have had huge selective effects on the human populations of the large continents. But no conclusive evidence has been obtained of any such correlations.

However, there may well be some significant physical advantage associated with each of the various human blood-group antigens, such as marginally higher fertility or longevity or capacity for endurance, which would be much more difficult to estimate in individuals than the incidence of the grosser and well-recognized clinical diseases.

Natural selection in progress

Interaction between the Rhesus blood groups produces haemolytic disease of the newborn, as we have seen. Each affected baby is Rh-positive, being the offspring of an Rh-negative mother and an Rh-positive father. Although Rh-positive, it will however be half Rh-positive and half Rh-negative (as a group A person can be half A and half O), and each time such a baby dies because of the disease, one Rh-positive and one Rh-negative gene will be lost to the community to which it belonged. Over a long time, this will have the greatest proportionate effect on the rarer of the two genes, which today is the Rh-negative one. Consequently we can guess that there has been slow and steady replacement of Rh-negative peoples by Rh-positives who have interbred with them.

There is also some interplay between the ABO groups and Rhesus haemolytic disease. If the mother's serum contains 'natural' anti-A or anti-B, and if the foetus is A or B or AB, an incompatible combination where mother's serum reacts with foetal cells on the ABO system tends to protect against Rhesus immunization of the mother. Consequently a population with a proportion of Rh-negatives (and consequently haemolytic disease of the newborn) has been selected differentially in favour of group O people (who have both anti-A and anti-B). Today, medical treatment is of course modifying these trends by preventing infant deaths from haemolytic disease of the newborn.

Even if there were not these current indications of natural selection in progress among the blood groups, we should be led by evolutionary theory to postulate that these inherited characters in the human race must be reacting either positively or negatively to evolutionary pressures. Genes are either on the way in or the way out. Some, like those which determine the blood groups, are in various local balances because diversity gives some biological advantage, but the balances are not stable. An animal like Man, who left the uniformity of his tropical rain forest to spread so explosively in the last million years into just about all the land surface available on earth, might be expected to exhibit a broad polymorphic diversity of inherited characters — such as is shown by his blood groups — as evidence of his recent arrival, his patent adaptability to varying surroundings, his enthusiastic outbreeding, and his psychological capacity for moving off before he can be 'selected' locally into a single uniform type.

Nevertheless, before any association between disease (i.e., biological disadvantage) and certain blood groups was known, there were many blood-groupers who considered that the world patterns must have been established by chance. They visualized a very few original humans suddenly becoming the ancestors of vast populations which magnified whatever local distributions of blood groups existed in those monkey families that first grew themselves big brains. But now that the whole matter has been considered for some time, it seems likely that natural selection rather than drift is the major influence.

But then how fast are the patterns changing? A million years of geologically 'recent' human wanderings and population expansions is one thing; the last two or three thousand years of partly recorded history is another. It is generally agreed that over the latter period the various selection pressures that we have noted may not have had a very marked effect on some, at least, of the various blood groups in the main human populations. And so a people with a particular blood-group pattern today may have had something reasonably like it during their early written history if there has not been too much mixing with other peoples in the meantime. And even where there has been mixing, quite good estimates about the probable ingredients of mixtures can sometimes be made on a blood-group basis. It is, of course, unlikely that selection operates at the same rate on all blood-group systems, and so blood groups subject to rapid selection will corroborate one another as race markers only among peoples who have very recently diverged from a common stock. Those groups which are selected very slowly will indicate the more ancient racial relationships. Allowing for these limitations, blood groups are useful data for the anthropological study of human migrations and mixtures in the hazy few thousand years that merge into modern times.

The ABO blood groups have been tested far more widely than any other throughout the world, and so from this anthropological point of view it is perhaps unfortunate that they may be among those most subject to selection pressures. Everywhere O is fairly common, usually with lesser proportions of A and B. All three antigens, A, B and O, are found in the bloods of the higher apes, and so none is an original, humanly speaking, from which the others could have diverged by mutation. It is likely that we have had all three since we dropped out of those trees. Indeed, the A and B substances are widespread in other animals, even in plants and bacteria. In chemical terms, they are polysaccharides (complex sugars), as are a number of bacterial antigens, although most of the classical antigens of immunology are proteins.

It is, as we have seen, something of an enigma that in human blood (and in that of the higher apes) the possession of these A, B and O substances in the red cells is invariably associated with the development in infancy of 'natural' antibodies in the serum which act against whichever A or B antigen the owner lacks. These antibodies, it seems, must arise as a result of active immunization of some kind, but of course this cannot be immunization with the red cells of another individual because spontaneous transfusion does not occur. Evidently the antigens must enter the body in the form of ubiquitous bacteria or food.

More curious still is the fact that the seeds of many species of the pea and bean family contain soluble proteins which have actions similar to those of anti-A, anti-B or anti-O antibodies, while some agglutinate human or animal red cells without reference to blood groups. These agglutinating proteins are very like 'antibodies', although plants have no antibody-forming mechanisms equivalent to those of the vertebrates. Perhaps the possession of soluble antibody-like agents capable of combining specifically with certain complex sugars may be a widespread necessity for living things, even for species as widely separated as the orang-utans and the leguminous plants. It could be related to a biological need to trap and hold sugars for specific defensive or nutritional purposes, the nature of which we cannot yet specify in chemical terms.

World patterns

O is the commonest gene in nearly all human populations, A is the next most frequent, and B is the least common. Only in eastern Asia does the proportion of B exceed that of A. In Europe, B is relatively rare, with much A in the central part and O increasing towards the west, especially in isolated parts of the peripheral seaboard. In aboriginal Americans one finds, amongst the Eskimos, A, B and O; amongst the North American Indians A and O; and in South America only O. In aboriginal Australians there is no B, only O and A.

Africa is an interesting country in terms of blood groups. Perhaps her special characteristics developed out of the ease with which primitive hunters and farmers could move around south of the Sahara, while at the same time they were isolated by sea and desert from the rest of the world. In Africa, O exceeds A, which exceeds B; the

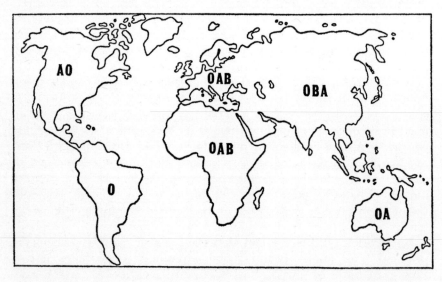

Map showing relative frequencies of genes A, B and O among the Aboriginal peoples of the world's continents, the most frequent gene being given first, the least last, and absent genes not at all.

GENE FREQUENCIES IN THE POPULATIONS
OF COUNTRIES IN EUROPE AND ASIA*
(*ranging roughly from west to east*)

Europe	O	A	B
Iceland	75	19	6
Scotland	70	23	8
Ireland	74	18	8
England	68	26	6
France	64	28	8
Spain	64	30	6
Portugal	60	34	6
Holland	67	27	6
Belgium	69	25	6
Denmark	64	28	8
Norway	62	31	7
Sweden	62	31	7
Germany	63	28	9
Finland	57	29	14
Poland	57	27	16
Hungary	56	29	15
Czechoslovakia	56	31	13
Italy	67	25	8
Switzerland	65	28	7
Asia			
Iran	52	25	23
Turkey	61	28	11
U.S.S.R.	59	25	16
India	59	18	23
China	60	20	20
Thailand	62	14	24
Indonesia	63	16	21

* The list of countries is arbitrarily chosen, to show the range of variation. It is based on information given by N. McArthur and L. S. Penrose in *Annals of Eugenics*, vol. xv (London, 1951), p. 302.

ABO gene frequencies are not the same as ABO blood-group frequencies. The reader will remember that many of those who belong to group A or group B carry an O gene as well as an A or B gene. Gene frequency calculations make allowance for this.

proportion of group B is slightly higher than in Europe, though not as high as in Asia, but in some of the other blood-group systems (such as Rhesus, MNSs, Kell and Duffy) the Africans show unique gene frequencies. To a lesser extent Australian aborigines also exhibit some unique patterns. As one would expect, isolation seems to produce sharper blood-group differences than those which are found between adjacent peoples that have had even slight contact.

Great Britain and Ireland form an area of special interest; they have been relatively, though not completely, isolated from Europe; they

Map showing the ABO blood-group tendencies in Europe. O is in fact the commonest gene everywhere, but the arrows show roughly the areas towards which there are relative increases in A, B or O gene frequencies

have a well-documented history going back to the time of the Roman Empire; they have been subjected to discrete invasions and immigrations; and are densely populated and very extensively blood-grouped, because of the existence of elaborate transfusion services. Group A is fairly common in the south of England, but gives way to increasing frequencies of O as one moves north and west into the highlands of Scotland and Wales. The pattern is continued in Ireland until in the west extremely high frequencies of O are found. Group B is uniformly low, and the Rhesus groups show little variation.

On the European continent, there are high concentrations of A between Scandinavia and the Alps. East of the River Elbe, group B becomes much more common.

Matching the peripheral densities of group O in the Celtic peoples of the British Isles there are similar high levels of group O in Iceland, in the Basque country, among the Berbers of North Africa, in Sardinia and in the Caucasus. The Basques are specially interesting, having by far the highest level in Europe of the Rh-negative gene, which otherwise is uniformly spread at lower frequencies. On linguistic, anthropometric and place-name evidence, the Basques belong to an ancient stock which was more widespread in prehistoric times.

Systems of blood groups other than ABO, such as MNSs and Rhesus, do not (except for Rhesus among the Basque people) show great differences within Europe. Their percentages vary between whole continents rather than between localities. One must therefore conclude that the ABO groups are subject to much more rapid local differential selection than the other groups. But still, one may legitimately consider the present ABO pattern of Europe and speculate upon how, and how recently, it was established. It could reflect recent historical migrations from one locality to another; or the prevalence in different localities of different diseases or advantages associated positively or negatively with particular ABO genes; or a mixture of these factors.

The present ABO patterns of England, Wales, Scotland and Ireland can be interpreted as reflecting two movements: the influx of continental Europeans bearing much group A, which took place in the Anglo-Saxon and Norman invasions of England; and the subsequent Anglo-Saxon adventures through South Wales into Ireland, which drove peoples with a high proportion of group O into the highlands and boglands of the west and north. But such 'archaeological' interpretations can never now be proved or disproved; they are matters of conjecture and likelihood. It is, for instance, also possible that wet or cold or stony country, or even isolation itself, selects, for unknown reasons, in favour of group O. One would also expect to see blood-group traces of the Vikings or Danes who were established in the British Isles in the eighth and ninth centuries, and there are none. (Of course, it is possible that their ABO blood-group frequencies were the same as those of the peoples whom they invaded.)

However, bearing such points in mind, it still looks as though the present general ABO patterns of Europe could be the result of a series of occupiers. The first, we may surmise, was a prehistoric high-O people; these were displaced by a very successful high-A people, origin unknown, who expanded from north Central Europe to push the Os into isolated areas of the west and south. At the same time, to the east a high-B people was moving from Russia through Poland into

Eastern Germany. Complicating this explanation is the fact that some of the peripheral high-O peoples show variations among the ten or more Rhesus antigens, and if they originate from a common prehistoric stock this seems to conflict with the opinion that Rh varies less sensitively than ABO, though the connexion with haemolytic disease of the newborn could make the Rh groups especially open to different selection pressures in cultures with differing marriage and family patterns.

When one looks around the rest of the world, the blood groups seem to offer some qualified support for such theories as that the Polynesian islanders originated either from American stock or from a northern stock common both to American Indians and Polynesians. There are other similar supposed relationships where blood groups help serious speculations. The peoples of China and the eastern Soviet Union have not yet been widely tested, and this is the last blank in the detailed blood-group maps of the world.

In our curiosity about the origins of our species and about long-lost mystery races and island peoples, we may well be inclined to press the blood groups too hard for such 'archaeological' information. The study of genetics, and the perhaps variable effects of disease in the past, warn us not to rely too heavily on blood groups as indicators of latter-day race patterns. At the same time, no one can deny their modest relation to the more recent history of the movements of peoples, and, of course, their absolute relevance to current inheritance problems such as disputed paternity. In the future, when stable populations whose diseases are recorded will have been blood-grouped at intervals of a hundred years or so, we may know more clearly how rapidly the patterns can change. The determination of the blood-group frequencies of past populations is not practicable. It is true that mummies can be grouped, but this can give only sparse data on a very small number of preserved people; tens of thousands are needed for significant statistical information.

CHAPTER SEVENTEEN

Heartache

In previous chapters we have considered a variety of blood diseases. Now we should look very briefly at diseases and disorders of the pump and pipes through which the blood must circulate if it is to perform its function.

Heart sounds

The normal heart sounds are caused by the slapping of the valves, the tensing of the muscular walls and the water-hammer effects in a thick fluid when it is squirted, forced around corners, accelerated and brought to sudden stops. You listen to all this through a stethoscope, which is the simplest of instruments: a couple of tubes connecting the listener's ears to an uncomplicated bell-shaped end-piece. The noise made at each valve in the heart is loudest at characteristic places on the front of the chest, so that these can be examined in turn by shifting the bell of the stethoscope from one to another.

Abnormal heart sounds are subtle and it takes practice to recognize them. Some have no serious significance. Some appear or disappear with exercise or deep breathing, or with a change in position. The doctor who deals with hearts has to have wide experience of them; acquiring it takes many years, and represents one of his major personal skills. The interpretation of the various abnormal loudnesses — murmurs, gallops, rumbles, clicks, knocks and rubs — has been laboriously determined over the last seventy-five years by co-operation between the heart specialists of many countries, listening through their stethoscopes, or recording the sounds electronically, or measuring cardiac function, or watching their patients' progress, or, when it becomes possible during an operation or an autopsy, by checking anatomical appearances.

When fluid is flowing smoothly through a tube, audible vibrations are set up if the tube is constricted, if a portion of it is dilated or if a taut string or membrane is inserted to shudder in the flow. Even when there are no distortions or insertions, noisy vibrations occur if the rate of flow is greatly increased or if it is partially reversed. Changes of these kinds cause most of the abnormal heart sounds. Narrowing, distortion, dilatation, valve thickening or rupture, displacement of the heart, lack of balance between the muscular work of the right and left sides; all can have noisy effects. Restriction of the openings guarded by the mitral or aortic valves (*mitral* or *aortic stenosis*), dilatation of the same openings (*mitral* or *aortic regurgitation*), or rupture of a valve so that a piece of membrane vibrates in the stream of blood: these cause characteristic murmurs. Abnormal openings in a heart, where the foetal circulation has not properly changed to the adult state, result in continuous so-called 'machinery-like' murmurs. The relationship of any murmur to the normal first and second sounds of the heart, and the point where it is most loudly heard, combined perhaps with other body signs, enable a physician to recognize it.

It is possible for a to-and-fro friction rub to occur if the bag, or pericardium, in which the heart lies becomes inflamed (*pericarditis*) so that its normally slippery surfaces are roughened. This often results in some fluid exuding into the bag (*pericardial effusion*), and this separates the surfaces so that the friction rub disappears again. But the fluid may restrict the action of the heart so that the normal heart sounds are reduced in intensity.

Galvani

The history of the science of electricity is full of eccentric people rubbing ebonite rods with cats' skins and collecting lightning in jars from kites flown in thunderclouds. In Bologna in the eighteenth century, Luigi Galvani was investigating frogs' legs.

He noticed wet, fresh frogs' legs hung by brass hooks from an iron railing. When a leg swayed and touched the iron, a circuit was completed and the leg jumped. Galvani jumped too—to a conclusion. He decided there was electricity in the legs.

He was right and wrong. Electricity was going through the legs, but it originated from the wet contact of the brass and iron acting like a little battery cell; it wasn't coming from the leg. But when Galvani continued experiments he found that as one leg jumped, it could 'galvanize' the nerve of a second leg by contact, making it jump too, so that the second nerve-muscle preparation was like a 'galvanometer' sensing the passage of electricity. This seemed to confirm the presence of a special animal electricity in the legs, and Galvani concluded that a contracting muscle generates electricity. And so it does, but not in a simple way.

The wave of excitation which passes along a nerve or through a muscle is essentially chemical, not electrical, though it can be started by a conventional electric shock. It moves fast, but not as fast as an electric current in a wire; it is more the equivalent of a speedily burning fuse. As this chemical change surges through nerves and muscles, it alters the balance of the electrically charged atoms and molecules in the constituent cells so that a wave of detectable temporary alteration in the electrical properties of the surfaces of the nerves or muscles accompanies the impulse or contraction. These electrical changes can quite readily be picked up by sensitive instruments, called galvanometers after the great Bolognese.

The wave of conduction and contraction which spreads through and over the heart has already been described. The electrical changes which accompany it can be detected by an electrocardiograph. This is a delicate galvanometer which makes a permanent record on a paper strip. Conducting wires placed directly on the surface of an exposed heart can pick up the changing electrical potentials while the heart is beating, but luckily it is possible to make a reasonably good record without opening the chest, by placing the electrodes on chosen points on the skin of the chest or other parts of the body. When all other muscles are at rest, the heart is the only part vigorously contracting, and so its electrical influences can then be detected by the leads of a sensitive instrument attached even to parts some distance off, such as the limbs, because the flesh and salty juices of the body are good conductors.

The electrocardiographic record looks like a regular series of squiggles. These indicate the timing of the heart-beat and the amount and nature (positive or negative) of the electrical charges produced by its contractions. These electrical tracings on paper strips are, in some ways, a more subtle and accurate guide to the state of the heart muscle than the skilled clinical methods of looking, feeling and listening, but all are used because they supplement one another. The importance of electrocardiography is that it shows, in terms of milli-seconds, any irregularity in the rhythm or duration of the heart-beat; any departure from the normal spread of the contraction as it moves from the pacemaker down over the auricles, down the bundle and up over the ventricles; or any increase or diminution in the muscularity of the walls of the different chambers.

Appreciating abnormalities in electrocardiographic patterns is a matter not only of experience, but also of applying mathematical analysis and knowledge of electrophysiology of the heart. Some of the signs are fairly simple. For example, a left ventricle which has been working hard in an athlete, or against high resistance (high blood pressure), will have become more muscular, in just the same way as activity against resistance thickens the muscle cells in a weight-lifter's arms. (Conversely, the heart of a bedridden person without vascular disease will become smaller than normal.) A thicker left ventricle causes more electrical changes when it contracts and this produces a bigger trace on the paper strip. Again, the atrioventricular bundle has two branches. If one of these is injured the contractile

17

impulse will be partly blocked and will arrive late in certain parts of the ventricular muscle, and this too will produce a characteristic change in the electrocardiographic tracing. Another example is in myocardial infarction where a portion of the muscle dies and so becomes electrically inert, leaving the electrocardiographic pattern unbalanced. The changes produced vary according to the part of the heart involved. Sometimes more than simple visual appraisal is needed for the interpretation of electrocardiographic results; they are suitable for analysis by electronic computers.

Blood pressure

'Blood pressure' in the medium-sized arteries is a product of the force and output of the heart-beat, the springiness of the arterial walls and the resistance to the flow of blood in the final vast net of narrow arterioles which are muscular and which can open and close in response to chemical and nervous influence.

There must be few whose blood pressure has not been measured at a medical examination. The doctor puts an inflatable band around the arm above the elbow. When he pumps air into the band, it tightens and compresses the brachial artery; when he lets air out, the band relaxes. As the artery is pinched the flow of blood in it becomes turbulent and noisy, so that it can be heard through a stethoscope placed over the artery where it passes in front of the elbow just below the band. (Pinch a flexible garden hose with water flowing through it and a similar noisiness will occur.) Now although the blood in the artery is flowing continuously, the pulse pressure in it rises and falls with each surge from the heart. First the doctor pumps up the arm band, tightening it until all arterial flow stops. Then he slowly relaxes the pressure in the band, listening to the noisy turbulence of blood as it flows through, first at the peak of each heart-beat, then broadening out through the pulse until the noise fades when the band is no longer tight enough to compress the artery even at the lowest point of its throb. The air pressure in the arm band at any time during the manoeuvre is shown on a dial or on a mercury manometer. So the 'pressures' a doctor may measure in this way are not blood pressures at all, and bear only a very indirect relation to the actual hydraulic pressures inside the brachial artery. But, though crude, the relationship is there: and the doctor writes down pairs of numbers, the first for the peak and the second for the trough of the pulse-beat.

The life assurance companies have accumulated much information about blood pressure, because it has now been measurable in this way for several generations. Generally speaking, people with high blood pressures can expect shorter than average lives. But if there was some aspect of another vital function, such as breathing, or food absorption, or kidney function, which could as readily be measured by any doctor and simply expressed in numbers, it is likely that the same importance would be accorded to it. Certainly everyone with high blood pressure need not look forward to an early death. It is only to be expected of organizations such as the assurance companies, who gamble on probabilities, and plan for the worst, that they should have a gloomier view of high blood pressure than would a family doctor who, knowing all the circumstances, often has a more cheerful outlook upon his patient's individual chances, and hopes for the best.

The simple fact is that your blood pressure is your own, related to your personal needs. Blood must be driven through the fine blood vessels or your body will cease to live. If there is obstruction to the flow, the left side of your heart will grow more muscular to compensate by increasing the force of the beats. This increases your blood pressure. Commonly it has no other consequences. Raised blood pressure can be looked on as a necessary and often harmless feature of certain physical constitutions, though in some cases it threatens rather than maintains life, and must be treated.

Obstruction giving rise to increased pressure is commonly caused by a degenerative thickening and narrowing of the arteries in the later years of adult life. Not much can be done about this, once it has happened. Obstruction may also occur in individuals who react with exceptional sensitivity to stimuli such as anxiety, cold or tiredness, which causes their small muscular arteries to contract so that more pressure is needed to push the blood through them. Constitution and heredity are important, since blood-pressure disorders tend to run in families.

There is a relationship between blood pressure and kidney disease. The secretion of urine is dependent upon an adequate blood pressure to maintain the filtration rate. If the kidney is not getting enough blood it releases a substance into the circulation which brings about a rise in blood pressure through a contraction of the arterioles in the rest of the body. A kidney which has in the past been damaged by infection or inflammation may have its blood supply reduced by scar tissue which slowly narrows and strangles the fine blood passages. This lowers filtration pressure, and then the compensatory rise in blood pressure is persistently stimulated by the release of the signalling substance.

But a sustained high blood pressure can itself cause degeneration and thickening of the walls of small kidney arteries, narrowing them and reducing their blood-flow, which will make the pressure rise further still, causing more arterial degeneration — a vicious circle.

Tendencies to high blood pressure are accentuated in pregnancy. There is also a rare tumour of the gland near the kidney, the adrenal

(Latin *ad renes*, by the kidneys), which manufactures adrenalin. The tumour may produce excesses of the substance, causing periods of high blood pressure which are cured by surgical removal of the tumour.

Heart 'failure'

Persistent high pressure may in the end affect the pump, though not necessarily; if the burden does become too great, the heart 'fails'. This is more often a progressive, slow, chronic process rather than a sudden, acute one. If during muscular exercise, when the circulation speeds up, blood cannot be cleared from the left ventricle because there is not enough reserve of heart power, it piles up in the lung, where the congestion causes poor oxygenation and consequent breathlessness. In the next stage, breathlessness occurs at rest, when the peak of the blood pressure falls, but the trough remains high. This is because the heart-beat has become weak but the peripheral resistance to the flow of blood is still great. Next, the right side of the heart begins to fail and blood accumulates in the liver and veins which become swollen and engorged. Back pressure raises the hydrostatic pressure in the capillaries so that fluid accumulates dropsically in the tissue spaces. This is accentuated by a tendency for the kidneys in heart failure to excrete only some of their excess salt which results in more water being retained in the tissues.

So heart failure is only 'failure' in a special relative sense. It does not indicate stoppage. In general it simply means that the muscle of the heart is not always sending the blood around the body at a suitable rate, because the flow is obstructed, or because the valves have become mechanically ineffective, or because the muscle itself has weakened or lost the rhythm of its contractions. As a result, not enough oxygen is supplied to the body, causing general inefficiency, just as in anaemia.

Heart 'failure' is treated by bed-rest and drugs. Some of the drugs encourage the kidney to get rid of excess water; some improve the quality and force of the heart-beat. The most valuable drug of the latter type is digitalis from the foxglove leaf, one of the half-dozen or so herbal medicines which orthodox 'scientific' practice has accepted from the folk tradition with approval and gratitude.

In non-medical usage the word 'drug' has come to mean something more potent and dangerous than 'medicine'. No such distinction is made by doctors themselves. 'Drug' has the same origin as 'drought' — most medicines were originally dried plant or animal substances — but today it seems to suggest to many people not so much a remedy as an opiate or draught which 'drags' the recipient into an altered mental or physical state.

Consideration of the blood pressure has diverted us from other medical methods of examining the heart and blood vessels. A dramatic one is cardiac catheterization. A long fine tube (a catheter) is passed up along an artery to the left side of the heart, or by a vein to the right side, and by measuring the pressures and the degree of oxygen saturation of the blood in the chambers of the heart, the doctor can obtain valuable information. For instance, if there is an abnormal opening between the left and right sides (as in congenital heart disease), the oxygen content of the blood in the right auricle or ventricle, before it passes through the lungs, will be greater than that in the great veins.

Catheterization can be combined with X-ray angiography, a technique whereby a dye opaque to X-rays is injected and then a rapid succession of X-ray photographs are taken to outline the shapes of the chambers and blood vessels as the mixture of blood and dye passes through them.

It would be convenient if somewhere in your body there was a small translucent inspection window through which a doctor could observe the state of living blood vessels. And indeed there is. Through an ophthalmoscope the arteries and arterioles of the back of your eye can be seen as they run on the surface of the retina. There it is possible to discern the kind of thickening that complicates persistent high blood pressure, and also the changes characteristic of kidney disease and of some other conditions.

Heartache

Any muscle deprived of blood by narrowing or blockage of its arteries will quickly run out of oxygen if it has to contract repeatedly. For example, if the blood supply to the leg is reduced, attempts to walk will lead to cramping pain in the calf or in the foot. Muscle tissue which has demands made upon it in excess of its oxygen supply invariably signifies its distress by pain signals. Were this not so, a competing athlete could drive himself to destruction.

The heart muscle during life cannot avoid constant rhythmic contraction. In the ordinary way it has plenty of reserve capacity, but if its own coronary arteries are narrowed by degenerative disease oxygen will become the heart's desire whenever a spell of harder-or-faster-than-usual contractions has to be nourished. In which case the heart responds like the leg muscles, by sending out pain signals.

However, these 'heartaches' are often felt apart from the heart itself, and are therefore sometimes misinterpreted, for although the heart has a few nerves, pain is seldom felt right in it, even when it is touched or cut. When the coronary blood supply is reduced a severe cramping or crushing pain may be experienced, but usually it is 'referred' to the breastbone, chest and arms. It is traditionally called *angina pectoris* (literally 'a choking of the chest'). Evidently the conscious levels of your brain do not ordinarily learn to localize and appreciate 'pain' in internal organs in the same way as they learn from babyhood about the surface parts of your body. Nerve messages may come in great strength to the brain from heart muscle running short of oxygen; but it cannot discriminate between such messages coming unfamiliarly from relatively few nerve-endings in the heart, and others which enter the nervous system along nearby channels at the same levels but from more superficial parts of the body which are richer in sensory nerve-endings and more commonly stimulated. Consequently the mind will 'refer' the unaccustomed intense sensation to 'the chest wall' or 'the arm', though a few people do localize it rather vaguely in 'the heart'. At the same time, perhaps partly because of this equivocal behaviour in the brain, the feeling is sometimes accompanied by a conviction that more than pain is present, an anguished overtone of things terribly wrong, the *angor animi* of impending dissolution.

In hearts with thickened, narrowed or hardened arteries, this heartache may be provoked by anything which increases the work of the heart muscle, either by accelerating the beat or by raising the pressure against which the heart works. Exertion, emotion and cold are common causes. There may be no actual pain but only a feeling of discomfort and pressure or heaviness in the chest. Damage to heart muscle can even occur without any painful symptoms and be revealed later by electrocardiography.

The emergency treatment for angina pectoris is to give drugs containing nitrite, which causes a general relaxation of small arteries and an increase in the blood-flow to the heart. Nitrites relieve heartache, but they cause headache, by dilating the branches of the carotid artery supplying the scalp and skull. In fact dilatation of these vessels, from various causes, is a common source of headaches, because when stretched, the nerve-endings in their walls send out pain signals. The headache of high blood pressure is of this kind, and so is that of migraine, which may occur on one side of the head only.

Migraine, or *megrim*, is a corruption of *hemicrania*, meaning '[pain in] half the skull'. It can be successfully treated with ergot, a drug which, given in the right doses, can make arteries contract. But excessive doses, or ergot poisoning, cause very severe and prolonged spasms of the small arteries — sufficient to prevent blood getting through to the extremities — and this in turn produces extreme pain because the muscles are deprived of oxygen. Ergot is produced by a fungus that grows on grain, and in the Middle Ages outbreaks of painful afflictions caused by eating grain spoiled in this way were known as 'St Anthony's fire'. (The same sobriquet was given to erysipelas, a painfully burning red infection of the skin, caused by the streptococcus.)

Heart disease

Diseases can be classified by causes (parasitic, degenerative, obstructive, traumatic, nutritional, endocrine, genetic, cancerous, etc.) or by the sites in which they occur in body systems, organs or parts of organs. When we considered disorders and diseases of the blood we related them mainly to cause and only partly to site, because the blood is a diffuse 'organ' and has few distinct sites. But in considering now some characteristic diseases of the heart and blood vessels, we can deal with them more definitely by relating them in turn to the anatomical parts which are affected.

These parts are the smooth outer covering of the heart (or pericardium); the muscular walls (or myocardium); the inner lining membrane (or endocardium) of the chambers, folds of which form the valves; the arteries; and finally the veins. In various ways, which should now be becoming apparent, disease in these parts can either weaken the pump or embarrass the blood-flow.

The pericardium may become diseased either because of infection or because of some general change in the connective tissue of the body. It is one of those membranous sacs which form during embryonic development to allow internal freedom of movement to organs such as the heart, or the lungs or the joints. These sacs are spaces in the middle layer of cells, and their linings are nothing very special – only condensed connective tissue. Consequently any general diseases of connective tissue will affect these linings so that they may become thickened or may exude fluid according to whether the predominant feature of the disease is a multiplication of cells and fibres, or an outpouring from capillaries. The symptoms of pericardial disease vary according to whether or not there is effusion of fluid. A pericardial effusion hampers the action of the heart in the same way as a fatal stabbing, because the presence of liquid in the pericardial cavity prevents the chambers from properly expanding in order to refill with venous blood.

The most significant present-day disease of the muscle of the heart in civilized communities is a 'heart attack' caused by blockage in the coronary arteries. The disease takes two forms. The mildest is *angina pectoris*, brought on by any stimulus to an increase in the heart's work, such as exertion. It is caused by a narrowing of the coronary vessels and it is relieved by rest, or by drugs that dilate the small arteries.

The severe and sudden form of the disease is *myocardial infarction,** also called *coronary thrombosis* (a 'thrombus' is a clot), or just 'a coronary'. It results from a sudden block in a branch of the coronary

---

* The word 'infarction' is unusual and comes from the Latin *farcire*, to fill up. The same word is seen on menus in the French form *farci*, meaning 'stuffed'. In the old days it meant 'a consolidation of the humours'; now it has come to indicate the lesion resulting from a plugging, stuffing or blocking of a blood vessel.

artery supplying a patch of heart muscle, and causes great weakening
of the heart which leads to a drop in blood pressure or 'shock'. Tissue
dies after losing its blood supply, and heart muscle is no exception.

Myocardial infarction is commoner in men than in women, commoner in affluent societies, and commoner in the fifth and sixth decades
of life. Between a quarter and a third of those who get it die instantly
or within a short time; the rest recover with some limitations of heart
function. The first two weeks after an 'attack' are the dangerous ones,
and most complications occur within four weeks. The treatment at
first is absolute rest, and perhaps the use of drugs which prevent clot
formation in the heart. If the contractile impulse loses its normal
rhythm or power, there are electronic monitoring devices which can
detect this and restore the natural beat. Unlike angina pectoris,
nitrites do not help this condition. Later it is essential for the patient
to become really 'fit' again by graded exercise, because a 'fit' lithe
muscular body greatly reduces the load on the heart. Active muscles
with a good open blood supply do much to massage the blood around
the circulation.

The course of the disease depends upon the size and position of the
infarct. If it is large, involving the whole thickness of the muscle of a
chamber, the affected tissue will soften and after a few days the heart
may rupture, filling the pericardial cavity with blood and causing
death in the manner of a stab wound. This is the only authentic
'broken heart', and occurs in about a tenth of the fatal 'coronaries'.
What one must hope for, however, is that the dead area of muscle is
not so extensive that it cannot become threaded through and through
by the fibre-forming cells which will knit the part into a firm scar —
a process taking some weeks. Scar-forming cells are less complicated
than specialized cells like muscle fibres, and will survive in low-oxygen
conditions where others cannot. Such a 'heart scar' may permanently
interfere with the spread of the rhythmic contractile impulse, but also,
with luck, it may suffice for a long quiet life. A disadvantage of scar
tissue is that although initially it knits and heals and draws together,
it is not elastic under pressure, and it may slowly stretch until some
time later the affected part of the wall of the heart becomes thin and
somewhat ballooned.

Another occasional and unfortunate complication of myocardial
infarction is the accumulation of clotted blood in a lump against the
damaged inner lining of the heart in the infarcted area. Blood platelets
inevitably adhere to such an altered surface and initiate a clotting
process. The clot may later detach itself or break up, and then the
pieces will travel as emboli in the arterial branches and block the blood
supplies of another organ, such as a limb or the brain, which can be
crippling or fatal.

The risk of getting a 'coronary' is increased if you are overweight, if there is much fat in your blood, if you eat much sugar, if you take little or no exercise, if you are a heavy cigarette smoker and if your blood pressure is high. All of these predispositions can be adjusted, personally or medically. Others, which cannot, are maleness and belonging to a family with an inherited tendency to get coronaries.

Rheumatics

Inflammation of the heart muscle (*myocarditis*) sometimes occurs in association with bacterial disease elsewhere in the body. Poisonous substances released by the germs are carried to the heart and affect the muscle, weakening its conducting and contractile properties. This disorder usually recovers when the infection is over and the germs have gone, as in diphtheria where it is a well-known complication. But there is a special kind of myocarditis which complicates a streptococcal sore throat in some unlucky people and which can cause permanent damage. This is rheumatic carditis.

'Rheum' or 'rheumatism' has always been a vague term, originally meaning a flux of the humours of the body. Then it came to signify fleeting joint pains and snuffling winter colds in the head. Its use for diseases of joints led to such designations as 'rheumatoid arthritis'. Certain young people, after a streptococcal sore throat, get serious myocarditis, persistent fever, and joint pains. This disease is named 'acute rheumatic myocarditis', and is one of the three major causes of heart disease, the others being high blood pressure and coronary infarction. A famous pathologist (William Boyd of Canada) whose textbook was used by generations of medical students once wrote graphically that this form of rheumatism 'licks the joints but bites the heart'. The poison from the streptococcus in the throat seems to set up a reaction in the connective tissue of the body affecting the joints and other parts, including the heart. Sometimes it can even interfere with the brain, causing the involuntary elaborate slow movements known as St Vitus' Dance, or *chorea* (Greek, 'dance'). The streptococcal germs themselves do not reach the heart, but a diffuse patchy inflammation appears in it. The disease lasts for weeks, perhaps months, long enough for these multiple small inflamed areas to become scarred by fibrous tissue. This can happen in any part of the heart, in the pericardium and valves as well as in the muscle. The small scars may do little harm, but being widely scattered and numerous there is always the chance that they will later contract and cause interruption of the atrioventricular bundle, or distortion or narrowing of one of the natural valvular passages such as that between the left auricle and ventricle (*mitral stenosis*), or between the ventricle and the aorta (*aortic stenosis*). Surgeons can reopen these narrowings, and scarred and damaged valves can be removed in suitable cases and replaced by grafts or by artificial ball valves while the patient is temporarily connected to a heart-lung machine. The artificial machinery clicks noisily in the chest, but it works.

Rhythm trouble

If the atrioventricular bundle is damaged by scars, poisonous substances or drugs, it may fail to transmit all the normal auricular beats originating from the pacemaker—perhaps every second or third beat gets through. Such a disturbance is easily recognized on an electrocardiograph tracing, where the ratio between auricular and ventricular squiggles will then be 2:1 or 3:1. There may be periods of complete block lasting some seconds, which cause the output of the heart to fail momentarily, and the patient may even lose consciousness for a short period until the beats get through again. Small artificial pacemakers have been constructed, consisting of electronic circuits and small batteries, and the wires from them can be surgically implanted in the surface of the heart, so that rhythmic galvanic stimulation can keep it beating during periods of complete block of the atrioventricular bundle.

Similar disturbances in the heart muscle can also result in other irregular forms of contraction. 'Fibrillation' is a state where the pacemaker loses control of the rhythm, and a tumultuous rapid twitching

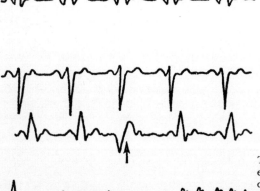

The type of electrocardiograph tracing obtained from (*top to bottom*) a normal heart, a heart with a very muscular left ventricle, a heart with an occasional (*see arrow*) irregular beat, a heart beating abnormally fast (tachycardia), and a heart which is fibrillating.

courses around and around the auricles which no longer can be said to 'beat'. The speed of this wave, which reaches the atrioventricular node at greater than the normal frequency, means that irregular and rapid impulses enter the atrioventricular bundle. Not all of these impulses get through to the ventricles but enough do so to make their beat irregular too. The fact that the bundle does not conduct all the impulses is important and makes auricular fibrillation compatible with life, because the ventricles still give full though fitful contractions. If fibrillation occurs in the ventricles it is almost immediately fatal. Another form of muscular twitching is termed 'flutter'. This is less rapid than fibrillation, but is still too fast for the doctor with his stethoscope to distinguish individual beats. All of these irregularities in either auricles or ventricles have characteristic electrocardiographic tracings.

Excessive sensitivity of the nerve relay mechanisms that originate in the rest of the body and influence the heart rate can make it excessively rapid (*tachycardia*) or excessively slow (*bradycardia*). Sudden paroxysms of rapid beating can occur in some people, during which they feel unpleasant palpitations. This is not dangerous and the individual often learns a trick of body movement or a pressure point that counter-stimulates the inhibitory nerves and abruptly restores the rate to normal.

In conditions where the thyroid gland in the neck is overactive the heart may be beating rapidly and working hard, even to the point of 'failure'. This is because the thyroid secretion is a general accelerator of the living rate of the whole body. Under thyroid stimulation, tissues need more oxygen and produce more heat. The heart responds like a willing horse, but begins to race away, pumping into a peripheral circulation which is wide open because of the dilated capillaries in the warm skin. It is important for a physician to recognize heart disease caused by thyroid overactivity because the condition is entirely curable. The gland can be quietened down by medical or surgical procedures, and then the heart will return to normal.

Foxglove tea

In 1775 an Englishman, Dr William Withering of Birmingham, a meticulous botanist and physician, was about to publish the first modern book on English plants arranged on the Linnaean system. The book was to remain a standard work for a long time, reaching its fourteenth and last edition one hundred years later, and in it Withering the botanist pointed out that the supposed curative powers of plants, widely established as folklore, were almost entirely illusory. But, ironically, Withering the physician was to validate the powers of perhaps the most effective plant medicine there is. One day he was asked his opinion concerning a family recipe for the cure of the dropsy.

He was told that it had long been kept a secret by an old woman in Shropshire, who had sometimes achieved cures after the more regular practitioners had failed. This medicine was composed of twenty or more different herbs, 'but', Withering wrote, 'it was not very difficult for one conversant in these subjects to perceive that the active herb could be no other than the Foxglove,' which on the Linnaean system of classification is *Digitalis purpurea.*

Dr Withering then spent ten years experimenting with the foxglove before he published a book on its medical use. He found that it cured only those kinds of dropsy that we now recognize as being caused by heart failure. He established a method of preparing the dried leaf and the way of finding the right amount to give. From the first he noted that it slowed the pulse rate. Dr Erasmus Darwin, celebrated naturalist and to be the grandfather of Charles Darwin, was a neighbouring practitioner, and Withering showed him how to use digitalis. Later Dr Darwin made a reference to it in the course of his long poem 'Botanic Garden':

> Bolster'd with down, amid a thousand wants
> Pale Dropsy rears his bloated form and pants.
> 'Quench me ye cool pellucid rills,' he cries,
> Wets his parched tongue and rolls his hollow eyes ...

The poem goes on to tell how 'Divine Hygeia' assumes 'bright Digitalis dress' and comes to cure poor Dropsy. Erasmus Darwin wrote much bad verse, including another botanical effusion, 'Loves of the Plants', verses of which were caustically parodied in 'Loves of the Triangles' by George Canning, an accomplished wit and later Prime Minister of Great Britain. There was a vogue for such cleverness at the time, and even William Withering, slowly dying of chest trouble at the end of the eighteenth century, did not escape a sally. 'The flower of physicians', the wits said, 'is indeed Withering.'

Strictly speaking, digitalis is a poison, but it is a useful one in many kinds of heart failure because it depresses the sensitivity of the impulse-conducting system of the heart. Disturbances of rhythm — fibrillation, flutter, tachycardia — are frequently the factors reducing the efficiency of the pump. If some of the irregular and crowding contractile impulses can be prevented from breaking through to initiate full beats of the ventricles, the situation improves. This is what digitalis does when given in suitable doses. It also improves the heart's output by increasing the capacity of the individual muscle fibres to contract fully and strongly, and it enhances the effects of those general nerve impulses which slow the heart. A wonder drug, foxglove leaf, and still, two hundred years since Withering's day, the most generally useful in the treatment of heart failure. We owe it to the herbalists, along with quinine from cinchona bark, aspirin from the sally bush, and opium from the poppy.

Disease of the valves

The valves of your heart are thin tough membranes, moving snugly into their well-fitting positions of closure when the current of blood reverses, and flapping unstrung, relaxed and unencumbering, when it flows with them. The thin valve material has few nourishing vessels of its own, relying for its maintenance mainly upon the surrounding wash of blood. These valves can become scarred as a result of past acute rheumatic inflammation, which distorts their bases and may leave a series of small nodules on the valve edges. Changes of this kind seem to render a valve prone to bacterial infection.

Occasionally bacteria enter the bloodstream, from locally infected areas of the body or from the bowel, and in the ordinary way they are rapidly cleared by antibodies and scavenging cells. But sometimes bacteria establish themselves in a heart valve and cause a local irritation which alters the lining membrane and attracts a deposition of platelets and fibrin. Once covered by this the germs grow steadily and cause further damage to the valve underneath. They can also distribute themselves around the body: some members of the colony on the valve crumbling away with fragments of fibrin and floating off as emboli in the bloodstream from time to time, setting up small abscesses in other organs, perhaps in vital ones. The disease they produce is prolonged and dangerous, and is named *bacterial endocarditis*. Many cases can be controlled by antibiotic treatment, but the severity and response varies according to which kind of bacteria are involved.

Blue babies

A small number of children are born with congenitally abnormal hearts which have not developed properly. Rarely, these abnormalities are inherited and appear in more than one child in a family, but more often they occur as single instances.* Some cases result from the mother having contracted a virus disease (particularly *rubella*, German measles, for which there is now a vaccine) in the early stages of the pregnancy. The abnormalities take the form of narrowed vessels, distorted valves or a failure of the natural foetal shunts to close off between the left and right sides of the heart.

Some of these plumbing troubles can be adjusted surgically, and it is therefore important that they should be recognized early in life. If they cause serious lack of oxygenation the child will be dusky purple—

---

* 'Congenital' is a general term used to mean 'present at birth'. 'Hereditary' means 'determined by the chromosome-gene mechanism'. Thus hereditary diseases present in infancy are congenital; but the reverse is not necessarily true. 'Familial' diseases are usually hereditary if they are otherwise uncommon in the community.

the 'blue baby'. The main cause of this is narrowing of the pulmonary artery. On the other hand, an affected child may not be 'blue' but may have an output of blood insufficient to supply the normal needs of limb and trunk muscles on exertion. The cause of this is likely to be a persisting of the foetal openings between the left and right sides of the heart. Then excessive blood flows through the lungs because the pressure is naturally higher on the left, and where there is a left-right passage some blood will pass more than once through the pulmonary circulation before flowing round the body generally, making a heart-lung system like that of a frog.

Another congenital defect is a narrow constriction in the aorta below the point at which the great arteries branch off to the head and arms. This produces a situation where the pulse and blood pressure is greater in the upper than in the lower part of the body. Many of these conditions can be diagnosed only by cardiac catheterization. When such disorders are being repaired by surgeons, a heart-lung machine is used to keep the circulation going while the heart is temporarily prevented from beating. Another procedure sometimes used is to chill the body so that it may survive for longer than ordinary periods without any circulation while an operation is being performed.

Disease of the arteries

To some extent all your arteries become thicker and narrower as you grow older, and maybe this is designed to counter their opposite tendency to lose elastic tissue (and therefore to stretch) in old age. However, even if this thickening and narrowing is basically a natural process, it is, as we have seen, seriously exaggerated by high blood pressure. But a more threatening degenerative change that affects all arteries, particularly the aorta and its main branches and the smaller arteries of the heart and brain, is *atheroma*. This is not a uniform degeneration, but a patchy one. Collections of soft pasty material (Greek, *atheros*, gruel) accumulate in the walls of the arteries, weaken them and produce shallow ulcers in the lining. The vasa vasorum can bleed into these patches and make them suddenly swell inwards until they block the main flow itself. Or a blood-clot can form on the damaged lining and may block the vessel. Or a piece of the clot or the ulcerated area may break off and travel in the bloodstream until it impacts in one of the finer branches of the artery and blocks it. In these ways atheromatous degeneration is responsible for most cases of coronary infarction. Similar arterial changes can cause limb pains on exertion, or even gangrene of an extremity by cutting off its blood supply.

The blood vessels of the brain are poorly supported in their soft surroundings, like tense little tubes in nerve slush. Unlike muscle vessels they are not held in an elastic massaging organ that helps their flow and takes pressure off their walls. They have to deliver a very large amount of blood per minute. No wonder they sometimes block or break when weakened by atheroma. The blood supply to a brain area is diminished, disrupting or inhibiting important nerve pathways and connections, and causing paralysis or mental changes which when they come on suddenly, as they usually do, are called 'strokes'.

This atheroma is very common in all civilized peoples and is a major medical problem of our day. The atheromatous material is fatty, and it has been thought that our high consumption of animal fat may have something to do with it. Opinion shifts about, and at the time of writing has moved somewhat towards blaming a high intake of refined sugar. However, it is generally agreed that the present plentiful food supply of civilized peoples has some bearing on it, and that in some people this disturbs the blood-clotting system so that small collections of platelets and fibrin become incorporated in the arterial wall. As the years pass by, these degenerate, in the end becoming an accumulation that constitutes an atheromatous plaque.

Other rarer diseases of arteries take the form of allergic inflammations, or the accumulation of calcium salts which turn them into rigid pipe-stems. These, and the others which have been described above, are physical structural disorders, and are technically called 'organic', as opposed to 'functional' changes where the blood vessels are temporarily contracted or expanded, to the disadvantage of the patient.

Chilblains, frost-bite, bedsores

It is the 'function' of small arteries supplying your skin to become constricted on exposure to cold, in order to avoid undue heat loss from the body. But in some people this response is extra sensitive, and perhaps one or more fingers or toes may become remarkably white or blue on an ordinary cold day. This is seldom serious or disabling. In people whose exposed skin is always cool both in winter and summer, severely cold conditions may mildly injure the capillaries so that they become swollen and leak extra fluid into the local tissues to produce a 'chilblain'. This is a kind of 'cold-bite', but a long way short of real 'frost-bite' which kills local tissues by actual freezing. A larger version of the chilblain appears in frosty weather in the form of cold reddish-blue areas on the legs of girls. The medical name for it is *erythrocyanosis frigida crurum puellarum*, which means 'cold reddish-blue areas on the legs of girls'. Contrariwise, one finds some people whose small skin arteries are in a permanent state of dilatation so that their hands or feet are always red and warm.

Those who are bedridden may lie in one position for long periods. This squeezes areas of skin against bony protuberances of the skeleton, and prevents a free flow of blood and lymph because the capillary vessels are compressed. In these circumstances the areas of skin may die for lack of a proper blood supply. They break down into pressure ulcers or 'bedsores'. This is why careful and regular turning of a bedridden patient, and massage of the back parts, are an important part of classic nursing care.

Pins and needles

Sensation 'felt' in a limb depends upon the working of the nerves which connect it to the brain. Nerves are active chemical structures; they are not the equivalent of wires of inert metal which conduct electricity. A nerve impulse has more the nature of a moving chemical change, or of a burning train of gunpowder. Energy is needed to maintain its passage; therefore, like the brain, nerves have to be well supplied with blood because the constant chemical activity of the cells of their fibres requires oxygen.

If the oxygen supply to the brain is interrupted for a short time, the result is unconsciousness. It is the same with the peripheral nerves. If their oxygen is cut off at any point along their lengths, they will not uniformly transmit the chemical impulses which on reaching the brain become 'sensation'. The blood supply to a gross nerve (a bundle of individual microscopic nerve fibres) comes through successive small arteries entering it and splitting up into a longitudinal network of fine capillaries running deep among the component fibres. Because it is like a piece of tape or string, a nerve is easily compressed, perhaps where it crosses a bony area on which the body is leaning (such as a buttock or elbow) or where a joint is stretched. Hard pressure on a nerve-cell fibre itself inhibits its function, but milder pressure also inhibits it by interrupting the capillary flow of blood. Then it quickly runs short of oxygen fuel so that some or all of its cell fibres can no longer chemically transmit a nervous impulse through that part of the line.

After many hours of continuous compression, the nerve fibres might actually die from lack of oxygen, but in the ordinary way temporary interference is with nervous function rather than with absolute vitality. It is in our arms and legs that we experience the effects. Sit on the edge of a hard chair or bench and you squash the great nerve running down to the leg from the buttock region. Lean your elbow or forearm on the edge of a hard table and one of the main nerves to the hand is pressed against bone. Throw an arm casually over the high hard back of a chair in which you are side-sitting and the nerves of the arm will be compressed in the armpit. The same nerves may be compressed by stretching, when the hands are put behind the head while sleeping flat on the back. All these can cause the numbness where parts of limbs 'go to sleep' or 'get pins and needles'.

Different nerve fibres, connected to different types of nerve ending, carry different qualities of sensation. Some transmit impulses which are interpreted as pricking, some as burning, some a deeper ache, or a sense of position. The whole, under normal conditions, adds up to the feeling of the part being 'there'. But when some of the fibres are unequally disturbed by having the local blood supply irregularly reduced, the experience is the tingling burning of 'pins and needles', and this is also felt when a limb that has completely 'gone to sleep' is recovering sensation. The experience that feeling is 'flooding back' is related to the restoration of blood-flow and recovery of function in the nerve segment, not in the whole limb. When a large artery in a limb is blocked, the experience is usually one of muscular pain, not one of pins and needles.

Varicose veins

There are sluggish parts of the venous blood-flow, just as there are back and stagnant waters of a river. Some people inherit veins with less effective valves. Others take up postures or have occupations that put a strain on their leg and rectal veins. Others again have a belt or corset or a pregnancy, or a gut swollen with overeating. All of these can compress the great returning vein (the inferior vena cava) that runs beside the aorta. Less frequently, a scarred liver may obstruct the return of portal blood from the gut. Veins which have to endure the back pressure may become distended, tortuous and *varicose* (Latin *varix*, a dilated vein).

Cirrhosis of the liver is a fine fibrous scarring process which can appear after severe damage to the liver by virus hepatitis or by liver poisons such as alcohol. When it occurs, the portal flow through the liver is obstructed and the very considerable volume of blood from the intestines has to find its way back to the inferior vena cava by ordinarily narrow alternative routes connecting with the veins of the gullet, rectum and sometimes the umbilicus. The connecting veins may become swollen and varicose. Their appearance around the navel is given the picturesque name *Caput Medusae* (one Gorgon had snakes for hair). Such veins can break and bleed dangerously into the stomach at the lower end of the gullet. In the rectum they become piles or haemorrhoids, but raised venous pressure is not unusual in this region and does not necessarily indicate liver trouble. It is possible for a surgeon to link the portal vein directly to the inferior vena cava in some cases of portal obstruction. This relieves the congestion and reduces the risk of bleeding from the dilated internal veins, particularly those at the top of the stomach.

Varicose veins are common in the rectums and legs of otherwise healthy men and women, and usually they are trivial, medically speaking, and do not indicate any major disorder of the circulation. Like fainting, backache and creaking knee joints, they are no doubt another human biological penalty for walking upright. However, if very severe, varicose veins in the lower limbs can lead to a waterlogged skin which becomes pigmented because of repeated leakage of blood and fluid from distended capillaries and venules. Such skin may be very itchy, and chronic ulcers can form after minor injuries to it. Luckily, most of the effective flow of blood in the legs is in the veins deep down amongst the muscles, and surface varicose veins can safely be eliminated surgically, by being tied off or injected with an irritant which blocks them with a clot. Clots produced in this way are harmless because a wide area of the vein wall is inflamed and the clot sticks firmly to the sides. Inflammation of a vein, whether deliberately produced in this way or caused by bacteria invading the vein wall in an area of infection, is termed *phlebitis* (Latin *phlebs*, a vein).

Embolism

'Embolism' is a general term for any obstructive mass, or 'embolus', moving in a blood vessel (Greek *embolismos*, to cast in, *embolon*, the penis; English *embolism*, an extra prayer inserted in a religious liturgy, or a day—such as February 29th—inserted in a calendar to complete a period; Latin *embolus*, a wedge, peg or stopper). Now, when clots form in a loose way purely as a result of stagnation, without inflammation, in an otherwise normal vein, their attachment is uncertain and their composition soft. Then when the individual makes a sudden movement, such a clot may be moved along a vein in the natural current of blood, and can pass through the right side of the heart and into the pulmonary artery in a branch of which it will stick, suddenly cutting off the blood supply to part of the lung. This is 'pulmonary embolism' and the cause of many deaths, for when a large clot arrives in the pulmonary circulation, a set of nerve reflexes comes into action which can stop the heart. Pulmonary embolism is one of the major causes of unexpected deaths after otherwise satisfactory surgical operations, because manipulation of organs at operation followed by complete bed-rest can encourage loose-clot formation in local veins. Then after some days, when the patient gets about again, these clots can drift off in the venous circulation and reach the lungs. Therefore early movements and exercises after surgical operations are nowadays encouraged in almost all types of patients in order to avoid stagnation and clot formation in the veins. Very rarely an abnormal right-to-left opening in the heart allows a venous clot to by-pass the lungs, moving 'paradoxically'* from the right to the left side of the circulation where it will do damage by blocking an artery in the general arterial tree.

* *Paradoxical embolism:* a pathologists' term.

Pieces of clot or pieces of atheromatous arterial wall are the commonest emboli. Others are masses of cancer cells, large droplets of fat, or bubbles of gas. Fragments of cancer tissue or single cancer cells may travel in the blood to areas of the body (such as the lungs) away from their origin, and there set up secondary centres of tumour growth. Large drops of fat may enter the venous bloodstream when a broken bone releases loose fat from the marrow cavity (which is not all occupied by blood-forming tissue – the rest is filled with body fat which is liquid at the normal body temperature). Such embolic drops of fat can impact temporarily in any capillary bed, but some of them may squeeze through the lungs and cause noticeable changes in the brain and kidneys.

Earlier in this book it was explained how small bubbles of gas can appear in the blood of a diver and have painful effects; but a large volume of air suddenly forced into a vein can produce fatal air embolism, a sudden tragedy which may accidentally complicate surgical or medical procedures. It is characteristically caused by unprofessional attempts at abortion when air (rather than fluid, as intended) is pumped into the blood spaces behind the placenta of a pregnant uterus. Air embolism has been known to be fatal since the seventeenth century. At that time it was discovered that animals could be killed very quickly by blowing through a quill into a vein. There is a record of an experimenter 'who only by inflating with his mouth the jugular vein, did once on a time, lay prostrate and kill an ox, of a stupendous size'.

What happens is that the air, if there is enough of it, churns to froth as it mixes with blood in the right ventricle. Death is then partly the result of the heart valves failing to work in froth, and partly the result of widespread blocking of the branches of the pulmonary artery by small bubbles, which the smaller they are the more they resist deformation and therefore become effective plugs of capillary blood vessels. So much for the ancient belief that arteries naturally contain a gross mixture of blood and air.

Elephantiasis

The lymph vessels are multiple and intercommunicating and rarely become blocked, but in a certain tropical disease thousands of small parasites clog the lymph channels of a limb, and the part swells as lymph fluid accumulates in the spaces between the cells. This fluid is rich in protein and an ideal medium in which the fibre-forming cells of scar tissue will grow and multiply. Therefore unless the swelling is soon reduced, it sets permanently into the fibrotic enlargement known as *elephantiasis*.

New graft on old rootstock

And elephantiasis is what this book will get if I clog it with any more 'bits'. But it is hard to know when to stop; for as a stream bearing evidences of physiology, the blood reflects a sizeable amount of the science of physiology itself, how sizeable I can only guess. No one will be able to tell until all the molecular constituents of human blood have been specified and related to the activities of the human body. And after the blood of man has been dealt with in this scientific way, there will still be the rest of the mammals, and then the rest of the vertebrates, and then the rest of the bloody animal kingdom, of which there is a great deal; for many a beast has no backbone, but does have blood. So haematology, grandly conceived, is perhaps a legitimate tenth of all the physiology of animals in the size-range from fleas upwards. Which is a lot of biology, especially when one of the animals is man's own favourite and best subject—Man.

Rational biology began in the minds of the ancient peoples of the Mediterranean and has been undergoing exceptionally rapid development in the last three hundred years. Not yet mature, its application becomes wider every day. The advance has been by searching out new things, along with a steady elimination of such untenable lore as does not stand up to strict inquiry and experimental test. It has been a slow process—the nature of the human mind is not to seek facts and make deductions against prejudice, except by special effort. It is hard to learn new tricks.

Physicists and chemists may consider themselves lucky, compared with biologists, to have got off to what amounted to a totally fresh start in the seventeenth century. No rival systems now bother their modern orthodoxies. The physics of flight or television, or the chemistry of dyes or plastics, for instance, are accepted and applied within a decade or two of passing the checkpoint of a little handful of scientists and technologists. But scientific human biology has rivals. Before being accepted by the whole community it has to contend with the biologies, and the words, of Moses, Aristotle, Galen, and the alchemists, which still survive alongside it today—even at high political levels— and influence social policies and human attitudes. After all, the whole dead weight of humanity is made up of millions of 'applied biologists' directing living organisms—our own precious bodies. Consequently a far greater degree of proof and repetitive demonstration is required by us before any generalization from scientific biology is accepted as 'true' by all, and so knowledge generally applicable to human eating, learning, loving, mating, ailing, fighting, and so on, has to satisfy almost the total consensus of opinion in a community before becoming operational.

But if we can agree that scientific biology has a better relation to the rest of reality than have any of the medieval or ancient biological systems, then this is the biology which must become a classic part of our everyday education. But neither should older ideas of biology be forced out too brusquely. The non-biological sciences such as physics and chemistry may yet find that their connections with the broad humane culture are too weak, that they have to remain permanent mandarin activities enclosed in scientific reservations and dangerously unrelated to the general experience of mankind. A slowly growing graft on an old rootstock is often a better gardening prospect than a cutting; yet the stock must be trimmed if the scion is to have a chance.

FURTHER READING

Readers seeking more information about human blood and its circulation in respect of structure, function or disease should read any modern books on anatomy, physiology, pathology or medicine. Anatomy books, in particular, will have labelled pictures of the dispositions of all the blood vessels, for which reason it has not been thought necessary to have such diagrams here. For special details of particular blood diseases, a textbook of clinical haematology should be consulted. Similarly, there are books on blood transfusion.

There follows a short list of works which specially elaborate some of the matters touched on in this book.

Fishman, A. P., and D. W. Richards, eds. *Circulation of the Blood.* New York: Oxford University Press, 1964. In the series 'Men and Ideas'.

Gunz, F. W., and W. Dameshek. *Leukaemia.* New York: Grune and Stratton, 1964.

Humphrey, J. H., and R. G. White. *Immunology for Students of Medicine.* Oxford: Blackwell, 1970.

Macfarlane, R. G., and A. H. T. Robb-Smith, eds. *Functions of the Blood.* Oxford: Blackwell, 1961.

Mourant, A. E. *The Distribution of the Human Blood Groups.* Oxford: Blackwell, 1954.

Race, R. R., and Ruth Sanger. *Blood Groups in Man.* Oxford: Blackwell, 1968.

Titmuss, R. M. *The Gift Relationship: From Human Blood to Social Policy.* London: Allen & Unwin, 1971.

INDEX

adenoids, lymphocytes in, 53

Adonis/Osiris: river of, 12, 128; flowers of, 57

adrenalin: accelerates heart rate, 68; effect on circulation time, 72; liberated by fright, 177; tumour excess causes blood pressure, 259

albumin: binding functions, 47, 193; small-molecule plasma protein, 74, 193; solution for transfusion, 193; bovine, plasma substitute, 195

alchemists: accepted discovery of circulation, 92; and Mars, fire and iron, 206; biology of, 276

Alexander the Great, and blood in bread, 125

amoeba, streaming of protoplasm, 16

amphibian(s): circulation in, 34–5; red cells, 102

Amphioxus: see lancelet

anaemia: from blood loss, 98, 209; iron treatment, 194, 196, 206; diagnosis, 194; term, 206, 209; chlorosis, 207, 212; varieties, 209, 210; symptoms of, 210, 211; pallor in, 210, 211; in pregnancy, 212; haemolytic, 214, 222–3; pernicious, 214; Vitamin B$_{12}$ and, 215; tapeworm provokes, 216; aplastic, 225; from radiation, 228; see also haemolytic disease of the newborn

anatomy, anatomist, 61

angina pectoris: see heart disease

angiography: by X-rays, 64, 261; by radioactive scanning, 65, 108, 111; of lymphatics, 75

animals: two-layered, 19; three-layered, 23

antibody, antibodies: production, 54, 137, 139; function, 54; lymphocyte-bound, 54, 141; term, 54–5; nature, 137; typhoid, 137; laboratory tests for, 137, 150, 160; precipitating, 137; auto-antibodies, 138, 222; varieties of, 141; pass placenta, 149, 156; in first milk, 149; in egg-yolk, 149; antivenoms, antitoxins, 149; against sheep blood, 150, 151; naturally occurring, 151, 249; plant juices agglutinate blood cells, 151; in blood donors, 152; in recipients of blood, 153; for blood-grouping, 154, 243; anti-Rhesus, 157; effect on foetus, 161; for identifying species, 170; against white cells, 189

anticoagulant: to stabilize plasma sample,

31; sodium citrate, 118, 187; natural anti-clotting effects, 121; citric fruit juice, 185; unwettable surface, 187; in leech's saliva, 218

antigen(s): term, 54, 137; in vaccine, 149; in cowpox, smallpox, 149; in blood substitutes, 195; and genes, 244

aorta: term, 61; values of, 61; filling of, 61; branches, 63, 64; flow rate, 71; constricted, 270

apoplexy, 65

aristocrat, breathless, 67

Aristotle: view of heart, 84; on tendons, 84; classifications, 85; Harvey's challenge to views, 91; perfect circular motion, 92; emphasis on qualities, 120; biology of, 276

arterioles, 65

artery, arteries: term, 61; air in, belief, 61, 84, 275; pulmonary, 61, 63, 67, 270, 274; coronary, 64, 198, 261, 263; innominate, 64; carotid, 64, 103; end-arteries, 65; blockage of, 65, 261, 270, 275; pulse, 67, 258; vasa vasorum, 68, 270; pressure in, 70, 258–60; flow rate, 71; Circle of Willis, 72; of umbilical cord, 77, 78; ductus arteriosus, 78, 79; artiers, 89; response to blood loss, 180; brachial, 180; thickening and narrowing with age, 259, 261, 262, 270; contraction in cold, 259; degeneration and thickening under pressure, 259 262; of eye, looking at, 261; atheroma of, 270, 271; pipe-stem, 271

arthropod(s): complete external skeletons, 28; hearts, 28; haemocyanin in, 29, 67; circulatory system, 29

'artiers' (arteries, q.v.), 89

atheroma: of arteries, 270; term, 270; thrombosis and, 270; of brain arteries, 271; causes, 271

athletes: hearts of, 70, 257; muscles saved by pain, 261

atmospheric pressure, and boiling point of water, 173

atrioventricular bundle: conduction of heart-beat, 63, 258; partial block in, 258, 266; in auricular fibrillation, 267, 268

atrioventricular node: heart-muscle contraction and, 63; in auricular fibrillation, 266

atrium, 60

auricle(s), 60; valves, 61; contraction, 61, 63, 267; foramen ovale, 78, 79; fibrillation in, 267

Bacon, Francis, and new way of investigating, 115
bacteria: *see* germs
balloons, fainting while blowing, 179
bat: wing 'hearts' in, 37; blood-sucking, 214; bedbug parasite of, 220
beans, peas: Pythagorean prohibition on, 80, 223; dietary iron in, 208; disease (fabismus, favism), 223; symbolism and turning to blood, 223; blood-group antibodies in, 249
bedbug, 29, 220
bedsores, 272
'bends, the', divers' disease, 273-4
benzene, effect on bone marrow, 226
Bernard, Claude, and *milieu interne*, 24
bilateral symmetry, 59
bile, black: *see* melancholy
bile, yellow: produced by liver, 50, 66, 88; gall bottle, 88; bilious children, 93; colour, 107, 162; *see also* choler
biological variation, disease and, 22
biology: of blood, 276; of Moses, Aristotle, Galen, 276; physics, chemistry, compared with, 276
birds, warm blood of, 40-41
birth, circulatory changes at, 78-9, 163
Bismarck, Prince Otto von: 'Eisen und Blut', 206; herring, 206
bleeding: 'coffee grounds' vomit, 97; into stomach, 97; clotting and, 111; remedies for, 113; epistaxis, 113; cobwebs for, 113; Host (miracle), 125; first aid for, 180; cause of fainting, 180-83; internal, 181; plasma loss in burns, 181; estimate of losses, 196; iron losses, 207; treatment of haemochromatosis, 209; inherited, 232-5
'Bless you!', 85
blister, nature of, 181
blood: folklore of, 11, 182, 190; evolution of, 40; and sea-water, 40, 174; warm, 40-43; 'dragon's', 43; functions, 44, 48, 276; as carrier, 47-50; tests for diagnosis of disease, 48, 107, 109, 110; test for identity, 48, 129, 167; white cells in, 49; as exchange pool, 50; buffering of acid, 50; manure, 57; flower legends of, 57; portal, 65; blue blood, 67; paramount humour, 82, 83, 84; Pythagorean views of, 82, 83; Hippocratic view of, 83-4; Galen's views of, 85-7, 276; Rabelais on, 87-8; Elizabethan view of, 89; other 'humours' in, 96; 'cleaned' by purging, 98; foetal development of, 101; quantity in adult, 103, 177; cell counting, 107; microscope films of, 107; menstrual, 126, 211; in literary symbolism, 127-8; individuality of, 129; quantity in newborn, 163; species identification, 170; sensitive chemical tests for, 170-71; stains, shape of, 171; haemolysis of, 172; stains, removal of, 172; as food, 172, 219; effect of heating, 172-3; boiling at high altitudes, 173; loss of, effects, 180; traditional cures using, 182-3; storage, for

transfusion, 187; from a stone, 196; primary diseases of, 204; secondary disorders of, 204; and iron, 206-11; oranges, 208; biology of, 276
blood-clotting: primitive cellular, 30, 56; evolution of, 31; factors, measurement of, 110, 112; mechanism, 111-12; plasma and serum factors, 112; time, 112-13; localization of, 113; neutralizers of, 113-114, 121; prevention by citrate, 187; in haemophilia, 234; in myocardial infarction, 264
blood diseases: *see* diseases. *See also* anaemia; leukaemia; etc.
blood donors: well-being after donation, 94; 'universal donors', 152, 153; fainting, 176; modern, 190; amount donated, 190; recovery of, 191; frequency of donation, 191; risks, 191; voluntary, 192; technique of bleeding, 197; grouping of, 198; for heart-lung and kidney machines, 199-200, 266
blood group(s): of individuals, 129, 135-6, 167; two in one person, 147; determination of, 150, 169, 185, 243; 'natural' antibodies, 151, 249; antigens shared, 151, 247; ABO, 152, 153, 156; water-soluble ABO antigens, 154, 170; inheritance of, 155, 160, 167, 168; Rhesus (Rh), 156; Rhesus group frequencies, 158; Rhesus sub-groups, 159; sex-linked (Xg), 159, 169; inheritance of Rhesus antigen, 159, 167-8; effects of foetal-maternal immunization, 165; origin of Rh-negative gene, 165; in paternity testing, 167; naming of, 168-9; 'honorary', 169, 243; 'private', 169; of the dead, 169; criminal investigation and, 169-70; from dried secretions, 170; tissue groups, 189, 243; of white cells, 192; why present?, 243, 245; systems, 243; antigens and genes, 244; race differences, 244-5; antigens, number and frequencies, 245, 252, 253; stability, 245, 246, 248, 254; natural selection of, 246, 247-50; possible functions, 246; ABO substances in apes, plants, bacteria, 249; world frequencies of ABO, 249, 250-54; of Basques, 253
blood-letting: for plethora, 93; procedure, 94; Patin on, 94-5; astrological indications, 96; from the 'leech' finger, 96; effect on sick people, 98; cause of anaemia, 98; seasonal, 98; veins used, 197
blood platelets: formation and activity, 55, 104; ingest bacteria, 56; numbers, 105; in clotting, 112, 264; transfusion of, 192; lack of, 192, 225; auto-antibodies against, 222; thrombocytopenia, 225; purpura and, 225, 239
blood pressure: and kidney function, 52, 259; skin flow and, 68; in arteries, 70, 258, 261; in capillaries, 71, 260; in veins, 71; in shock, 176, 177-80, 197; measurement of, 197, 258, 261; enlargement of heart in, 258, 259; and life-span, 258-9; causes of, 259; in families, 259; in preg-

nancy, 259; a cause of heart failure, 260; and headache, 262

blood transfusion: usefulness, 56; cadaver blood for, 121, 185; early attempts, 150, 181; animal bloods, 150; haemolytic reaction, 150, 152–3, 157; multiple, 153; cross-matching, 153, 198; importance of ABO groups, 153–4; red-cell survival after, 154; compared with tissue grafting, 154; MN and P groups, 155; Rhesus antibodies and, 156; husband to wife, 156–7, 165; of Rh-negative women, 158; second and subsequent, 159; exchange, 163–4; for haemolytic disease of newborn, 163–5; intra-uterine, 164; at Royal Society (1667), 184; made safe and easy, 187; blood bank, 187, 189; character traits and, 191; allergies transferable in, 191; infections transferable by, 191; of white cells, 192; of plasma fractions and albumin, 193, 194; of fibrinogen, 193; of anti-haemophilic globulin, 193, 235; of globulin antibodies, 193; of packed cells, 194; for anaemia and shock, 194–5; 196–197, 198; blood substitutes for, 195–6; response to, 196; in burns, 196; of large volumes, 197; risk of overloading, 197; technique, 197–8; arterial, 199

blood vessels: lining of, 23; first, 25–8; consistency in human, 64; aids to dissection, 64; degenerative changes in, 65; control of, 68; of umbilical cord, 77, 78; fibrinolysin and, 121; response to over-breathing, 178; changes in bleeding diseases, 239; constriction of aorta, 270–271; see also arteries; capillaries; veins

'bloody', etymology, 99

blushing, 69

bone: arteries supplying, 72; calcium store, 72; radioactive phosphorus, 111; broken, and fat embolism, 275

bone marrow: blood-flow in, 29; foetal, 102; adult blood formation in, 102; white cells in, 105; stimulated by oxygen lack, 105; samples of, 109; effect of radiation, 188, 227–8; preservation by freezing, 188; effect of lack of Vitamin B_{12}, 215; poisoning of, 225–6; contains body fat, 275

'Box, The' (Abram's Box), 203

Boyle, Hon. Robert: sees bubble in snake's eye, 173n; 'Father of Chemistry ... ', 183; views and experiments on blood, 183–5; Sceptical Chemist (full title), 186

bradykinin, 69

brain: end-arteries, 65; apoplexy, 65, 271; blood-flow in, 72, 179; arteries of, 72, 270; Circle of Willis, 72; Galen's view of, 85; and mind, 143; number of nerve cells, 143; electric and chemical codes, 143; tumour, 143; brainy people, 183; localization of heart pain, 262; fat embolism and, 275

Browne, Sir Thomas, and 'leech' finger, 96

bruise, 106, 181; purpura, 225; devil's pinches, 239

buffering, action of blood, 50

burn, plasma losses in, 181, 196

Burnet, Sir Macfarlane, 138

Burton, Robert, on humours, 89

bustard, thick-kneed (stone curlew), 203

Butler, Samuel (Erewhon), on egg, 101

Butler, Samuel (Hudibras), parody on Boyle's experiments, 183

cadaver: see death

caisson disease (bends), 273–4

calcium: and sol-gel changes, 16; bone store of, 72; radioactive, 111; in blood-clotting, 112; citrate anticoagulant, 187

campfires, fainting while blowing, 179

cancer: mutation and, 133, 148; lymphocyte surveillance, 141, 148; loss of order in, 148; anti-cell drugs for, 189; of white-blood cells, 228; embolic spread, 275

capillaries: term, 28; in earthworm, 28; of kidney, 28, 50; none in arthropods or bone marrow, 29; in human, 65; pressures in, 65, 71, 73; of lungs, 67; flow rates, 72; lymph formation, 74; plasma loss through, 181, 263; chilblains and, 271; bedsores, 272; fat embolism and, 275

carboxyhaemoglobin, 227

cardiac: see heart

cartilage, bloodless tissue, 72

cell(s): structure, 14; cytoplasm, 14; diffusion in, 14–15, 74; cohabiting, 20; excretory, 23; reproductive, 23; number in body, 48; death of, 48, 189; microscopic examination of, 53; and disease, 93; human egg-cell, 101; scar formation, 101; differentiation, 102, 135; or corpuscles?, 102; numbers in brain, 143; preserved by freezing, 188; cultures, 189; effects of radiation on, 228, 230, 231; cell-wall activities, blood groups and, 246, 249; see also lymphocytes; red blood cells; white blood cells

Charadrius (thick-kneed bustard), 203

chilblains, 271

chimera, 147; and grafting, 188

chocolate, iron in, 208

choler: human, 82; Rabelais and Burton on, 88, 89; in 'overheated' blood, 93; apparently in blood, 96; see also bile, yellow

Christmas disease (haemophilia), 236

Christmas factor, 112

chromatography, 110

chromosome: see gene

circulation: in proboscis-worms, 25; in round-worms and molluscs, 26; in squid and earthworm, 27; in arthropods, 29; hydraulic adaptations, 32; in primitive vertebrates, 33; human, control and times of, 69, 71–2; human foetal, 77; changes at birth, 78; discovery of, 90–93

clitoris, erection of, 69

clotting: see blood-clotting

coal-gas poisoning, 227

cobalt deficiency and Vitamin B_{12}, 216

cobweb, as bleeding remedy, 113

cold, 42, 93, 265
colostrum, antibodies in, 149, 165
companage, 88
'complexion', 83
'congenital', 269n
connective tissue, 23
constitution: humoral, 82–4; individual, 242, 259
contraceptive pill, 76
copulation, and internal development of foetus, 76
cord: see umbilical cord
coronary: see artery; heart; heart disease
corpse: see death
corset, compresses inferior vena cava, 177
cousin marriages, 237–8
cramp, swimming and, 179
critical days, 84
crucifixion: basil at place of, 57; cause of death in, 178
cubit, length of, 197
cupping, 97
cytoplasm: see protoplasm

dandelion, iron in, 208
death: corruption after, 57, 212; cadaver blood for transfusion, 121, 185; post-humous blood-grouping, 169–70; drown-ing, tests for, 174–5; blood groups of mummies, 254
defence: by scavenger cells, 52–3, 75; against 'not-self', 52, 139; by lymphatic system, 75, 139; against second infection, 140
dextran, plasma substitute, 196
dextrocardia, 60
diagnosis, 201, 202
dialysis, for kidney failure, 200
diatoms, in drowned person, 174
diffusion: rate of, 14, 17; flat shape and, 14, 25, 45; and osmosis, 73
digestion, 66
digitalis, 260, 268
Dioscorides, Pedanius, 115, 182
disease(s): variation as, 22, 104, 204, 209, 225; stroke, 65, 271; Hippocratic view, 83; infectious, 136; resistance to, 137; naming of, 201, 205–6, 236, 263; diag-nosis and prognosis, 201; as abstractions, 201, 204; variability of, 203; auto-immune, 222; biological evaluation of, 229; sex-linked, 232–4; cure by genetic manipulation, 235; medicine and here-ditary, 235; and cousin marriage, 237; and ABO groups, 246–7, 254; and Rhesus groups, 247–8; classification of, 263; organic, 271; functional, 271
divination by internal organs, 33
dizziness, 178, 179–80
'dorsal', 32
Dracula, 214
dragon's blood, 43
dragonfly, jaws of larva, 70
dreams: of blood, 126–8; interpretation of, 126
drisheen, Irish food, 172

dropsy: in kidney disease, 199; in heart failure, 260; foxglove tea for, 267–8
drowning: diatom test for, 174; blood salts in, 175
drug(s): active against cells, 189; occasion-ally damaging marrow, 226; bacterial endocarditis in addicts, 226; term (versus 'medicine'), 260; relaxing heart arteries, 262, 264

ears, 'burning', 69
earthworm, 27–8
egg: waterproof, 75–6; of fish and reptile, 76; human ovulation, 76; yolk sac, 76, 101; yolk, choler in, 93; -white, fixation of, 108; identical twins from one, 129; cell, mutation in, 133; sex chromosomes in, 133; antibodies in yolk, 149, 160; boiled, at different altitudes, 172–3; yolk, and iron absorption, 208
electrocardiograph, 257–8, 262, 266–7
electrophoresis, of plasma proteins, 110, 193
elementary particles, 13, 130
elements, 82, 90
elephant: heart rate, 70; venous return from feet, 71
elephantiasis, 275
Elizabethan view of blood, 89
ell, 197
elvers, leaf shape of, 45
embolus, embolism: gas, 173, 275; diatoms and, 174; air, 198, 275; clot, 264, 270, 274–5; bacterial, 269; pulmonary, 274; paradoxical, 274; fat, 275; cell masses, 275; blockage of lymph vessels, 275
embryo: see foetus
emotion, 68, 177
endocarditis, bacterial, 227
endocardium, 263
enzymes, 66; measurement, in plasma, 109; and maturation of garum, 122; in traces of blood, 171; in red cells, 223
épinards à l'anglaise, iron in, 208
epistaxis, 113
erection, of penis and clitoris, 69
ergot, poisoning, 262
erysipelas, 262
evolution: hypothesis, 21, 116; natural selection and, 21, 133, 246; further, 36–7, 51, 225; of antibody types, 141; and disease, 204, 209, 225, 246, 248; of sickling, 224; of self-consciousness, 225, 240; natural selection of blood groups, 246, 247–50
expiring, 44, 85
eye(s): central artery, 65; blood squirted from, 70; bloodless parts, 72; black, 106; looking at blood vessels in, 261

fabismus, favism, 223
fainting: Burton on syncope, swooning, 90; at sight of blood, 127, 177; of blood donors, 176; and shock, 176–8; and preg-nancy, 177; and corsets, 177; in soldiers on parade, 177; 'gravity suit' for, 178; in

upright crucifixion, 178; recovery and first aid, 178, 180; schoolboy trick, 178; from over-breathing, 178; uncommon in elderly, 179
fear: pallor in, 68, 69, 210, 222; cause of fainting, 176, 177
feathers, 41, 75
fever: 'stuff a cold and starve a', 42; yellow foods bad for, 93; 'blackwater', 97; 'plethora' and, 98; red flannel for, 98; ague, 221
fibrinogen, fibrin, 111, 117, 193
fibrinolysin, fibrinolysis, 121, 193, 211
first aid: for fainting, 180; for haemorrhagic shock, 180; cardiac massage, 198–9
fish: heart, 33–5; in hot water, 42; gasping, 45; without haemoglobin, 45; red cells, 102; sauce (the *garum*), 122
fixation, 108, 172
flatworm, 23, 25
flea, 219
Fletcher, Phineas, *Purple Island*, 127
foetus, foetal: as parasite, 76, 77, 212; heat production, 77; genetic constitution, 77; umbilical cord, 77; haemoglobin, 77; circulation, 78–9; short circuits in, 78–9, 269; rudimentary blood in, 101; red cells in, 102, 103, 161; white cells in, 102, 103, 138; tolerance of self and non-self, 138, 147, 222; damaged by mother's antibodies, 156–7; hydrops foetalis, 161; liver, 162; nutritional needs, 212
foramen ovale, 78, 79
foxglove tea (digitalis), 120
frog: heart, 35–6; electric effects in legs, 256
frost-bite, 188, 271

Galen: his 'innominate' artery, 64; views, 85–7; Harvey's challenge to, 91; on menstrual blood, 126
Galvani, Luigi, 256
garum, fish sauce, 122
gelatin, blood substitute, 195
genes, chromosomes: particulate, not blending, 129, 244; pattern analogies, 130, 133; in cell nuclei, 130; paired, 130; expression of, 130–31; self-copying, 132; in sex cells, 132–3, 134, 232; mutation, 133, 224, 228, 232, 236–7, 243; crossing over, 133–4; determining blood groups, 155, 167, 168, 243; inheritance of Rhesus antigen, 160, 161; Rh-negative, European origin, 165; control of iron absorption, 209; effect on population, on individual, 209; for haemoglobin variants, 224; effect of radiation on, 228; inheritance of haemophilia, 232; sex-linked disease, 232; manipulation of, 235; cousin marriages and recessive, 238; view of individuality, race, 242; congenital, hereditary, familial, 269n
germs: souring milk, 50; in body, 52, 55; rotting, 57, 212; killed by dyes, 108; in food, 125; chromobacterium prodigiosum, 125, 223; as marker, 125; as parasites,

136; typhoid, 137; effects of antibody on, 137, 140; viruses pass placenta, 147; vaccines, 148–9; killed by boiling, 185; restrained by chilling, 187; transferable by transfusion, 191; pasteurization of plasma albumin, 193; cause unresponsive shock, 198; produce Vitamin B_{12}, 215; few cause disease, 216; spread by biting arthropods, 220; overcoming defences, 226; bacteria in bloodstream, 226–7; cause of myocarditis, 265; and rheumatic carditis, 265; streptococcal, 265; virus of rubella (German measles), 269
'Gesundheit!', 85
gills, 27, 34
girls, green, 211–12
gladiator, blood of, for epilepsy, 182
graft(s): rejection of, 141; of tissues, organs, 154, 188–90; matching for, 165, 189, 192; autografts, 188; of bloodless parts, 189; future possibilities, 189, 190
granulocytopenia, 225
Graves, Robert James ('He Fed Fevers'), 42

haematology: nomenclature, 168, 205–6; development of, 205–6; *see also* blood; disease; etc.
haemochromatosis, 94, 209
haemocyanin, 27
haemoglobin: advantages of, 25; nonvertebrate and vertebrate type, 34; and haptoglobin, 34; properties, 45; foetal haemoglobin F, 76, 224; adult haemoglobin A, 77; rate of production, 103; measurement of, 106; breakdown pigments, 106, 163, 212, 223; spectroscopic identification, 171; no substitute for, 195; abnormal, 224; carboxyhaemoglobin, 227
haemolysis, 161, 172, 222–3
haemolytic disease of the newborn: caused by antibodies, 149, 161; erythroblastosis foetalis, 156, 157, 162; mainly in western Europeans, 159, 165; prevention of, 160, 163–5; tests for, 160, 161, 164; effects on foetus, 160; hydrops foetalis, 161; effects in infant, 162, 163; icterus gravis neonatorum, 162; kernicterus, 163, 164; transfusion for, 163, 164; green teeth, 164; premature delivery for, 164; in nonhuman animals, 165; selective effect on Rhesus groups, 247, 254
haemophilia: anti-haemophilic globulin, 112, 193, 235; inheritance of, 232–3; blood-clotting in, 234; folk beliefs about, 234; bleeding in, 234; stiff joints, 234; transfusion for, 235; marriage and, 235–236; Christmas disease, 236; in Queen Victoria's descendants, 237
haemorrhage: *see* bleeding
haemorrhoids, 273
hagfish, four hearts in, 35
hair, 41, 76
hand, biological account of, 145–6
haptoglobin, 34
haruspicy, 33

Harvey, William, and discovery of circulation, 58, 90–93
head, arteries of, 64, 262
headache, 262
healing: by scar formation, 101, 164; by functioning cell replacement, 101
heart(s): squid and earthworm, 27; fish, 33–5; amphibian, 35; accessory, 35, 36, 52; human, 35–6; comparison with pumps, 58; output, 58; rate, 58, 63, 70, 266–7; control, 58, 68, 266–7; sounds, 59, 255–6; position, 59; on right side, 60; pericardium, 60, 263; stabbing the, 60, 263; chambers of, 60; valves, endocardium, 60, 263; shape, 60; heartstrings, 61, 84; muscle, myocardium, 61, 263; pacemaker, 63, 68, 257, 266; beat, 63, 257; atrioventricular bundle, 63, 257; coronary arteries, 64, 198, 261–2; veins, 66; nerves of, 68, 261; pressures in, 68; chemical control, 68; athletes', 70, 257; Galen's view of, 85–6; 'invisible pores', 86, 87; Rabelais on, 88; failure, congestive, 94, 197; first beats, 102; filling with blood, 176–7; muscle in anaemia, 194, 197; overloading by transfusion, 197; cardiac arrest and massage, 198–9; heart-lung machine, 200; electro-cardiograph, 257; cardiac catheterization, 261, 270; oxygen needs, 261; pain in, 261–2; broken, 264; air embolism in, 275
heart disease: congenital, 79, 261, 269; coronary (myocardial) infarction, 198, 258, 264, 270; bacterial endocarditis, 227, 269; heart sounds in, 255; mitral and aortic stenosis, 256, 265; mitral and aortic regurgitation, 256; valve rupture, 256; pericarditis, 256, 263; pericardial effusion, 256, 263; congestion in lungs, liver, veins, 260; breathlessness in, 260; failure, 260–61, 268; pain in, 261; broken heart, 264; myocarditis, 265; acute rheumatic carditis, 265; heart block, 266; artificial pacemaker for, 266; fibrillation, 266–7; tachycardia, 267; brachycardia, 267; and thyroid gland, 267; blue baby, 269–70; air embolism in, 275
heart-lung machine, 200, 266, 270
hepatoscopy, 33
herbal medicines, 260, 267–9
herring: Bismarck, 206; red, 208
hidalgo, 'blue-blooded', 67, 244
Hildegard of Bingen, migraine auras of, 90
Hippocrates: methods, 81, 83, 106; microcosm and macrocosm, 81; critical days, 84; view of arteries, 84
honey, for colds, 93
hookworm, cause of anaemia, 218
Horace, 122
hormones, carried by blood, 47
horned toad, 70
Horror autotoxicus, 138
horse, heart rate of, 70
humour(s): term, 82; four, 82–3; Hippocrates and, 83–4; Rabelais on, 87–9; Burton on, 89–90; knowledge of circulation and, 93; phlegm in 'colds', 93; choler in 'fevers', 93; in blood, 96–100, 110; current phrases relating to, 98–100; Ben Jonson on, 99; Shakespeare's usage, 99; flux of, rheumatism, 265
Hungarians: strength from 'Bulls' Blood', 208n; vampire neurosis, 214
Huxley, Thomas Henry, 61
hydrops foetalis, 161
hypothesis, 116

immunity, immunization: self and not-self, 136, 138, 147; persistence of, 139, 140, 141; to second infection, 140, 158; fading with age, 140; towards grafted tissue, 141, 188; vaccines, 148; active, 148; passive, 149, 160, 164, 191, 193; of mother by foetus, 156, 157, 160, 164–5; by transfusion, 150–51, 155–6, 185; against Rhesus antigen, 158; against grafted tissue, 188; auto-immunity against red cells, 222
in vitro and in vivo, 150
inbreeding: artificial, 129; human, 238
individuality: and identical twins, 129, 243; self, 136, 138, 147; mental experience of, 142; biochemical and genetic bases, 242–3; 'blood relationships', 243
infarction, 263n
infection: effect on white cells, 105; entry of, 136, 185, 225; second, resistance to, 140; vaccination, 149; heavy, overcoming defences, 226; sepsis, 226; 'blood poisoning', 227
inflammation: signs of, 55, 226; nature of, 55; lymphatics in, 75; not cured by blood-letting, 98
Innocent VIII, Pope, attempt to rejuvenate, 182
insects, air through portholes, 29
inspiration, 44, 83
iron: binding by plasma, 47, 194, 209; and haemoglobin, 106, 207; measurement, 109; radioactive, 111; for anaemia, 194, 196, 206, 209; and Mars, 206–7; quantity in body, 207; loss from body, 207; in men, in women, 207; in foods, 207–9; intestinal absorption of, 208, 209; medicines, 209; in cooking pots, 209; stocks in haemochromatosis, 209; needs in pregnancy, 212–13

Januarius, Saint, blood miracle, 122–4
jargon, medical, 200, 202, 205–6
jaundice, 162, 191, 192
jellyfish, non-living jelly in, 19
joints: in haemophilia, 234; in rheumatism, 265
Jonson, Ben, on humours, 99
Joyce, James, 127

kidney(s): blood supply, 28, 51–2, 65, 72; excretion of waste, 50, 51; structure, 51; filtration, 51–2, 259; new site for, 52; end-arteries, 65; blood formation in, 102; glomerulo-nephritis, 193; albumin leakage, 193; artificial, 199–200; dialysis, 200; disease and blood pressure, 259–60, 261; fat embolism and, 275

Lagrange, Joseph Louis, on Lavoisier's execution, 45
lancelet (Amphioxus), 32, 37
Landsteiner, Karl: discovery of ABO groups, 152; discovery of MN and P groups, 155; discovery of Rhesus groups, 156–7, 159
Lavoisier, Antoine Laurent, and oxygen, 45
leech(es): epithet for doctor(s), 94; use in medicine, 97, 218; jaws, 218; amount of blood taken by, 218; anticoagulant in saliva, 218; gathering, 219
leucocytes: see lymphocytes; white blood cells
leukaemia: bone marrow in, 109, 228; anti-cell drugs for, 189, 231; cancer of white blood cells, 228; radiation a cause, 228; rare but fatal disease, 229; diagnosis and treatment, 229–31
liver: gate of (porta hepatis), 32; divination by, 33; hepatoscopy, 33; functions, 33, 66; circulation through, 33, 65, 74; digestion by, 66; origin, 66, 101; portal system, 66–7, 275; Galen's view of, 85; 'natural spirit' in, 85; Rabelais on, 88; blood formation in, 102; foetal, 162; effects of heart failure, 260; cirrhosis of, 273
long-distance running, slow pulse, indicates capacity for, 70
lungs: development and structure, 35, 75; blood supply, 67; invented by amphibians, 75; placenta a 'lung', 76; changes at birth, 78; Rabelais on (lights), 88; in heart failure, 260; blood-flow in congenital heart disease, 270; pulmonary embolism, 274
lymph: in inflammation, 55, 75; formation of, 73–4; capillaries, 74; main returning ducts, 75; humour, 82
lymph nodes (lymph glands), 75, 226
lymphatics (lymph vessels, channels), 74–75, 226, 275
lymphocytes: disposition of, 53; surveillance function, 54, 140; circulation of, 54, 140; antibody production, 54, 137, 139, 140, 141, 160; origin of, 54, 102; growth of, 104; carriage of antibodies, 141, 222

Macbeth, and cream-faced loon, 210
macrocosm, microcosm: Harvey and, 58, 90–91; term, 81; scheme for, 81–3; identities between, 82; Rabelais and, 87; hypothesis, 90; universe and mind, 144
magic bullet, 149
magnitudes: cosmic tonic sol-fa, 104
malaria: black pigment in, 97, 221; transferable by transfusion, 191; cured by menstrual blood, 211; transferred by

mosquitoes, 220; n birds, 220–21; haemolysis in, 221; tertian, quartan, 221; and sickle cells, 224
Malpighi, Marcello, discovery of capillaries, 92
mammals, warm blood of, 40–42
manure: blood, 57; poultry, 216
Marlowe, Christopher, and 'artiers', 89
Mars: symbol of fire, bile, iron, 206; Bloody, 207
medical research, some difficulties of, 121
medical technology, human dependence on, 149
medicine: amateur interest in, 202–4; quackery, 203; effect on gene pool, 235; social policies for, 235; dependence on expert teams, 236
melancholy: humour, 82; sourish black, 89; Burton on, 89; apparently in blood, 96; supposed from spleen, 97; and stomach bleeding, 97
Mendel, Gregor, 244
menstruation, menses, menstrual fluid, 126–7, 211
microbes: see germs
migraine, 262
milieu interne, 24–5
milk: souring of, 50; and menstruation, 126; antibodies in colostrum, 149, 165
mind: unconscious, 126; and brain, 142; consciousness, 143; personality, 144
miracles: evidence for, 121; saints' blood, 121, 122–4; bleeding Host, 125; chromobacterium prodigiosum, 125, 223
molasses, iron in, 208
molecules, 14; diffusion of, 15; reactions between, 47
molluscs, 27
mosquito, 220
mouse, heart rate of, 70
mouth, primitive, 19
mummies, blood groups of, 254
muscle(s): of heart, 58–9, 61, 263; as 'meat', 59; massage of veins, 71; blood-flow in, 72, 264; massage of lymphatics, 75; injection into, 75; Aristotle's view of, 84; electric change during contraction, 257; painful contractions without oxygen, 261, 262
Mycetozoa, 17
myocardium, heart muscle, 263
Myxine (hagfish), four hearts in, 35, 37

natural selection, 21, 22
neck: arteries of, 64; veins, 67
nerve(s): Galen's view of, 85–6; blood supply to, 272; 'pins and needles', 272–3
nitrogen, 173
node, atrioventricular, in heart-beat, 63
'normal', conventional term, 105
nose bleed, 113
numbers: of cells in body, 48; of red blood cells, 103, 105; of haemoglobin molecules, 103; of white cells, 103, 104, 105, 109; of platelets, 105

oatmeal, iron in, 208
ophthalmoscope, 261
oranges, blood, 208
organ, 23
organism: organized protoplasm, 14; multicelled, 19
osmosis: and capillary function, 73–4; osmotic fragility of red cells, 109, 223; red cells in water and, 172, 221; plasma albumin and, 193, 195
oxygen: in air, 44–5; in water, 45; red cells and, 46–7, 103; foetal haemoglobin and, 76; lack stimulates blood formation, 105; in heart-lung machine, 200
oysters, iron in, 208

pacemaker: of heart, 63, 68, 257, 266; artificial, 266
packed cell volume, 109
pain: effect on pulse and colour, 68; protects muscles, 261; referred, 262; angina pectoris, 262, 263; in headache, 262; in ergot poisoning, 262; St Anthony's fire, 262
pallor: in cold, 41; in fear, 68, 69, 210, 222; in anaemia, 210
palpitations, 267
Paracelsus: view of microscosm, macrocosm, 90; full name and title, 92; and animation of matter, 92
parasites, 136, 147, 216–21; germs as, 136, 147, 220–21; blood-sucking, 219; adaptation to man, 219
parsley, iron in, 208
Pasteur, Louis, 45; avoiding bacteria, 187; pasteurization, 193
paternity, blood-group tests for, 167, 168, 244
patient (term), 93
Patin, Guy, advocates blood-letting, 94–5
peas: see beans
pelican, as symbol for blood donors, 190
penis, erection of, 69
Pepys, Samuel, mentions transfusion, 184
pericardium, 60; disease in, 264
Person, David, compares earth and body, 127
phagocytes, 49; see also scavenger cells
phlebitis, 274
phlegm: humour, 82, 83; Burton on, 89; and 'cold' in head, 93; chill on liver, 93; 'laudable' pus, 93; 'chicken-fat clot', 96, 97; apparently in blood, 97; greatest disease-producer, 97
piles, 273
'pins and needles', 272–3
pituitrin, 69
placenta (afterbirth): development of, 76–9; structure, 77; umbilical cord, 77; of twins, 147; immunization across, 155, 159; and grafting, 188
planetary motion, and circulation of blood, 92
plant(s): circulation in, 37–9; photosynthesis, 37–8; water losses, 38; sap movement, 38, 39; blood manure and, 57;

juices agglutinate red cells, 151; derivatives for transfusion, 195; foods, iron in, 208, 209
plasma: in proboscis-worms, 25; term, 31; compared with serum, 31, 112; binding of metals, 47, 193, 209; binding of pigments, enzymes, drugs, 47, 162, 193; complexity of, 47–8; as exchange pool, 50; proteins, 74, 193; proteins in disease, 110; globulins, 137, 193–4; protein groups, 169; loss in burns, etc., 181, 196; storage of, 193; fractionation of, 193–4
platelets: see blood platelets
plethora, 85; blood-letting for, 93
Pliny the Elder: account of elephant and dragon, 43–4; miracle at Gnatia, 122; and garum (fish sauce), 122; on menstruation, 211
pneuma (vital spirit), 45, 83
polycythaemia, blood-letting in, 94
pregnancy: heat dissipation in, 77; stillbirths in haemolytic disease, 157; compresses great veins, 177; morning sickness, 208, 213; iron needs in, 208, 212–13 anaemia in, 213; blood pressure and, 259; German measles in, 269
private ponds (internal water), 24
proboscis-worms, 25
prognosis, 201, 202
prothrombinase: in blood-clotting, 112; from tissue cells, 112; effect of spiders' web on, 118–20; and haemophilia, 234; see also thrombin
protoplasm: molecules of, 14; streaming in, 16–17; works against the gradient, 18; of heart muscle, 61; limitations of human, 132
protoplasmic hairs (cilia): make water current, 17, 20; wash food to 'mouth', 19; a colonial current, 21
pulmonary embolism, 274
pulse: emotion and, 68; rate and heart-size, 70; Hippocratic knowlegde of, 84; pressure, 258; when aorta constricted, 270
pump: molecular or chemical, 18, 52; heart a mechanical, 58
purging, 95, 98
purposive language, 21, 22
pus, 53; 'laudable', 87, 93
Pythagoras, Pythagorean: contraries, 80; lyre-string experiment, 80; numbers, 80; macrocosm, microcosm, 81; harmony, 81, 104; and beans, 223

quackery, 203–4

Rabelais, François, 87–9
race: similarities, differences, 240–42, 244–245; biological view of, 242; blood-group characteristics, 249, 253
radiation: fatal, 188; sickness, 227–8; effects on cells, 228, 231; a cause of leukaemia, 228; a treatment for leukaemia, 231
radioactivity: mapping blood-flow with,

64; organ tracing, 108, 111; for tagging cells, 111
red blood cells: in vertebrates, 45; shape and properties, 46, 243; life-span, 47, 50, 207, 225; nucleated, non-nucleated, 102, 170; numbers in human, 103, 104; rate of production, 103; production stimulated by oxygen lack, 105, 109; immature, in blood, 109; reticulocytes, 109, 223; sedimentation rate, 110, 194; electric charges on, 110; rouleaux formation, 110; whether alive, 189; abnormal without Vitamin B$_{12}$, 215; abnormal, inheritance of, 222; sickling of, 224; vital for human life, 225; in aplastic anaemia, 225; polycythaemia rubra vera, 231
Red Sea, nature of redness, 128
reticulocytes, 109, 223
Rhesus factor: see blood groups
rheum, rheumatism, 265
rheumatoid arthritis, 265
Robespierre, Maximilien, 'sea-green Incorruptible', 212
round-worms, 26

Saint Anthony's fire, 262
Saint Vitus' Dance (chorea), 265
salt, depletion of, 179
sangre azul, 67
'sanguine', 98, 99
sardines, iron in, 208
scar: healing by, 101; formation in heart, 264, 265; cirrhosis of liver, 273; elephantiasis, 275
scavenger cells: in primitive animals, 23; in flatworms, 24; removing waste, 49–50; in spleen, liver, bone marrow, 50, 51; multiplication of, 51; defence function, 52–3; in black eye, 106; tolerance of self, 137, 138; removal of antibody-coated red cells, 160, 222; in tissue graft, 188; lack of, 225
scientific method: 'spirits' confuse, 81; discovery, nature of, 92; the question 'Why not?', 115–16; an experimental investigation, 116–21; controls, 116–17; publication, 117–18, 121; in 17th century, 183; naming, 201, 236; splitting, lumping, 205; final form of a science, 205
scurvy, 98, 216
sea-cucumber, oxygen exchange in, 31
sea-squirts (ascidians), 32
segmentation, 27
sepsis ('blood-poisoning'), 226
septicaemia ('blood-poisoning'), 227
serology, 31
serotonin, 69
serum: term, 31, 112; compared with plasma, 31; antibodies in, 31, 149, 151; antivenoms, antitoxins, 149; treatment, 150–51
Shakespeare, William: and liver, brain, heat, 89; and melancholy, 96
shock: the two kinds, 176, 180; term, 176; blood pressure in, 176, 177; in water- and salt-depletion, 179; pulse rate in, 180;

after bleeding, 180; appearance in, 181; 'wound shock', 181; from plasma loss, 181; 'shell shock', 181n; transfusion for, 195, 199; irreversible, unresponsive, 198; in myocardial damage, 198, 264
situs inversus, trap for medical students, 60
skin: enclosing milieu interne, 25; of amphibians, 35; temperature, 41; lymphatics, 75; injections, 75; wound permits infection, 226; always cool, always warm, 271; bedsores, 272; varicose ulcers, 274
slime fungus, 17
sneeze, loses 'vital spirit', 85
sol-gel change, 16
soul: transmigration of, 80; Galen's spirits and, 85–6; risk of sneezing out, 85; Burton on, 90; angor animi, 262
soya beans, iron from, 208
sperm cell(s): of bedbug, 29; genes in, 132; mutation in, 133; union with egg-cell, 133; sex chromosomes in, 133; preservation by freezing, 188
spiders: lung-book in, 29; web of, for staunching blood, 113, 116–21
spinach, iron in, 208
spine-skinned animals (echinoderms), 31–32
spirit: 'vital', 45, 86, 87; natural, 85, 86; animal, 86, 207; Burton on, 90; angor animi, 262
spleen: scavenger cells in, 49, 50; structure and evolution of, 50; and portal system, 50; and liver, 51, 101; surgical removal, 51, 192; blood supply, 64; Rabelais on, 88; melancholy and, 97; and platelets, 192
sponges, colonial currents in, 20
squid, 27
staining: of cells for examination, 108, 109; antiseptic dyes, drugs, 108; of living cells, 109
starfish, oxygen exchange in, 31
steak: raw, for black eye, 106; iron in, 208
stethoscope, 59, 255
stomach: primitive, 19; 'coffee grounds' vomit, 97; bleeding into, 97, 273; absorption of iron, 208; absorption of Vitamin B$_{12}$, 215
stone, blood from a, 196, 207
storms, dispersed by menstruating woman, 211
stroke (apoplexy, paralysis), 65, 271
styptics, 113
sugar, and iron, 208
sun, energy from, 18, 19
swimming: slow pulse indicates capacity for 70; after meals, 179
Sydenham, Thomas: experimental medicine and, 183; use of iron, 206–7
symmetry, bilateral, 59–60
sympathies, doctrine of: 'like cures like', 98; red flannel for fever, 98; steak for black eye, 106; red wine and food for anaemia, 208

syphilis, transferred by transfusion, 191
system, 23

tapeworm: flattened for absorption, 25;
thief of Vitamin B_{12}, 216–17; life-cycle
of fish-tapeworm, 216
teeth: green, 164; septicaemia after extraction of, 227; extractions and haemophilia, 234
temperament, balance of humours, 83
temperature: control of, in human, 41,
44–7, 178, 222; of reptile and insects,
41–2; of blood bank, 42, 188; lowered for
surgery, 42, 270; why 37°C?, 42; and
living rates, 42–3, 188; relative, 104
tendons, Aristotle's view of, 84
'Thalatta! Thalatta!' cry of the Ten
Thousand, 224
Thermodynamics, Second Law of, 18, 148
thrombin, prothrombin: in blood-clotting,
112; deficiency, 239
thrombus, thrombosis, 263, 271, 274
throttling, 103
thymus gland, 53–4, 139
thyroid gland: blood-flow in, 72; radioactive iodine, 111; auto-immune disease
in, 222; over-secretion, effect on heart,
267
tissue, 23; cell 'turnover' in, 101
tissue fluid, private pond, 24
toad, horned, 70
tonsils, lymphocytes in, 53
transfusion: see blood transfusion
twins: identical, 129, 243; placenta of,
147; chimera formation, 147

umbilical cord, transfusion through, 163
universe: running down, 18; who wound
up?, 19; scale of magnitudes, 104
uraemia, in kidney disease, 199
urine: formation, 50, 52, 259; in bladder,
52; albumin in, 193

vaccination, 149
Valentine's Day, 60
valves: in fish heart, 33; term, 61; in
human heart (endocardium), 61, 263;
mitral, 61; tendinous strings of, 61, 84;
aortic, 61; in veins, 71, 273; in lymphatics, 75; of heart, surgical repair, 265;
nourishment of, 269
vampires, 214
variation, biological, and disease, 22
varicose veins, 273–4
vasa vasorum, 68
vascular hydraulics: in penis and clitoris,
69; in horned toad and dragonfly larva,
70
vegetable(s): see plants
vein(s): azygos (term), 72; hepatic portal,
32, 65, 273; from spleen, 50; inferior
vena cava, 52, 65, 273; flow in, 65–7,

71–2, 177, 273; renal portal, 66n; jugular
(term), 67; superior vena cava, 67; pulmonary, 67; colour of, 67; pressure in, 71,
273; azygous (term), 72; pressure-equaliz-
ing connections, 72, 274; umbilical, 77,
163; 'natural spirit' in, 85; of 'leech' finger, 96; engorgement of jugular, 197; used
for bleeding, 197–8; infection of blood in,
226; varicose, 273–4; Caput Medusae
(gorgon's head), 273; phlebitis, 274
venesection: term, 94; useful, 94, 209;
technique of bleeding, 197; for haemochromatosis, 209; see also blood donors;
blood-letting
ventral (term), 32
ventricle: term, 33, 60; valves, 61; filling
and contraction, 63; fibrillation, 267
vermin, dispersed by menstruating woman,
211
vertebrates, primitive, 32
Viola (Twelfth Night), 'green and yellow
melancholy', 211
Virchow, Rudolf, 98
viruses: see germs
Vitamin B_{12}: lack of, 109, 111; radioactive
tracing, 111; treatment with, 194, 215; in
foods, 215; absorption of, 215; sources of,
215–16; effect on non-blood tissues, 216;
taken by tapeworm, 216; taken by
bacteria, 217
vomit: bile in, 93; 'coffee grounds', 97
voodoo, 177

water: movement over cells, 17; dependence of life on, 20; movement in plants,
38–9; sea-, 40, 174; properties, 41;
drowning in, 174–5; depletion, shock in,
179; held in capillaries by albumin, 193;
blood turning to, 222
watercress, iron in, 208
white blood cells: leucocytes, 49; stained
appearance, 49; types and locations, 49;
polymorphonuclear, 49; nuclei, 49; movement of, 53; pus, 53; in foetus, 102;
numbers, 104, 105, 109; life-span, 104,
225; infection and, 105, 226; immature,
in blood, 109; female sex chromosome in,
134; antibodies against, 165, 189, 192;
transfusion of, 192; lack of, 192, 225;
effect of radiation on, 228; leukaemia,
228–31
Willis, Thomas: circle of, 72; experimental medicine and, 183
wind instruments, fainting while blowing,
179
wine: dry, 83; bread and, 88; iron in, 208
Withering, William, 268
Wordsworth, William, and leech-gatherer,
219n
Wren, Sir Christopher, and intravenous
injection, 183

X-ray angiography, 64, 261